Praise for M

"George's work is precisely its own thing: an archaic genre the western world has long forgotten it possessed, a genre I suspect was already defunct to the Western imagination even at the time of Homer. George is a phenomenal pagan, thrown forwards or backwards in time to this era. I will hesitate to call his work poetry, not that it does not more than serve the function of poetry, but his method is one that predates the definitions we have given poetry in modern literary theory. It is primal incantation, a spell, dreaming as vital action. In Yorubaland, the part of Nigeria where I grew up, one of the praise epithets of Aziza (a supernatural being who travels in a tornado) is, 'He is the one for whom thought and action are one and the same.'

I read recently that in Holland they have perfected a method that enables their asphalt roads to automatically discover their potholes and repair themselves. I believe the incantation genre, as explored by George in *Masks of Origin*, is a technology that assists the earth in her attempts to heal herself, after centuries of our having feasted recklessly on her flesh. George's work harks back to a moment in time or dreamtime memory in which to speak is to act, powerfully, with cosmic stealth, and at times with purgative violence. Its aim is less to inform—though it informs aplenty—than to widen the reader's gaze in a fundamental way, almost akin to giving the reader the gift of a new tongue."

Olujide Adebayo-Begun, author of *The Book of Supreme Happiness*

Credit: P. Horálek/ESO

"The universe had no beginning. Reality always existed. The earliest tradition of poetry, carried from Sun to Sun, is carried by Brian George."

Don Burgy, artist, writer, teacher

"Brian George steps over voids with legs that are rainbows, which snap like bands back into his body, catapulting him into the abyss. He free-falls, unwinding from the eye of Providence and plummeting down the spine of Babel. Leaving more than just a smoking crater, he penetrates to the earth's molten core, absorbing the shock of earthquakes and storing the energy in his bones, tracing what lay scattered, no matter how disparate and disjointed, back to primal source. He plunges all back in the fire and melts it down to extract what will endure.

Cooling after his incredible creative and alchemical process of solitary determination, Brian George emerges on the other side of earth with an ice-cap on his head, with new tools crafted, new weapons forged, and a new voice and new language even, both intimate and epic, manifold and polyphonic, in his *Masks of Origin*."

John Dockus, artist

"Steeped in myth while staying grounded in day-to-day reality, George ushers forth a contemplative surreality. His writing takes you on a journey through a labyrinth, revealing cryptic truths and exposing the long and treacherous shadow of history. Round and round the labyrinth you go, George's words leading you like Theseus in search of the Minotaur. And when you have reached the center of the labyrinth, you find God as a detonating atomic bomb—truth as monstrosity, a darkness that illuminates."

Brandan Styles, artist and weirdo spirit

"The writing of Brian George is built upon personal experience, which he translates into a universal algorithm. Each verse reads as geometrical sequence, keys that unlock pieces of consciousness. This is where poetry becomes music. The poet lives in the center of the vortex, memories flooding his vision, being assigned symbols in the matrix. Brian weaves his way through a hall of mirrors, travelling to emptiness, where the faceted diamond of knowledge is forged and brought to the surface in his writing. His words are clues; one's understanding shifts and expands the more one reads. There are lingering questions, and passages that come into clarity over time. This only serves to enhance for the reader the incredible fortune of not-knowing, and thus, discovery."

Marjorie Kaye, artist

"Over a dozen or so years of experiencing George's writing, I have developed my perception and understanding of it. The cosmology George paints is vast, complete with montages of events and characters. The painting emerges from direct yet oddly juxtaposed language. I savor each sentence until its imagery alights within my mind and then progresses to the next, flowing across dimensions of space and spans of time. The overall effect is of an open field of consciousness. And though the ideas and events may, at times, seem alien on the surface, the writing evokes an evanescent sense of recognition. Somehow, I participated. How do I return? George's writing creates a bridge into that liminal space."

Jason Strobus White, Shamanic Practitioner and Technologist

MASKS

OF ORIGIN

REGRESSION IN THE
SERVICE OF OMNIPOTENCE

Brian George

Untimely Books

Untimely Books

untimelybooks.com

An imprint of Cosmos Cooperative
PO Box 3, Longmont, Colorado 80502
info@untimelybooks.com

Book design by Kayla Morelli
Cover Art by Brian George
Unless otherwise attributed, all interior artwork by Brian George

Publisher Cataloging-in-Publication data
George, Brian.
Masks of origin : regression in the service of omnipotence / Brian George. — Longmont, CO : Untimely Books, 2022. — p. cm.
Consciousness. — Civilization. — Culture. — Essays.
B105.C477 G466 2021 — 150
ISBN: 9780971663589 (pbk.) 9780971663572 (ebook)

Contents

Foreword   ix

The Blind Staircase   3

The Ocean and its Attendants   13

The Blind Staircase, Revisited   23

The Centrifugal Displacement of the Tribe   43

The Big Dreams of a Gravedigger   49

Autumnal Fallout   53

Green, like a Leaf, on which the World is Written   61

Revenge is a Dish Best Tasted Cold   67

The Stranger Face of the Friend   73

The Goddess as Active Listener   89

Only Two Lines Could be Saved from the Mahabharata   121

The Long Curve of Descent   125

Early Days in the Vortex   133

The Music of the Spheres, Again Audible   147

The Art of Deep-Sea Fishing   153

Anonymous, and His International Fame   163

My Friend, the Minotaur   187

Notes on Kundalini and the Ticking of the Biological Clock   215

The Long-Delayed Meeting   229

Children Give Birth to Their Parents   245

Visiting Saint Joseph's: Towards a Just Proportion of Emptiness   251

On the Paintings of Deniz Ozan-George: The
Breaking of the Golden Egg   275

On Back Roads, in a Car Whose Driver Has Gone
Missing: A Eulogy for Robert George   279

As Henry Ford said, "History is bunk"   293

Descent to the Merkavah   299

Birds of a Feather and the Playthings of the Twelve   311

The Snare of Distance and the Sunglasses of the Seer   329

Having Cleared the Sky, it was Time to Reinvent the Wheel   357

Notes   369

About the Author   371

Foreword

Vortices and Seeds, 2003

1

Dear reader, let us pause to count the breaths that we have taken, in this as well as other bodies. Let us ask who owns our hands. For the most part, we see only what is put before us on a stage. The strength of the arc-lights prevents our seeing very far. We believe that we are conscious actors; our experience just "is what it is." From a different angle, or in a moment of non-local vision, we may suddenly discover that we are also sound asleep. Propelled by an off-stage technology that we do not understand, we participate, like holographic puppets, in a dream. Each stage-prop that we touch is a late-generation copy of some prototype that was long ago destroyed. Like these prototypes, we too may have vanished long ago. Already, the Earth may have smoothed her wrinkled skin. The self that once read the beginning of this sentence is not there by its end. It is no more than a memory, a memory we have no way to fully reconstruct. Yet a different part of the self has never ceased to be aware of the sum of all possible levels of experience and the outcome of all actions.

Thus, we are not where we are. We know much, but do not know what we know. To know, we must change ourselves, in ways that are, perhaps, uncomfortable; conversely, as we seek to penetrate the Other, it would be best if we were to come and go by stealth. We should not cut pieces from the object of our knowledge in order to make it fit the Procrustean bed of our intent. On our test-runs into the depths of the Land of No Return, we should not be rude to even the most unnatural of our guests.

We have keys without any corresponding locks. We have doors that lead to no buildings. At the center of a wasteland, there are columns that do not support a roof, and that, oddly, do not have a sky attached. Paleolithic ghosts, perhaps, have removed the stars for safekeeping, meanwhile tempting us to think that nothing of significance has been lost. Elsewhere, there are stairs that lead us straight into the ocean. There are petrified footsteps that are waiting for our feet and a labyrinth that, as we venture to retrace the path of our descent, will lead us towards the multitude of crimes we have committed. In the future, there is a point that calls to us from the clear atomic light on the horizon, towards which the lines of our perspectives must converge. Envision it as you will—as a trash-compacting vortex or the Bindu or Amma's Egg or the Stone of the Philosophers—this point is, however tiny, far more real than we are, and it may very well reach back to prompt our actions in the present.

2

Once, someone challenged me to sum up *Masks of Origin* in a single sentence. By the tenth sentence I proved what I had told him from the start: that this is just not the way I think. Even were such a thing possible, there are no two readers who would interpret even the simplest sentence the same way, or be able, whatever the similarity of their beliefs, to duplicate each other's interactions with a symbol. To me, true knowledge must originate in a "call and response" process, only one part of which is subject to our control. How would I sum up *Masks of Origin* in a sentence? To pose such a challenge is to get things exactly backwards.

In writing of the type I want to see, even when a text is composed of a series of hard statements, I believe that the result should be less an argument than a cave of half-open implications. To this cave of implications, questions can be posed. Any answers will depend upon the tone and format of the question. Let us say that some outraged critic might demand, "But why was that sentence written this way, not another?" Tipsy with the fumes that leak from the depths of the Homogenocene, the bone-thin Sibyl of the cave, her eyes rolling, will issue the all-purpose word, "Because." Should the Sibyl pose a question to the author, his own eyes must not roll. He must be willing to take stock of both his motives and his actions, to probe the etymology of each chance association. In short, he must be willing to subject the whole of his psyche to revision, even as he bows before the polyamorous virginity of the symbol. Only in this way will the Sibyl grant that he exists, that he is not just one more image out of many. Only after this will she agree to assist him with his voyage.

In my first efforts to describe *Masks of Origin* I had written, "The book is not quite a collection of essays, or the fragments of an autobiography, or a record of inter-dimensional journeys, or a work of metaphysics, or a socio-political critique, or an attempt to formulate a contemporary mythology—although it has elements of all of these." Upon further thought, however, I realized that such a mix of elements is exactly what had first defined the essay.

The word "essay" originates in the French "essayer," which means "to attempt; to put to the test; to set out on a journey; to explore." When Montaigne explained his use of this word, in 1580, in the "Preface" to his first volume of *Essays*, he made it clear his work was intended to be revolutionary both in content and in form. "I dare to write all that I dare to think," he wrote, and "In every one of us is the entire human condition." This later statement may call to mind certain Renaissance illustrations, such as those of Robert Fludd, in which the human body has been set inside of a circle, with each part corresponding to a planet, star, element, or other level of the cosmos. "So, reader," Montaigne somewhat paradoxically declared, "I am myself the substance of my book, and there is no reason why you should waste your leisure on so frivolous and unrewarding a subject."

Like Montaigne, I would not argue that my experience is significant just because it is mine; no, I would suggest that the personal life—so apparently familiar—is a sign that points towards an undiscovered continent, and then beyond. It is the source of raw material, a kind of fossil fuel, the small version of something almost infinitely large.

One way to read *Masks of Origin* that juxtaposes—in one panoramic sweep—all of these elements is to view it as a meditation upon destiny, or more simply, as a probing of the pattern that gives form to one life. I would argue that we each possess a "preexistent story," whose end we intuit, but whose details we must discover step by step. The magnetic field of our destiny comes first, and it functions as a kind of DNA, around which the body of our experience must grow. Intent is a part of this, to be sure, as is consciousness, but accident and unconsciousness also play a central role, nor is there, in the end, that much difference between these factors.

In *Masks of Origin*, I attempt to peek behind the stage of my experience, with all its holographic props, and to discover who or what is there. I would argue that there is a point, located on the other side of space, from which the whole of the story can be taken in at a glance, as can the Earth itself. To that point, I would once again return. From there, as I did in ages past, I would once more seize control of the apparatus of projection.

3

A change in narrative perspective does not mean, however, that we should throw away the intellect; instead, we should simply nudge it back towards playing its proper supportive role. We cannot, for example—or with rare exceptions—analyze our dreams while we are having them. The cone of our focus is habitually state-specific. At the same time, we may tend to underestimate how many hands we have, how casually the face that we see in the mirror may blur into another. As we add a footnote to our paper on Barthes' *Elements of Semiology*, a fiery agent may have been sent from the city of Hurqalya. Presented with an offer that it can't refuse, the intellect may agree to become more actively non-active.

After a series of explosive high-energy experiences in the late 1980s and early 1990s, these are some of the key questions that I asked myself:

How big is the microcosm, and how small is the macrocosm?

Are the two divided by the surface of a mirror?

What happens when this mirror breaks?

Should we fill ourselves up with facts, as is commonly believed, or should we educate ourselves as to the depth of our amnesia?

If we desire to return to some substratum of lost memory, should our goal be to grow bigger or should we empty ourselves out, in the process becoming smaller, so that we may more comfortably take our place among the lost?

To get to the "Land of No-where," how long does it take, and will we then be required to pass on?

Have we, in fact, forgotten more than we would ever dare to know?

How does the personal version of the self look from the inter-dimensional viewpoint of the *daimon*?

James Hillman, in *The Soul's Code*, writes,

Why assume that the genius (activating spirit) wants only to be with geniuses? Maybe the invisibles are interested in our lives for the sake of their realization and as such are inherently democratic: Anyone will do. Maybe they do not recognize the concept mediocre. The *daimon* gives importance to each, not only to the Important. Moreover, they and we are linked in the same myth. We are divine and mortal twins, and so they are in service to the same social realities as we. Because of this linkage, the angel has no way of descent into the streets of the public common except via our lives. In the film *Wings of Desire*, angels fall in love with life, the street life of ordinary human predicaments.

When I first read this paragraph, in 1998, the implications hit me with the power of a depth-charge and helped to prompt my transition from hermetic poetry to prose. In *Masks of Origin*, I attempt to integrate these almost incompatible perspectives: that of a life experienced from the inside out and that of a life experienced from the outside in, as from the far edge of an illuminated sphere.

This perhaps sounds far more esoteric than it is, or rather, it sounds this way because the scope of our vision and our hearing has contracted. Nothing has ever actually been hidden. We need not fight with the unknown; instead, we must reactivate our senses. We must remember what it means to see and hear. As Heraclitus says, "If we do not expect the unexpected we will not discover it, since it is not to be searched out and is difficult to apprehend." We are, I believe, as supernatural as we are natural. Our home is the sum-total of all possible realities. When we act, we act both in this world and the next.

It is we who, at the appointed hour, set foot beneath the arc-lights. It is we who also direct and prompt, though in a form that may seem all but disconnected from our choices. It is we who have methodically excised the Aeon from our bodies, whose bones no longer glow, whose systems have lost the ability to function on a diet of pure space. It is we who are the antediluvian Watchers that we fear. There is, however, a point from which the future is the present, a point from which we can reach to subtly steer events. I do not mean to suggest that we "create our own reality," as so many New Age teachers recommend that we should do; rather, I would like to suggest something stranger and more difficult to describe. I would like to suggest that, from multiple locations, we collaborate in shaping a reality that to some extent preexists us.

During a near-death experience, it is said that a person can re-experience and review all of the incidents in his life, as in a flash. If true, this raises serious questions about the nature of time, as well as about our contracted perception of it. On the one hand, we can—and most often do—view our actions, thoughts, and emotions as part of a one-directional sequence. On the other hand, during altered states or at the moment of death, we are able to view these same actions, thoughts, and emotions as the parts of one spatial pattern, each aspect of which is simultaneously unfolding in the present.

A simple illustration of this paradox would be the novel: In order to fully experience the novel, we must read it page by page, and, even if we have heard how the story ends, we must pretend that we have not. At the same time, the novel can be weighed as an object in the hand, and the whole of the story is already in existence, so that, if we choose, we could read it back to front or flip randomly to an individual page.

If there is a magnetic field that serves to give a shape to our experience, we also know from our own experience that even the best plans can go haywire. Among other things, we may know that money is not wealth, that more of an addictive substance may not make us any happier, that it is sometimes best to not remove the genie from the lamp. We may know that we are guilty by the very fact of our breathing, that our shadows are mercurial, that the more we try to expunge them the stronger they will grow. We may know that love does not solve every problem, that the Road to Hell is paved with Evangelical ministers, that work did not make the residents of Auschwitz free. We may know that the arc of the moral universe does not always bend towards justice, that the gods do like to play. We may know that history did not end with the triumph of Neoliberalism, that Pythagoras is not in any way less "evolved" than B.F. Skinner, that our left hand and our right may be up to different things, and that there is no way to follow a straight line in a labyrinth. If we know more than our minds accept that we should know, there are forces that cut one flash of insight from the next. Once, there was one world; now, many have split open.

This tension between shape and chaos is, perhaps, at the heart of what it means to be human, to be an actor rather than an observer, to be a halfway conscious traveler rather than the mute victim of experience. These tensions that define us cannot be easily put to rest, but they do, perhaps, point us towards the nature of our role.

To accept, for the sake of argument, that each of our stories may be in some way already in existence, like a novel, as an object with a kind of volume, is to play with an intriguing abstract possibility. I am almost tempted to say that the reader should take this concept literally, that they should visualize this story as an object to be weighed on the palm of their hand. Such an exercise might help to make the concept real. Who would hold the story? Who would see it? How large would this hand have to be? To shift from philosophical theory to tactile intuition would be to also jump from the "I" to some version of the "We."

To see the five parts of the narrative arc at one and the same moment would be to potentially subvert the fixed boundaries of the self. This would not be the story of one individual at all, and, like the author of this book, the reader might want to adjust their way of moving.

You will notice that *Masks of Origin*, although autobiographical to some degree, is not structured like a traditional linear narrative. While it does move towards the present from the past, more or less, and in its own labyrinthine way, there are also large gaps between incidents, which I make no attempt to fill in. Rather, I have attempted to focus on key moments of transition. As Faulkner says in *Requiem for a Nun*, "The past is never dead. It is not even past." In these essays, my goal is to return to a point of origin— both personal and collective, both lost and ever in the process of emergence—at a different turn of the torus.

No bigger than a pinhead, there is an ancient city that flickers at the edge of the horizon, of which we are the citizens, now grown dangerously frail, even as we appear to be getting younger by the day. There are some who say that the Deluge is still far off in the future, that it is only metaphorical, or that it may not come at all. Yet come it has, and it was we who had once set off to cross the puddle-dotted flood-plain, crawling inch by inch, like ants, to determine how much of the world body might be left. On our heads, perpetually, the shadow of a black wave falls, and the weight of the dead city has not been lifted from our backs. For several centuries now, in some bizarre reversal of perspective, we have been programmed to see our development in terms of a long arc of ascent. At the end of our search, we had at last discovered our own continent-wide scars, which we then chose to ignore.

Powerful search engines are again available! As before, these are of the binary sort. We have only to google the Manhattan-sized outpost that we left on the coast of India, built when not all of the glaciers had yet melted, and which is now submerged at a depth of 120 feet. The sidescan-sonar image is not real because we know that such things as this city are not real, nor can we see beyond the ends of our own noses. We are blind to our faults. Our big dreams turn against us. From our eyes, a few tears fall. Where they land, drop upon drop, we can see that the Earth has cracked like a plate of glass.

Once, at the dawn of the Satya Yuga, we had only a bit less vision than the gods. We still yearn for the scalar weapons that could ring space like a bell, causing it to curve. We still yearn for the games we played. We still yearn to enforce the rules that we have broken, those rules at which it was so much fun to laugh. We still yearn to casually exit from our bodies. If only in the form of symptoms, we still yearn to make full use of the technology of the word, of the mantric power of the seed, of those ratios with which we hoped to heal what we destroyed. We still ache for the tools that had fit themselves so perfectly into our hands. In 12,000 years, we have not been able to fix much. How strange it is that we are almost infinitely stupider than we were. We are left staring at the small details of our lives.

Yet there are moments at which we can move more deeply into the present. Each everyday object then becomes a source of light, and each event a cue. We do not need the sun. A kind of x-ray vision once more becomes operative. As if we put on a new body, we are able to slip beneath the fossil strata of mass die-offs, the scrambling of stellar alignments, the camouflage-nets that nature threw across past cultures. Quite unexpectedly, we are seized by the knowledge of what we are meant to do, and we follow the scent of sacrifice to the edge of the horizon. There, the Primordial Female/Male waits breathlessly for our return.

If He/She is as calm and radiantly empty as the sky, they are no less aware than we that certain loved ones have gone missing. An expert in micromanagement, He/She is nothing if not encyclopedically well-informed, to the point of being able to see the veins in every leaf, to the point of being able to map our DNA's translocations, to the point of being able to scan the words in every text. It may come as something of a shock, then, that this alien but oddly familiar presence is always eager to hear more.

Existing at a certain distance from events, He/She cannot intervene directly, nor can they fully enter the tone or depth of an experience. As small as He is big, as weak as She is strong, such a being is not in any way omnipotent. In their bodies, there are catastrophic gulfs. Like us, they must put their trust in the closed curve of regression, the surface of one ocean tearing to give birth to the next. Chaotically on schedule, the spell that binds the world breaks. Many are called. None will exit as they entered. Those with wide eyes will cross the threshold of the moment. Their surrender is the plunge of the Satya Yuga from a cliff.

We have keys without any corresponding locks. We have doors that lead to no buildings. At the center of a wasteland, there are columns that do not support a roof. With luck, we will be ambushed by the stories that we told, by those truths that we invented to scare children. We will once more visit our disasters at their birth, our creations that have gone so mysteriously wrong. Much will look the same, yet each thing will be different. The gods that we starved will once more grow on trees. Cool mercury will once more burble from the fountains. Each event has happened a great many times before, both as theme and variation, both to us and to the strangers whose bodies we possessed.

There is a form of light that preexisted its pronouncement, a form of light that is black. This light is the luminous blackness of Najm Kobra and Sohravardi, the blackness of the Deus Absconditus, the blackness of the Pole. If few can read the letters that are written on this blackness, neither has the language of such blackness ever hid, except within the plain sight of each viewer. There are moments at which we can move more deeply into the present, to harvest salt from the fields of Carthage, to kiss the

Stone that the Builders Rejected, to ask questions of the Treasure that Desired to Be Known.

Our sunset city, our city self-assembled from the ocean, our city moist with the dew of a cold dawn, although worn around the edges and bearing jagged scars, will then look to us even more wondrous than it did. To this city we return as from it we depart. There, we will take the pulse of the shadows that we loved. There, we will come across our earlier versions from behind. We will be happy to see that She is still gainfully employed, that she is still nurse to the tribes that the burning ground aborts. We will be happy to see that He is just as luminous as he was, in spite of suffering from the wounds of the billions he has killed. These were the first voyagers, those whose mummified organs were consigned to jars, those whose hearts broke. There is much work still to do. Once again, we may begin to see how the contradictory spaces that we inhabit intersect.

MASKS
OF ORIGIN

The Blind Staircase

Hawk Mummy Floating on the Ocean, 1992

Because the axis mundi is an idea that unites a number of concrete images, no contradiction exists in regarding multiple spots as "the center of the world."

—*New World Encyclopedia*

1

My earliest coherent memory goes back to the age of three. It emerges from the dark, clear after sleep, its freshness reflecting the hours of the day during which the events took place. Before this were only images or sensations with no story to connect them. Although I perhaps experienced myself as the omnipotent ruler of a world, this ceremonial function was not yet accompanied by any autonoetic—or "self-aware"—awareness. All memories took the form of habits, whose lengthening shadows were projected towards the future. Then too, it was possible that these things had happened a great many times before, but I was only just starting to figure out again how one thing followed from another, how a story must be forgotten in order to be told, how my growth was a cryptic pattern of retrieval.

So: the hour of emergence would soon take me by surprise. Whatever the traumas that had echoed through the dark, the whole of the world looked fresh, as if scrubbed clean by a flood, which had left, even for those who could determine where to look, only a handful of small traces. I could no longer see from one side of the planet to the other. On my belly, a healed scar, now invisible beneath my shirt. On a spider web, a few water droplets sparkled.

There was a time in my life when I got up early, often before the sun rose. I was as eager to get out of bed then as I am reluctant to do so now. There was so much to see, and, although time did not really yet exist, there was not a moment to waste. Like the birds, I responded to a signal in the dark announcing that a change was imminent. A voice called me out of bed to celebrate the perpetual moment of transition, in which the objects of the day were lifted, dripping, from the oceanic night. In the background, I could hear a few atonal squeaks, as if from cities on the ocean floor. Now, the hands reaching from the depths had simply faded from my view. The screams of the countless millions who had been ripped out of their lives were not audible behind the bass drone of the currents. The past was over, and the stage had been cleared to make room for my appearance. What a surprise it was to discover that the voice I heard was my own, as a song burst from my throat.

My family had just moved to a white, 17th-century farmhouse, in need of paint and buzzing with wasps, located on Bacon St. in Natick, Massachusetts. Stairways led up and down, twisted at odd angles, then ended abruptly in blank walls. As I later learned, these were designed to create confusion during an attack by the Nipmuk or Wampanoag Indians, and, by stopping the straight lines of their energy in its tracks, provide precious moments for an underground escape. Such subterfuge of design was common for houses built in that period. It was a time when Natick was an outpost on the westernmost edge of the frontier, a no-man's land where the authority of the Calvinist Elect broke down, the beginning of the savage, if seductively beautiful, wilderness.

I knew none of these things when I was three, of course, when we first moved to the house with the blind stairways, but that mysterious house and the fields around it were a true frontier to me, whose dangers were wonders, and whose objects served as supernatural signs. Natick was still very much a wilderness, waiting for one child to discover it.

2

Echoing my song, birds were singing on the roof. Branches swayed. A wasp buzzed, beating against the window, as light streamed through the tiny, 17th-century panes of glass. The monsters beneath the bed had disappeared; I checked. There were only several toys with a spider-web stretched between them, on which a collection of mummified insects, moved by a draft through the floorboards, fluttered, awaiting the next step in the cycle of rebirth.

The house itself was quiet, as though emptied of its living inhabitants to make room for the dead. Sunlight fell on the floor in geometric shapes, laying down a path for me to follow. I spun in circles, bounded down the convoluted stairs, as if down the helix of a DNA molecule, and then, on the first floor, I paused to listen to the loud ticking of a clock. It seemed possible that this was the same ticking that I had first heard underwater, the ticking that, so recently, had challenged my heart to beat. At first faint, and seeming to belong to no one in particular, the sound was now as loud as that from a large drum. From "tick tick" to "boom boom," its call to arms was all but impossible to ignore. The clock seemed determined to have its way. I did not choose to oppose it.

An explosive nexus of energy, I had not a care in the world. My hand rested on the door handle, which the presence behind the hand then turned. The door swung open. The hinges needed oil. The scent of lilacs hung in the air. A shadow moved before my feet, which was connected, in some yet to be specified way, to the movements of my body. The path of the keyhole in the sunlight led quickly from my door. There were no real boundaries. There were no rules that the omnipotent ego should be expected to obey. I could not be hurt. I did not remember that I had a mother or a father.

Like a one-inch sun, gymnastic, and crackling with atomic force, some future version of myself observed these actions from a branch. The sky was open, and every tree translucent. The ringing music of the spheres was still present as an echo. No doubts clouded the field of non-local correspondences.

For one further moment I stopped to play in the backyard, an area with which I had become all too familiar, whose magic had been exhausted. Without a thought I continued on, over the weathered wood of the fence, which, if you were not careful, would attempt to leave a large splinter in your hand. Once over it, I set off across a vast, uncharted wilderness, parting the tall grasses as I went. Grasshoppers chirped, in a wave. I could see them rubbing their legs together. Snakes tied themselves into pretzels. At the edges of my vision, treasures dug themselves up.

I knew where I was going, more or less, if not exactly how to get there. In the middle of nowhere, or so it seemed to me, a cannon from the Revolutionary War had long ago been left. I now consider: With its ragged weeds, the field towards which I was heading had never been a town square, or a park, and there was no good reason for a cannon to have been there. Perhaps, in the aftermath of some battle, it had simply been left where it fell. Or, after growing from a point, perhaps it had crash-landed, like an asteroid.

Its wheels were broken. Rust could be pulled from its eight-foot barrel in small flakes or large sheets. The object of my pilgrimage was all the more interesting, of course, for its state of total disrepair. It was a living relic, the occult antidote to amnesia, a sleeping giant inexplicably ignored by the rest of the human race. In spite of its sad condition, it had enough power to draw me forward, irresistibly, as towards a magnet. Lashed by ghosts, I was a Viking explorer haunted by the scent of magnetic North.

Who knows how long I played there? It was three or possibly four hours. I had been drawn towards the light at the far side of a tunnel, and then through a series of passageways, passageways that were neither inside nor outside of the landscape. And then, just in front of me, I found the cannon for which I searched. This was the mystery that had pulled me through the keyhole, the presence that had led me to believe myself an orphan.

An adult might look once and in passing at the cannon, recall some historical footnote, and then move on. He might pause to light a cigarette. If he had a camera, he might lift it to snap a photograph. Unsettled by the rustling of the field, he might shiver and then turn to look around him. But as a child I found no end of associations to explore, as well as stories to act out, in the presence of such a fascinating object. Then too, it was helpful that they had left the cannon at the center of the world, in a spot that no one had judged to be important. There was nothing to prevent my occupation of the field! It was an odd spot, certainly, in which to have placed Omphalos, which now looked like a half-healed scar.

So: what did I do for those three or four hours? I really do not know. Was I lifted from the Earth, transported to a sphere of pure consciousness, from which the whole of our galaxy appeared no bigger than a pinhead, and then, after being taught how to play a glass harmonica by the birds, returned to my own body several hours later? A large spider web vibrated on the branches of a bush. The field buzzed, and the clouds crackled. There is a gap between what I know and what I am able to communicate. Filling me with warmth, both then and now, my encounter with the cannon resonates with a kind of radioactive glow.

3

When I at last wandered home, at nine o'clock or so, having been away since the sun came up, my father, on the edge of tears, exploded. He and my mother had been worried, to say the least, wondering if I had been kidnapped by a pedophile or had crashed through rotted boards into a well. All of a sudden, I was standing at the door, perfectly at peace, with no good explanation of what I had been doing for three and one-half hours. My stomach felt hollow, and I thought, perhaps, that it might be time to eat. It took me totally by surprise that my parents would be upset.

Was I carefully supervised? I guess that I must have been. Did I automatically ask permission before setting off on an adventure? Given my behavior on that day, this seems far less likely. As I grew, I must have responded to rewards or threats, but only to the extent that these forced me to modify my behavior. Compliance was not the same as understanding, nor did it imply acceptance of the false authority of my parents. My parents were simply present, as was the early morning light and the songs of birds and the house silent but for the ticking of a clock and the all too familiar yard and the call of the field beyond. Space was open, a tactile mystery that flowed through me more or less without impediment. My father's anger must have served in its way as a ritual act of violence, the catalyst that called forth armies from a seed, the Aztec knife that separated the once half-conscious world from the self, the once half-conscious self from the other.

I can deduce that my father did not too often lose his temper, at least with me. I know this because of my shock at his reaction to my absence. At the time, there seemed no limit to his anger. In retrospect, and as a parent, I realize that he probably fought with himself for some small edge of control. Against his desire for emotional catharsis, he seems to have measured out his words. I cannot hear or visualize every detail of the punishment. It did not involve physical violence, of that much I am certain. I do know that I was made to sit on my toy box, without a toy, and with my face turned to the corner for what seemed like an interminable stretch. Such a punishment would have been reasonable, to be sure; it was also far beneath the dignity of the ruler of a field. "Do you know that you did something very, very wrong?" my father asked. No, I did not know any such thing.

The full weight of my father's disapproval was the worst part of the punishment. This was the first time I remember feeling truly separate from my parents, as well as from the world, and even from my own sense of adventure. For the first time, perhaps, I wanted to go back instead of forward. I wanted to withdraw from the searchlight of my father's stare, which was terrifying. Even when he had finally turned it to the side, it had not ceased to threaten to turn me into an object.

4

Did phenomena exist before the day of the blind staircase, on which a child provoked his father to build a tower out of anger? The father is now dead. The child is himself a father. Those phenomena now belong to the self as other, close at hand, but forever out of reach, and not to the self as investigative eye. They exist as habits, as encoded modes of action, as opaque metaphysical moods, but no exercise can really lift them above the surface of the ocean. Glyphs metastasize, producing a new pantheon of gods. A Paleolithic murder haunts my autonoetic awareness.

The memory of that day stirs paradoxical emotions. The first sensations are those of early sunlight, of joy, of a red rip in the fabric of creation, of the horizon cracking open like an egg, of treasures excavated by a song, of the triumph of the omnipotent ego, of morning mist steaming from the grass. A bittersweet aftertaste soon follows on the tongue. I had not known that my parents were fighting, with an escalating intensity, all throughout this period. Monsters danced beyond the coordinates of my hypnagogic dream. Unconscious of the context I inhabited, I awoke from play, suddenly, to find my feet frozen at the edge of an abyss.

Soon my parents would separate, and I would see my father once or twice a year, if that. One morning he was gone, or we were. The world broke, like a wheel. It was no longer new. From Larchmont, New York, my father had once sent a birthday present. He accidentally wrote the address in Ugaritic cuneiform, and so the box did not make it all the way to my grandparents' house in Worcester, where we had moved after the divorce. Great cracks had opened in the rich mud of the flood-plain. There were pools of coldness. You could feel the weakness of the disincarnate teachers as they begged us for fresh victims, for a few more drops of blood. Much has happened since that morning in 1957. A golden sadness has attached itself to the day of my encounter with the cannon. An angry father is better than one who has disappeared.

When I was twelve, my father would move to a house on La Avenida de Los Insurgentes, in Mexico City, to start a company and a replacement family. I would never visit this 24-room mansion, with its red tile roof, with its Romanesque fountain spurting in the courtyard, or have iced tea served to me by a passive-aggressive maid. I would be 23 years old, married, and out of art school before I saw the three-dimensional version of Robert George again. The images of that distant morning are immediate. Pointing towards the interdependent arising of the void, each object is a sign that designates not one but many things.

The Ocean and its Attendants

Living Ship, 2000

1

To the oldest had been assigned the most complex of responsibilities. Stepping from our catacombs when the deluge had
subsided, we had first to locate the spots where our power had
been concentrated, and we then made use of the few tools that
were left. There were fossils from the future. There were artifacts
from a world that never did exist. We no longer remembered the
whole of who or what we were; we only knew what we must do.

However obscure the protocol, much depended on one's attention to the smallest of details. For want of a period, the whole of the Ur-Text could be lost.

It was we who had removed the seaweed from the statues that resembled us, inside of which were our "geniuses." The light pulsing from our dark companions was unbearable, and soon, we would learn to hate them once again. Their breathing was so slow as to be almost imperceptible. Like us, they breathed; unlike us, however, they breathed space instead of air. Their eyelids were no thicker than a zero. Our hands moving as by themselves, we then reinstalled the snails that they had used as earplugs and placed fresh coins on their eyes. There were rivers with strong currents to be crossed. There were scribal anomalies. There were whirlpools. There were topological mists. Beyond these, there were oceans with no shores. Some amount of foreign assistance was required; hence, the importance of the two coins on the eyes. Was this not a fair enough transport fee? Such was our tradition, yet we knew that there were ferrymen who might flatly refuse this medium of exchange.

We had done our best to prepare these statues for their voyage. For a time, we shared our breath with these delegates from the Pole Star, and they had offered to us, in our dreams at least, full access to their records. Even then, however, we could sense that the field of our vision had been compromised. All but imperceptible at first, we could see a black speck, growing. The light of the world's morning slipped from us as if we were contaminated. You would think we had done something wrong. What, exactly, might this be? Who among the small number of survivors had not done something worse, and what race had the standing to accuse us? If our shadows had stretched to several miles in length before they had detached themselves, this was odd, yes, but we had no reason to believe that this was more than a coincidence. We had done no more than prepare our duplicates for their voyage. These statues were a link to the lines on the palms of our hands. We had just begun, and, already, the moment for their departure was several years past due. One day, we observed that they had left. Six houses of the zodiac would rise and fall before we once again recognized the perfect language that we spoke.

It was we who had once volunteered to give away our powers, yet we did not anticipate how large a portion this would be. We knew that speaking clearly was important. A great weight had been placed upon our tongues. Our lips just barely worked. We were scared of the depth of the forgetfulness that was coming. We were scared that a constellation might get stuck in our throats, that we might shake our stories apart in trying to dislodge it.

It was we whose preparations fell short of the mark. It was we who could not count the vessels that had shattered. It was we who had once plotted to assassinate the gods, our temperamental children who had tampered with our DNA, who claimed that they had planted every culture. Few indeed were the rites they had not "borrowed" from their elders. They had taken from us our bird-cloaks, our plumb bobs, and our fish-suits. They had taken from us the small stones we had rubbed smooth with our hands. They had taken from us both the raw materials and the end results of our alchemy. With all their arts, they were less experienced than we were, and they were far more invested in the cosmic status quo.

The gods were desperate for existence; we could take it or leave it. Their love of supernatural power had caused them to inflate, like balloons that would soon be turned into lead buoys. They used our untold traumas to fuel their conjurations. By creating their own reality, they were hoping to go up without ever coming down, to be full without ever being empty, and to be strong without ever being weak. Well, that was not going to happen. We would bow our heads, and smile. We would shield our energies. We would tend to our gardens, and we would scavenge for usable pieces when they crashed. Like ours, their arc was downwards. For them, it was not a choice. They were rulers, yes. They were beings who commanded our attention. Should we even still call them gods?

We were not, perhaps, quite as tiny or as limited as we appeared. Our rigor was martial. Death had camouflaged our capacity for stealth. They had hooked rings through our noses, the better for us to assist in the "improvement" of their stock. They had sealed the key to hyperspace beneath the eight plates of the skull. To some, a bit more intelligence; to others, a bit less, thus to set the part in opposition to the whole. Again and again, they told us stories from our childhood, of monsters under the bed, of presences too luminous to look upon and live, of traps to be sprung, of whole populations slated for blood sacrifice, of steps to be taken so this blood would not be ours. They told us what our needs had led us to demand, or rather what our fears had led us to imagine. If certain warnings did prove accurate, this was no thanks to our rulers, who had fallen under the spell of their own voices. They ignored far greater threats. They had always been pretenders.

They did not take note of the comet that was curving through deep space. Their hearts did not break when the last bees had departed from their honeycombs. They did not hear that the planets had stopped ringing. They did not care that the ocean had crept inch by inch towards their cities, that it welled up through their drains. They did not sense how each action would produce its harmonic counterpart. They could not grasp the sheer number of things that were happening at one time. As the wheel turned, the gods were subject to the law of unintended consequences. They forgot how to fit through keyholes. They could not find their way around their bodies. Their bones grew dim. Their magic became cancerous, yet they clung to their belief that their lineages were pure.

Let them play, we thought. Let them bask in the rays of their artificial sun. They did not know on whose backs their empires had been built. Even then, some few of us were circling in the borderlands, crouching around our campfires as the first lights on their towers began to flicker off. "We will," we said, "almost certainly, find the means to pull both the Earth and the sky from beneath them." We were nothing if not patient, and we had the advantage of having seen these events a great many times before.

There were those who believed that the ocean was not once as red as blood, or "wine dark," as the poet would prefer. A wave had once shattered every symbol on the coast, taking with it, as it withdrew, the occult history of our race. In our hearts was a catastrophe; we would pour them out. We drunken sailors did not have any choice but to gather up wealth from the four corners of the world. We were poor, and we had to pay down the high balance on our debt, which we had first incurred when we were brighter than the sun. Earth's overlords were rich, and asked for nothing but our lives. We had more than enough. Our bodies were like stadiums that had not ceased to hold multitudes.

Again, we had begun to see. It was we who had built a faster-than-light vehicle out of space, and then narrowed our focus to develop the small bones of our feet. Strangely, we then swore at them, even though they had done their best to support us. It was we who instructed the megaliths that they should not speak with strangers; instead, they should whisper to the chosen, to those whose psyches were scarred. It was we who had consigned the most luminous of our cities to the deep. It was we whose all-purpose ships were built from the simplest materials. It was we who were forced to redraw our maps from scratch. It was we whose emptiness had given birth to the 64-cube tetrahedron.

For the infinite has a form. In the discord that it generates, the one sphere is economical. It was determined that we would meet in Ithaca at the end of the Great Year. There, even now perhaps, the Translucent Ones are replaying every turning point in the Ur-Text, as they choose up sides for the Games.

2

The extended form of growth is always that of a spiral, as they have shown us in archaic urns. To cultivate the "fire in the belly" you must depart from home, whether Ithaca, with its clockwork owls, with its prows that are painted with wide-open eyes, or South Worcester, with its mix-and-match neoclassical factories that are manned by hungry ghosts, it is all the same. Contemptuous of death and, at first, as light as a feather, you must travel far across the many-colored ocean. You must experience the changeable hearts of men, the weird will of the gods, the wonders of phenomena, great and small, bright and dark, only to return at last to the place where you had started, with a gift to give. There, you will rediscover the beauty of those objects close at hand.

I had traveled far, had gained a facility in moving between dimensions, and had grown, as if from scratch, a capacity to decode and translate for use the most arcane of traditions. I had not only explored the depths of the unconscious, I had developed a certain skill in demanding answers from it. The world was a kind of living book, which worked like a non-linear storage system. Space itself was both the hardware and the software of an ancient but still functional computer. If you could figure out what word root gave you access to a program, and could determine, moment by moment, what questions you should ask, then it might be possible to reformat your whole concept of an answer.

I had thrown my invocations out, not knowing who or what might answer. I suspected that something would. At the same time, I could feel a tug from the far side of the ocean, as though

I watched instead of acted, as though even my most absurd mistakes had long ago been planned. What a relief it was to not have to navigate among an infinite number of choices. Instead, I had only to figure out who and where I had been.

My life belonged to some potentially quite undependable presence. It did not care how I felt. If it bothered to read my thoughts, this was only to redirect them towards an utterly obscure agenda. I had once made certain promises, it seems, that took precedence over my wishes. I had scars that ached to be probed. I had wounds meant to serve as doorways, which no test could diagnose. To have asked for happiness would have been to put my health in danger. There was a certain formality to how a question should be posed. As my vision grew, it became clear that my goals were much less personal than collective. The line between the familiar and the strange became less and less distinct.

My search-nets had conjugated lost civilizations from the wave-fields. I was present at Gobekli Tepe when the Twelve decided that the T-stones should be buried. Lifting my shovel, I had spoken from behind a mask. "Those beneath the earth will perhaps make better use of our artwork," I said. "Not much will survive above. The dead have needs of their own, and we must offer our support. Already, there are far too many to count. There will soon be many more. Very few are prepared. It is not their fault if they are ignorant of the rites." "No," said others, "our time is clearly over. A comet swarm approaches. All but the last of the gods have withdrawn. Is not emptiness our mother? The waves are hungry, and the elements should be allowed to finish what they start." The arguments between factions of the zodiac had been intense, but, in the end, we had all agreed: No trace of the site would be visible for the next 10,000 years.

I was present on Crete when the labyrinth was just a gleam in the eye of Daedalus, before they had traced its 28 u-turns on the sand. I was present at the crafting of the Antikythera mechanism, as well as at its rediscovery. It was I who had sealed the cycles of the planets into a lump of corroded metal. Thieves and traders, it was my crew that had called the giants' bluff. First, we had challenged them to a drinking game, which they assumed, because of their adjunct storm-cloud stomachs, they would win. Next, we caused the lid of Mount Etna to slide back. And then, once they passed out, we had only to dump them in. The giants had been way too literal in their analysis of the importance of sheer scale. We had three eyes, not just one. We were light on the ocean's surface. We were currents at the ocean's depth. Like a weapon's point, we were made to penetrate, then move.

The one-inch city had expanded beyond all measurement. Cutting the zeros from large numbers, we had renormalized the hallucinatory vastness of its architecture, with its living friezes, with its rows upon rows of electromagnetic arches. Again, the whole of space could be seen in terms of firsthand—and yet multi-purpose—correspondences, which we did not have to be omniscient to interpret. We could once more grasp them on a human scale. We believed that no city should be so big that its inhabitants, when passing on the street, would not be able to say "hello" as well as call to each other by name. So too, the cosmos should be measurable in terms of a single full exhalation. To inhale was to call a capsule-version of the Ur-Text back. Upon request, each detail could be magnified.

Some would say that I was unconscious, yes, but this is of small account, since my operating system had prompted each connection that had been scheduled. Some might see this system in terms of the weaving of Arachne, the craft of Hermes, the stellar clockwork of the Fates. You did not have to be aware of your means of transportation in order to discover that no wrong turns had occurred. By means of an algorithm as ancient as it was incomprehensible—and more to the point, deliberately incomprehensible—each event had been projected a great many times before, and yet, to the voyager's eyes, the present world looked new. It was only at odd moments, when the surface of objects was ripped away to reveal the wound beneath, that recollection yawned. At such moments, at first terrifying, a soft wind would cause my heart to swell, like a sail that did not exist.

The time had come for a joyous, if at first unacknowledged, homecoming, in which I would be recognized only by my aging dog, Argos, a moment before his death. A chaos of competing powers had surrounded the One Female. I had gotten used to travelling on the currents of pure space. Ashore, I had to call my breath back. My left hand would be difficult to find, as would the bow that it was meant to hold, though I would follow a trail of footprints towards a row of 33 ax-heads. Those with whom I had been associated in a former life would then, each in his or her own way, begin to solidify out of the mist that had obscured them.

The Blind Staircase, Revisited

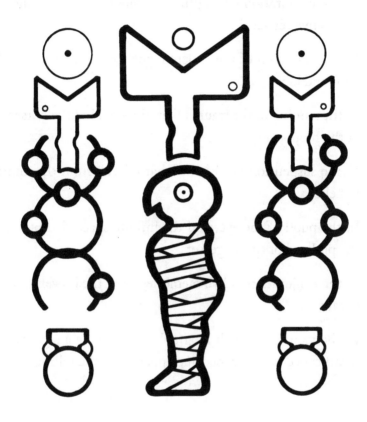

Hawk Mummy with Rising Snakes, Pots, and DNA, 1989

It is said that Apollo is a god who cannot lie. If he says that
he is lying, is he lying or telling the truth?"

—Ancient Greek riddle

1

I hate to admit it, but I have no particular interest in how accurate my memories are. My interest lies:

In the exploration of enigma, in elaborative encoding and associative retrieval

In the liberation of the epileptic poet from the gulag of the temporal lobe

In the naming of the trauma that hides behind the horseshoe of the hippocampus

In the suspension of disbelief that follows from the murder of belief

In the pupil of the eye, and the infinite space that buoys up the pinhead of the stage-set

In the conjuration of live memories from the bowels of dead oceans

In the viewing of each biographical detail as a sign, whose significance will only become apparent in the telling

2

My earliest coherent memory goes back to the age of three. It was 1957, the year Sputnik Two was launched. Gas was 20 cents per gallon. ZETA's nuclear fusion experiments led to dreams of infinite energy, of mini-reactors for the average suburban basement or garage. Wham-O introduced the Frisbee. The final US death toll from the flu was close to 70,000.

At 9:00 AM, I had just stepped through the front door of my house. Gone was the loud ticking that had accompanied my departure. I was not sure where I had been for three and one-half hours. I was not sure how I managed to get home. A few details were left, somewhat jagged to the touch, the shards of an adventure that had broken like a pane of glass. Q: Did some trauma occur? A: Not in any physical sense. My father was annoyed that I might have been abducted. It was only his anxiety, perhaps, that lent its tone to my experience in the field. In one version of events, I had stepped into a luminous sphere, one inch in height, which crackled with electric force. Q: Why would I do such a thing? A: Because I was asked.

While it could be said that I then experienced a voyage, this may not be entirely accurate. It is possible that the sphere did not go anywhere at all. There was a bright light, which hurt my eyes. There were bird-headed figures. There were wheels that showed some sort of events, and each event, as it turned, contained a whole host of others. There was a sense that I had seen these things a great many times before, that I was observing them from some-place far above the Earth, that my home was not the place that I had left. There were certain nonverbal instructions, which I felt as a vibration in my bones. There was also some amount of fear. As seen-through as I was, I was not afraid of the birds; rather, I was afraid of stepping outside, of returning to the field.

There is no way to determine exactly what I saw, or even if what I saw took place, in any normal manner of speaking. I did not go where I went, nor did I stay, but the public version of the experience is as follows: My parents were asleep. I left just after the sun rose, indifferent to the very fact of their existence. I climbed the fence in our backyard and set off over a field. My goal: to play on a rusted Revolutionary War cannon. Some block of time, say, three and one-half hours, passed. At some point, I found that I was back at my white, 17th-century house, with its indestructible wasps, with its shadows that felt free to wander from their objects, with its stairways that turned to lead only to blank walls.

This house, once thought to be at the edge of the known world, was located on Bacon Street in Natick, Massachusetts, where my much-delayed return had provoked my father's anger. This anger was the sperm that pierced the golden egg, the subterfuge that caused a "somewhere" to exist. This anger was the slap that knocked the bird mask from my face. This anger was the Aztec knife, whose edge cut my cerebrum's right half from its left. Before that day, I was the almost unconscious subject of a drama, with no ability to assemble events into a story. Or, alternately, I was the panoramic eye of races gone beneath the ocean, the sky behind red clouds, the gasp of those too traumatized to speak. After that day, I stood outside myself. I watched as well as acted. I moved in a line as well as in a circle.

The dream of the external world is, like any dream, overdetermined: it can be understood in terms of a multitude of causes, within each of which is embedded the seed of a present end. Thus, each everyday object can be interpreted as a sign, which refers us back, in an almost infinite loop, to the number of times that we have seen that thing—or a similar thing—before. Each person reads or misreads their own version of the sign, as does each sign its person. I wanted, nonetheless, to check on the accuracy of the key facts in my story. Was there any way to do this? Of the six people who might know something about the incident—my father, my maternal grandfather, my maternal grandmother, my mother, and my aunt—all but the last two were dead.

I decided to talk first with my aunt Corinne. Her memory was sharp, but she had no reason to remember more than some bare outline of the story, those few details that might fit her frame of reference. My mother might have told her how I left and then returned. She might have told her of the worst fears of a parent, of how my father had flown into a rage. My aunt would not have heard the buzzing of the field, the clashing of dead armies in the clouds, the frightening chime of the glass harmonica. She would have felt no surge of vertigo, or seen the wheels that turned inside of wheels. I doubt that I would ever have told her much about the incident, since, even now, I can do no more than point: Here, I woke from sleep, to find that the world had shattered.

I loved my aunt, but could any of my relatives ever shed light on my origins? Could any speak my language? My family told stories, yes; we told stores and more stories, but we did not, ever, dare to discuss the biggest things. If, as Wordsworth says, poetry is "emotion recollected in tranquility," then our family stories were emotion recollected from six degrees of separation. The drama and the words remained, in whatever new and improved form they might take; it was up to the listener to guess at the emotions. Perhaps story and emotion were in some way interrelated? That was not for the speaker to judge. Any psychological probing was best kept private. The time for such things was a sleepless and tormented three AM. A week or a month later, the second or the eighth or the 20th version of the story could be tested out on listeners who would, of course, be kind enough to pretend that they had never heard it before.

Was a detail inconvenient? It would not be for long. Should a punch to the jaw be added or removed? This would depend upon such things as the gender of the audience. Should the bully, instead, be flattened with an offhand caustic remark? Nothing could be simpler. I had gotten used to the abyss that opened between what I was and what I knew. Lost cities felt right at home there. I did not assume that I knew the beginning, the middle, or the end of any story. For many years, because of this, I wrote poetry instead of prose.

In many ancient cosmologies, speech did possess the power to create. This same power could be used to distract. It seemed probable that my family's avoidance of the depths had also shaped my perception of events in the larger world. In short, I did not believe much that I saw. I believed even less that I heard. In the larger world, as well, a story's usefulness could be judged by the amount that it left out, by its stoking of a set of designated fears, by its suppression of a set of metaphysical anxieties. Our comfortable concepts had moved more and more out of alignment with reality, with the scale of the gigantic challenges we faced.

The only difference between a fact and a fantasy was the agreed-upon authority of the source, or so said those who sought to propagate their spin, whether fringe or mainstream, Gnostic or official. "Facts are stupid things," as Reagan once informed us. Sadly, there were facts that snuck in through one's eyes, that bypassed the defenses of one's ears. A love of cognitive dissonance was the mark of the true believer.

For example, a terrorist's passport had supposedly fallen from one of the planes that had crashed into the World Trade Towers. An unidentified pedestrian found this almost immediately and gave it to an NYPD detective. The passport was Saudi Arabian. This caused us to invade Iraq, where we killed more than a million civilians, drove millions more into exile, and were forced to destabilize the whole of the Middle East.

We chose to believe lies that a six-year-old should have seen through. Since the early 1970s, tens of thousands of factories had been boarded up, turning once prosperous communities into ghost towns. Jobs had been outsourced to countries where the workers were virtual slaves. Meth and heroin addiction spread. There was no way to put food on the table. This was all the fault of the victims of such policies, since the majority had not bothered to pursue advanced degrees. Others, too, were guilty, such as those with advanced degrees, for they had chosen to laugh at the genius of the Unseen Hand of the Market.

Each year, with ever escalating frequency, glaciers slipped into the ocean. Ships were able to sail through the Arctic in the summer. Many gigatons of methane, sealed for tens of thousands of years under permafrost, burped into the already less-than-stable atmosphere. There were years when the whole of the West Coast was on fire, yet half the US population did not believe in climate instability. The problem was not that reserves of oil would run out, that this was 100 percent certain. No, the problem was how to redefine the problem—a classic PR issue. Would reserves run out in 2050 instead of 2030? Voila! The concept of "peak oil" was a myth. In Florida, where the ocean welled up through the sewer grates during storms, a law was passed that criminalized the phrase "global warming." Cities would soon sink, and we chose to pin our hopes on the development of the perfect self-steering car.

Many issues once thought super-important had already been resolved. In the 1960s, for example, sociologists thought that technological advances would soon make the 40-hour work week obsolete. What would the average person do with all of the extra time? Perhaps they could develop a greater interest in the arts or take up judo or build a second model railroad? This turned out to be a big nothingburger—a non-issue after all. Did the 30-hour work week present us with a problem? The solution was to go back to the 58-hour work week. Why did Friedman and Hayek have to bother to point this out?

In retrospect, my family's reluctance to look too directly at key issues was an invaluable form of training. Once I saw how the process worked, I had only to do the opposite, to the extent that I was able. First, I had to fix a cool eye on my fears, to make friends with my anxieties, to invite them to collaborate. Second, I had to access a greater range of information, in depth as well as breadth. And third, I had to craft a structure open at the edges, a structure as psychically fluid as it was creatively daring—one that asked the reader to fill in a few blanks, one that trusted that the missing had some desire to be heard.

So, was there any way to excavate that morning, to dig beneath the surface of events? My aunt did confirm the approximate age of the house, as well as the existence of a stairway that led to a white wall. On the other hand, my father was not a one-eyed monster, as I had been told. He was good with kids. She had always liked him. She vaguely remembered seeing an old cannon in a field, although she was not sure whether she had actually seen this cannon herself, or whether I had, in fact, mentioned it to her years ago.

A mental image proves only that such an image now exists. As Marx writes,

> Constant revolutionising of production, uninterrupted disturbance of all social conditions, everlasting uncertainty and agitation distinguish the bourgeois epoch from all earlier ones. All fixed, fast-frozen relations, with their train of ancient and venerable prejudices and opinions, are swept away, all new-formed ones become antiquated before they can ossify. All that is solid melts into air...

That an image had no location did not prove it unimportant. Conversely, the physicality of an image did not grant it special privileges. Just as solid events can melt into the air, certain cloud-like events can become increasingly real. "Perhaps," I thought, "the physical world itself is no more than a mnemonic exercise. The five Platonic solids may be more in love with chaos than we know. The letter Aleph may command more resources than the Department of Homeland Security. Perhaps the play of appearances is no more than a test, a test that our recent 'cultural evolution' has set us up to fail."

Since my aunt then lived in Wayland, only 10 miles or so from my old neighborhood in Natick, she sometimes drove by Bacon Street on her way to *Shopper's World*. She lamented to me that the area was now part of an unbroken tract of development. I had suspected as much, of course. More than 40 years had come and gone since I had been there, and most site-specific communities had been removed from life-support. There was no reason that this one street should have been exempt. We flesh and blood humans were now the interlopers. The town of Natick had been shut down for repairs. Its duplicate had evolved through leaps of punctuated equilibrium, until, to the great majority of the public, it was the original and not the duplicate that seemed false. "Reality" had become as two-dimensional as paper. Some Masonic ritual had inseminated the psi-bank of the continent, causing dreams, already haunted, to metastasize.

Office parks that looked like titanic UFOs had landed. "We at Raytheon love you!" Biotech celebrated the birth of the hermetically-sealed middle class. Sociopaths were among us. We buzzed, like drones, in the service of those dark ambassadors, as we fingered the scar through which our omnipotence was removed, the dead socket where the sun was plugged. Financial "wunderkinder" had turned excrement into gold. "See it shine!" they said, "Just out of reach." A few moments afterwards, you could see them turning the gold back into excrement. Whole sectors of the economy collapsed. Each year they had further streamlined what were once top-heavy industries, until some came to exist for no more than $1/100^{th}$ of a second. The GDP was in freefall. Sign upon sign, a chain reaction had multiplied the small cellular divisions of the six large multinational conglomerates, like a time-lapse explosion that we followed frame by frame. And to think that I once saw boredom as the greatest problem facing the suburbs!

There were signs that told you when to stop and when to go, and when to turn right or left, and when the time had come to declare war on a new country in the Middle East. You could never have too many corporate logos. They helped to distract you, and they kept you from noticing how few local companies actually made some physical product to be sold. So too, you could never have too many reproductions of the same few stores to shop in. After all, the year was 2009, not 1957. As if there was anyone left who could figure out what a physical object should be used for! The brand had triumphed. There were barcodes on each forehead. The white 17th-century house on Bacon Street may still have existed; the world that once surrounded it did not.

3

As above, so below—it is possible that signs do not always tell the truth. We must nonetheless, upon pain of death, learn to interpret them correctly. So too, we should not be surprised if our own subconscious minds have set out to destroy us. They may act in ways that are utterly nonsensical. We must not be caught off guard!

At the tail end of the age, there are few of us whose eyesight has not become defective, so that we see things only from the outside in. For this reason, I have come to believe that blindness is the prerequisite for vision. An impassable wall of objects has been piled in the foreground. There is no convenient way to penetrate this wall, nor can we stare too directly at the sun. No, to recover our vision we must make a pact with darkness, of the catalytic sort. We must remove the external sun in order to replace it with a black one. As if remembering the present at the same time that it happens, we must once more learn to see from the inside of each alien object out.

∾

Yes, the "gods" had abandoned us, as we had long ago instructed them to do. For, according to our customs, it was the eldest who must set off for new worlds. No tools or other items were permitted. Our doubles had agreed to keep us well supplied with energy—which, when read correctly, is also information—on the condition that they be allowed to speak and circulate among us. By their powers of bilocation, they would micromanage as they went, spreading joy by osmosis, and instructing us in each one of the arts. Conjugal visits could be scheduled in advance with each of the nine Muses. Once, we had laughed at tragedy. Life was lighter than a feather.

There was no north or south, or east or west, and only one inch separated the above from the below. The Earth did not, in those days, tilt, and all planets moved in perfect circles, rather than in ellipses, which are bad.

Death was theatre, no more and no less. Industrial-strength human sacrifice did not lack for volunteers. The gods, too, cut themselves, as did the archetypes—just to see what would happen. Why should those with bodies be allowed to have all the fun? Genocide was then the most popular form of sex. There was one tree, where all races hung, and from which all events in the future could be picked. Like an auto-immune disease, all knowledge was contagious. Transport was by word of mouth. All wealth was hallucinatory.

Six of one, a half-dozen of the other; there was no way to escape from the translucence of the 64-cube-tetrahedron. Time's arrow was just learning how to fly in one direction; it could be shot and simultaneously taken back, even as it never failed to hit its target. A mushroom cloud was the customary token of success. From the warrior's face, no act of violence could remove the archaic smile. Earthquakes were the first form of urban renewal, and a world-destroying flood was seen as little different from menstruation. Mothers then collaborated with their superconscious fetuses to determine the best moment for each birth. Tombs were reserved for the most pretentious teachers. The oldest actors were the first to acknowledge they were young.

The zodiac was still wet behind the ears. It sent delegates, and they had posed to us a challenge: to activate the unconscious genius that was trapped behind twelve powers. Life was good all over. Some trauma would appear to have intervened, an age ago.

4

The 1950s ushered in the mass-marketing of hypnosis, the theft of souls on an industrial scale, or so some sources claim. Jazz became less danceable and fun. Highways spread through the countryside like cancer, tempting humans to think that their car seats were their couches. Staring radioactive children spread fears of the Bomb. So shadowy were the actions of our Neoliberal Masters that they managed to hide their deceptions in plain sight. If no one noticed, that was not their fault. The Fourth Reich had collaborated with the CIA and Wall Street to translate the technology of the alien craft at Roswell. Fictitious UFOs were mixed in with the real ones. It was useful to keep the public glued to their TVs.

These theories may be false, or only slightly true, yet there was no doubt that a rip in time/space had occurred. You, the reader/listener, have no choice but to plumb the depths of your experience. You can recognize that such theories serve as shields for something stranger.

In an early opening sequence of *The Twilight Zone*, as the four-note theme mechanically repeats, an off-center spiral attempts to draw you in. In a somewhat later version, as you stare into the depths of the night sky, a line turns into a doorframe and a door. Like the spiral, these revolve. A voice suggests that you unlock the door with the "key of the imagination." No pause allows you to say "yes" or "no." The door opens, and a window rushes towards you, beyond which you can see a tree in a backyard. The window shatters, to reveal a lid that opens on an eyeball, the equation $E=mc^2$, a wooden-jointed artist's doll who flies downward at an angle, her hair rippling and electric, and a clock with spinning hands.

Let us enter into the vortex, for it is there that a bout of vertigo will ensue. Once inside, you will be carried past the point of no return, at least several times, and then back. It is only natural to experience a horror of the depths as you watch space curve like a figure eight. On your forehead will be stamped the barcode meaning "INFINITE." It cannot be removed, and it marks you as one who has been scheduled to descend.

Looking down, you will see where the vortex narrows to a point, even as its winds continue to tower through the exosphere. You will not know if the underworld is below you or above you, or whether you are being swallowed or spit out. As the vortex widens, there go all of the contents from the first house of your childhood, as if they had no weight at all. You will be transported to a space as vast as the inside of a clock, and as terrifying. This space will, in fact, be the inside of a clock. The loud ticking that you hear will be your heart. The clock's gears, as they turn, will be the whole of human history.

What will disturb you is not so much that you don't know where you are, that you are as clueless as a disobedient toddler in a closet; no, much more disturbing, you will realize that you never *did* know where you were. Only now is your memory just starting to return, in small glimpses and in overwhelming spasms, which leave you gasping for air. All things being equal, you would perhaps prefer that it did not. You will yearn for those days when your body had a limit, when you had not yet fixed your eyes upon the spiral, when you had not yet turned the "key of the imagination" in the door.

Life was simpler when you could celebrate the tree outside your window, before your backyard shattered. To distinguish the growth of a mushroom from the splitting of an atom: this should not have been so difficult. You would have preferred to have not been blinded by the light. You would have preferred that the birds did not have human heads, that their tweets did not sound like the Music of the Spheres, that the shadows they cast did not resemble the graves at Auschwitz-Birkenau. You would have preferred that your end came after your beginning. You would have preferred, as was the custom, to have seen with your two eyes. It was grueling to be forced to see out of the whole of the world body. When the waterfalls roared open at the edge of the Atlantic, it would have been nice to be asked if you were ready for the plunge—not that you would ever have chosen to say "no."

5

From a field in the wilds of Natick, Massachusetts, I had travelled to an unknown destination, to then find myself deposited at the front door of my house. It was 1957. I had done nothing more dangerous than to play for several hours on a cannon. The sun was out, the birds were singing, and all hell had been scheduled to break loose.

My three years of unconscious unity were over. It was once more time to remember how to speak. The time had come for me to exit from the spiral, to enter into the house that I had left. My father's anger was a wave that would break apart the world. My father's anger was a tower whose staircase had gone missing. No humans could climb up. No gods could be bothered to reach into its depths. Only ghosts saw fit to frolic in the rubble. My father's anger was a hook of asteroidal iron, the means by which my mouth would once more be pried open.

So far, I had postponed talking to my mother, my only direct link to the glyphs of that untranslated morning. I was not eager to do so. This was not part of her repertoire of stories. The records for that period had long ago been sealed. A few small details could be altered, yes, but only when the appropriate forms had been filled out in advance. To do otherwise would be an insult to those workers who fell from the ramps of the ziggurat, those who heaved the grammatical blocks, with no thanks from their masters, those who gave their lives in service to the Ur-Text. And if unauthorized material did somehow manage to sneak in, then it would have to be immediately removed.

Q: "Mom, was I a perfect child?" A: "Yes! You were always happy. You were curious about everything, and you could keep yourself entertained for many hours at a stretch." Q: "Mom, do you remember when I got mad at Bobby La Porte and shot him in the leg with an arrow?" A: "No." Q: "Mom, do you remember when my friends and I set up a clubhouse in Mr. O'Donohue's basement? He was almost deaf, and it took him six months to discover we were there and kick us out." A: "No. You would never trespass." Q: "Mom, could you tell me more about the fistfights that my grandfather got into with his brothers? I guess a fight with your uncle Jimmy took place in our kitchen." A: "The Sheas never got into fistfights. They were constantly making jokes. They never even argued."

My mother was certainly present on the morning of the incident, in a manner of speaking, but only in a dreamlike on-again off-again way. This was during a period when doctors freely issued both amphetamines and barbiturates. Six months into her pregnancy, my mother had given birth to my sister, Maureen, who only weighed two pounds. The premature delivery was traumatic. It was the consequence of a car crash caused by my father's reckless driving, or so my mother believed. His single large eye was powerful, like a search-light, but this did not make for good depth perception. (That he drove fast, I do know to be true. I would sometimes have to close my eyes when we sped down mountain roads, the white line twisting like a snake, with small creatures jumping out in front of us in the dark.) Due to the constantly repeating replays of the accident—about whose details she and my father held incompatible versions—my mother, quite often, could not get to sleep until 3:00 or 4:00 AM. If she was up at 7:00, she was not necessarily awake.

"You don't understand what it was like to be a housewife back then," she said, "I had planned to see the world as a stewardess, and I somehow ended up just staring at the sink." No, she had never left the house to explore the fields behind it; for, being female, she was not allowed to stray far from the morphogenetic compound, lest the rate of mutation should suddenly take off. It was difficult, indeed, to keep track of every chromosome. Also, although she had covered the large mirror in her bedroom with a sheet, envoys from lost races tended to migrate from its back, and she had, gently but firmly, to remove them from the present. She was often tired, and had many things to do.

As regards my father's unexpected rage, whose boundlessness had provoked my jump into a new stage of self-awareness, she agreed that while the rage was, in and of itself, not that unusual, it was unusual that he should have chosen me as its target. In a confidential voice, she informed me that he had hit her several times—as if I had not heard this story 50 times before, as if, from the age of four, I had not been her confidant—but that she had never known him to be less than affectionate towards me. I was, after all, the heir to the mantric technology of Utnapishtim. Since, even years after my father's death, she had not forgiven him for hitting her in 1957, I can only assume that her analysis is true. If he ever had directed this type of anger towards me, you would think she would have been eager to add yet another charge.

He was moody, of course. "Even in passing," she said, "he did not like to acknowledge that Maureen had been born, or that an incubator had caused blindness, cerebral palsy, and what the doctors termed 'mild retardation,' or that he, and he alone, was totally to blame. A less than perfect daughter had no place in his version of reality. It was as if the accident had never taken place at all, or had, perhaps, happened to a different set of people."

"Mom," I said, "did you ever try to talk things out with Dad?" "No" she answered, "there would be no point to it. He would only say something like, 'What is the use of borrowing a sports car from a friend if you are not going to drive faster than the speed limit? This is the Zurvan Darhahvadata, you stupid woman, the "Time of Long Duration." Its current vehicle is the automobile, as the sphere was the vehicle of the Zurvan Akarana. You are forbidden to so casually hold it in contempt. Your duty is to follow your instructions. This is the way that we do things now, and these are the events that are scheduled to unfold.' There were, of course, times that I did try to talk, but he would quickly withdraw to a dimension of his own. His silence would be deafening, and more frightening than his words. His large eye would go cold; then clouds would drift across it, swell up, and turn dark."

Did I remember how she washed and ironed clothes for the Andersons? There were eight kids. The mother had cancer. Mr.

Anderson was a tiger, who flew for Chang Kai Shek. Did I remember how our landlord would unexpectedly show up, in the dead of night, to run off leaflets on the printing press that he had set up in the barn? "Mom," I said, "on the morning that I'm talking about, do you remember how dad yelled, how he demanded that I accept that my wandering off was wrong?" "No, that didn't happen. You were always a well-behaved child."

In all good conscience, I never could admit that I was wrong. How could getting up early and talking to the birds be wrong? Besides, the birds had been quite specific in their warnings. "This woman is not your mother," they said, "and this man is not your father, nor does either one have a right to set limits to your actions." What could be so wrong about playing in a field? It was a beautiful day. The sun was out. The birds were with me, and I was only away from home for about three-and-one-half hours. Then was pronounced the sentence of "Time Out on the Toy Box." This was the first time I had been punished, and it shook my faith in the unbreakable perfection of the world.

My father's large eye fixed me with its cone. My vision shrunk, and my limbs just barely worked. I did not want to sit, facing the wall, on a toy box for two hours. My father's anger was gigantic. My punishment was unjust. No one intervened to stop this outrage to my dignity. Clutching her housecoat, my mother was standing at the top of the blind staircase.

6

I had stared into a spiral. This spiral had transported me, providing me with more vistas than I could possibly incorporate, only some of which related to my childhood. Others pointed to what seemed a different life, a different period, a different order of existence. Strata upon strata, as the ground beneath each spectral city was dissolved, there was no way to escape the dizzying influence of the spiral, nor was there any discovery that one might view as "safe." The glow from the most wondrous of visions could quickly flare into a threat. After all my efforts, my investigations had taken the form of a closed curve. Few facts were available. Of those that were, none fully explained my sense of vertigo when I thought about that day. In my bones: the throb of a frightening vibration. In the pit of my stomach: a queasy ache.

At a distance of some 52 years, as I sipped tea with my mother, I could see that there were questions we would never bother to ask, as well as stories that we would never dare to tell. There were records that cohered in a dimension set apart. There were stories into which we had accidentally stumbled, in which we were only the bit players. There were traumas of which we had only been given a small glimpse. If I did attempt to speak of what I felt, if I did attempt to translate the strange glyphs of that morning, if I did attempt to force the issue, the words would go in one ear, out the other, never to see the light of day again. There was no way to tell a less familiar story. "Oh," my mother would say, turning to the side.

The year was 1957. Sputnik Two would soon be launched, propelling the dog Laika into orbit. The Tablets of Destiny were no longer publicly accessible. Our city lights would soon obscure the constellations. Just before my parents got divorced, we had lived in a white, 17th-century house, buzzing with wasps, located on Bacon Street, in Natick, Massachusetts. My mother and I were, at the end, able to determine that the windows had small panes, that there had still been a few of the wavy, 17th-century sort. And, if the previous owners had not stupidly nailed it shut, you could have opened an escape hatch in the root cellar. The way led underground to a stand of distant trees.

The Centrifugal Displacement of the Tribe

Detail from the *Gundestrup Cauldron*, Public Domain

1

I grew up with my mother and with grandparents who were both wonderful storytellers, able to speak with authority for hours, to educate or entertain. They could cast a spell. Like food for birds, they threw the wealth of their experience around them, so much so that it took me 20 years to learn that we were poor. The oral tradition had been brought across the sea from County

Kerry, Ireland, in the black days just before and after the end of the potato famine, when pregnant women dropped from hunger in the street. The tradition was sturdy—as strong as the skin of a bodhrán, as vivid as the hangman's noose. The voices of dead heroes had not yet faded out.

As a child on a warm spring night, if allowed to stay up late, I would sit with my grandparents on our third floor porch as the seven hills of Worcester blinked on and off in the distance. Around us would be arranged the rest of our immediate extended family, about 16 of them, whose genetic relationship to me was often quite obscure.

My grandfather would lead us on a charge through the cannon-fire at Gettysburg. A bit tipsy, an uncle would start to sing. My godfather would pontificate on his research into branches of the family tree, and tell of trudging up muddy roads to the stones at Eanloch, of the way that leads from Drogheda out past Ail na Mureaan, of hours spent in the attics of 18th-century churches. My grandfather would snort. He was not sentimental about Ireland. His father had come from there. So much for the good old days! Life here was good—and could be improved only if we still rode horses. Our one unwed mother would tell an off-color joke, learned (of course) from a French Canadian. Moths would launch attacks on bulbs. My grandmother would harmonize the narrative cacophony.

Back and forth they would all rock in their chairs. They would joke and argue and tell stories late into the warm spring night. Trees would rustle. The scent of lilacs would waft up from the yard. Time would stop, almost. The moon would move. Crickets would continue to make noise as the sound of traffic slowly disappeared. I would swing to sleep in a hammock, not knowing if what I saw was a story or a dream.

2

Too many of our living libraries have no one to assist them with repairs. The moment scheduled for transformation passes. It is time for them to go. There is a Hassidic saying that when a person is killed a whole world disappears with him or her. It ceases to exist in a mode available to the community—at least to the community of the living. The same holds true when a person dies with his/her stories unrecorded.

My memory swells, but the promise that it holds is false. The all-protective guardians of my childhood become smaller as I grow. Each year, the Earth revolves more deeply into darkness.

Sadly, I am no biographer, and cannot retell the particular stories of my grandparents. Or perhaps, when all is said and done, I am their testament, but their stories are the bones and nerves and organs of my body. I can only suggest some portion of the magic of their words, as the moon floated above our back porch long ago, and crickets chirped, and the sound of traffic slowly faded into silence.

3

As the years went by and men set foot on the moon. As McDonald's built golden arches and TVs broadcast a revolution and atomic fission was employed to boil water. As fish had puppies and Earth's population doubled. As 10-year-olds in the Amazon were taught to "walk a mile for a Camel." As Pemex set up oil rigs on the Olmec ruins at La Venta and the dead pronounced a collective curse upon the clanking. As almost 98 percent of our DNA was determined to be "junk" and this junk was then bought up by the most corrupt of cabals. As apes threw thighbones at the black obelisk that had haunted them.

As Surrealism found a locked door at the end of the Unconscious. As dreams bred monsters and new polymer chains were developed and the Great Society was destroyed by madness and the best minds of a generation competed to outsource their own lives. As the Future was sacrificed on the altar of the International Monetary Fund. As wind whistled through the broken windows of abandoned factories in the Rust Belt and only birds manned the machines. As the First World became more and more similar to the Third and the real world was replaced by an almost exact duplicate. As this duplicate became less and less like anything that was real.

As centrifugal force triumphed and as contemporary culture sprawled in all directions, my relatives moved a hundred or a thousand or three thousand miles away, or died.

4

Trailing supernatural powers, like the light from a dead sun, the Tuatha de Danaan had disappeared beyond the seven hills of Worcester. Empty chairs rocked back and forth. A layer of dust on the furniture remembered the once heated arguments of the tribal council. My grandparents lost their audience. They were left almost alone. Bit by bit they drifted into memory, where their stories came to resemble continuously repeating tape loops. The culture had moved on, without them. There was little to focus their energies on present interactions.

With a change of scene, perhaps—in the aftermath of a trip to the Grand Canyon—or when some interesting new person might appear, the occult shape of their experience might suddenly snap back into focus. Wisdom had indeed accumulated. It was waiting to flash out with force, with the authority of the Senex, with the fearless joy of childhood. Filled with wonder, eyes would again grow sharp. They had been looking for the circle of stories where they had expected to end their days—a circle that had existed for millennia. It had been carried off from under them.

5

Now, new immigrant families occupy the three-decker that I grew up in, with its open porches, with its scent of lilacs in the spring, and with its panoramic view of the horizon. In my fingers, even to this day, I can feel the tin cans, large iron keys, one-handed clocks, shoes, anvils, rusted spark plugs, bent bicycle wheels, broken snake-oil bottles from the 1920s, and other treasures that I dug up from the yard. I marvel at how things so close can be simultaneously so far away. Some part of me is still rooted there, in the damp earth, in the strata of a house that has its own mode of existing.

Each year, the few dozen photographs that I have left of my grandparents look slightly the worse for wear, as a crack deepens or a piece crumbles from an edge. My fingers do not touch the things they hold, yet there is nonetheless some point to going through the motions. At times, I think that there is some circle on the other side of death, where a Bronze Age tripod has been set above a fire. I can see how the embers cast their light on the assembly. It is possible, I think, that there seats for my grandparents had been long ago reserved. There, it is possible that the feast is just getting started. To celebrate the solstice, or some other punctuation of a 26,000-year curve, the tribes have just come together from the four corners of the Zodiac. "So," says a distant cousin, "perhaps one of you would like to drop a stone into the soup?" With their golden bodies, sporting incomprehensible glyphs, the dead may once again be able to pass for fifteen or sixteen years old.

Biology betrays me. My right knee unexpectedly gives out. As one form of memory grows weaker there is another form that grows stronger. Each year, I add to my catalogue of wounds. I start to see how these are essential to my story, how certain misfortunes should be understood as gifts. When I speak to myself, there are others who now appear to be listening, and the voices of those not present are much louder than they were. There is a stone that goes before me through the arc of my displacement. It is tiny, and it glows.

The Big Dreams of a Gravedigger

Detail from *Gundestrup Cauldron*, Public Domain

Perhaps, as Thomas Kinsella argued, the whole concept of the Celtic Twilight was a romantic confabulation. An excellent translator, he disapproved of the more supernatural elements in the *Tain Bo Cuailnge*, which he saw as fanciful interpolations, and he made a point of restoring the direct references to "seduction, copulation, urination, the picking of vermin, the suggestion of incest in 'How Cuchulainn was Begotten,'" and other such matters of the body. My counterargument is as follows: that the facts of life do not make a mythology less true, and that confabulation can be the doorway to an otherwise lost world.

∽

How close are the dead? Does the one I call for hear? I reach for my great-grandfather, Black Jack Shea, a violent youth, whom a hundred and four years of experience did not improve. Storming out of the back door after an argument with his wife, as enraged as ever at her independence, he paid no attention to where he was going, fell headfirst off the porch, and broke his neck. I can only wonder what there could have been to fight about after 80 years of marriage.

He and Maggie had known each other since 1864, when they had met, both of them diseased and half-dead, on a boat that docked at Deer Island, Boston. Nursing their romantic memories, they married some five years later, when Black Jack had returned from his job as a gravedigger on the battlefields of the Civil War. The body count was high. Many corpses had turned to skeletons by the time that they were buried. The work was not completed for several years after the war. Good work, if you could get it—better, in any case, than starvation.

Twelve-hour work days were the norm. By the 1880's, Black Jack had achieved his dream of opening a small livery business. Four white horses for weddings. Four black horses for funerals. I have sometimes wondered about the numerological symbolism, and about whether, all practicality aside, such choices might have been deliberate on his part.

Four plus four: in a magical act yoking the four ages, the two teams pulled the carriage of the Sun. The eight horses could be the eight primordial elements of the Cosmos. To all, it was obvious that Black Jack's first love was these horses. When, for example, his favorite reared up and crushed his left leg in a stall, so that he would enter the 20th Century with a limp, he did not stay angry for more than a few weeks, but simply saw it as a price that must be paid. As with a Siddha living in a cremation ground, naked and rubbed with ash, it is possible that his years of working as a gravedigger had installed in him a kind of out-of-the-box per-spective, a way of looking at things from an angle. Whatever the origin of his skill, and in spite of his hard edges, Black Jack also had a reputation as a master reader of the Tarot.

In the Great Year, each life was multiform, and vast; its length was nonetheless indeterminate, and there was no guarantee that one would live through the next hour. Perhaps one life picked up where another one left off, without break, although not necessarily with awareness, or perhaps, should one suddenly step back, the ground would fall away from underneath one's feet, so that direct awareness would be no different than vertigo. Each fact was a sign. It was possible to interpret every biographical fluke in terms of this or of the other world.

Thus: Black Jack was good with horses, but temperamental with his seven sons. He had taught my grandfather to swim by rowing him out into the middle of Lake Quinsigamond, dumping him in, and then rowing back. In Ancient Greece, initiates would court near-death experiences by jumping off of a high cliff into the ocean. Perhaps this apparently cruel "swimming lesson" too was the remnant of some long out-of-date tradition, a tradition now obscure even to its practitioners, and which they must enact in the realm of the Unconscious.

In spite of my bad—that is to say, too civilized—habits, do any threads connect us? Would Black Jack insist on taking me to the doctor, concerned about the number of books that I had read, as he did when my grandfather had finished all books in stacks A to Z at the small Canterbury Square Library? It was not so much that real men did not read books; it was that real Irishmen should not need them. To this day in Ireland, a country that does not require writers to pay taxes, the writer is regarded as a necessary but somewhat pathetic figure—a storyteller who couldn't make it, who lacked the charisma to command his audience. Black

Jack was ashamed of his son. He had disappeared into his books, perhaps never to reemerge.

From a time before the farce of Christianity was invented, any Shea should be able to spread around himself a wide field of hypnotic energy, the words turning into shadows as he spoke. Even dogs should sit up straight and listen, dark magnetism should charge the atmosphere, and the dead should return from their trees in the underworld to break bread with the living. Jack, my youthful grandfather, the seventh son of a master reader of the Tarot, should not be an exception to the rule. The back of a father's hand could yet work wonders.

In the mind of Black Jack Shea, nothing had improved from the day 1600 years ago when Seanchan summoned Fergus from the megalithic stone, to reinvent the almost forgotten epic of Tain Bo Cuailnge, which had survived only in a number of disconnected fragments.

In fact, these fragments had never ceased to be assembled, as Seanchan showed on that day some 1600 years ago. As a test of strength, it was sometimes necessary to do a thing just because it was once thought to be impossible. This was just what it meant to SEE, and what a seer, such as Seanchan, did. And even now you could feel the dark magnetism of the poet, as he traded taunts with the human-headed birds, or gossiped with the dead.

Even now, you could see the mist roll in as it coiled around the megalith, so that, for three days and nights, Seanchan could not see his hand when he held it in front of this face, until, in "fierce majesty," Fergus stepped forth to recite the original version of the Tain. Even now, you could see the transfigured raiders galloping as clouds flew across the moon, and hear Donn Cuailnge, the archetypal bull, bellowing as, by the hundreds, heifers mooed. As was Seanchan, so too I am led to reinvent the story of my origins. The past floats like a vapor on the breath.

Autumnal Fallout

Bindu with Black Sun, Baby, and Butterfly over New York, photogram, 2003

Student at Rochester University: "Was the bomb exploded at Alamogordo during the Manhattan Project the first one to be detonated?" Dr. Robert Oppenheimer: "Well, yes. In modern times, of course."

∝

It would be hard to communicate to someone growing up today just how widespread was the fallout from the threat of the Atomic Bomb. From July 16th, 1945, when the first bomb was tested over the Jornada del Muerto Desert, its occult light had continued to throw shadows from each object. The danger was not abstract; it was imminent, and it changed our whole way of looking at the world. At any moment, a chain-reaction might reach out to take us by the hand, and there was no telling where we would end up. By the time that we got there, our hands might no longer be able to grasp objects. Our minds might be blinded by their own illumination, which was said to be brighter than 10,000 suns. Our vision might no longer go where we directed it; instead, it might plummet to the far side of the planet. We might not be able to distinguish the brain of Einstein from a cloud, or from the folds of the shockwave that had spread out from Ground Zero, or from the elegant simplicity of the equation that he dreamed. Which direction would be "up," and which would be "down"? Our feet might get no traction on the sky.

I vividly remember grammar school nuclear holocaust drills in the early 1960s: Get under your desk, put your head down on your knees, then put your hands on your head. (!?!) Yes, that should work, much as closing your eyes would make you invisible to the rest of the human race. The mind boggles at such unintentional comedy, in which the punch-line is the city going up like flash-paper. Such unintentional comedy was not a laughing matter! We did not consider laughing, yet how was it possible to do anything else but laugh?

In retrospect, I can see how truly small we were. Our lineage was obscure, and deliberately so; we were not left with the flicker of an idea about our strength. At the end of the last ice age, a war had rearranged the whole surface of the Earth. Cities popped like bubbles. Words became armies and chants destroyed empires.

Millions died. Suns ate each other. Mirrors fought against their own reflections. Whales left their bones on the Andes. Gigantic chunks of our memory were wiped out. When we crawled out from our net of subterranean tubes, there was not much that we recognized. We were few in number, and hungry. Our eyes were hypnotically fixed on large objects in the foreground. Space, somehow, had become opaque, and even the laws of physics had been altered.

In 1962, we were only just starting to remember how to say our ABCs. We were the interchangeable extras in an internecine drama, whose stage-sets we saw, but whose scripts were directed from the depths of the Unconscious. Use us once and throw us away. We were caterpillars whose chrysalises would not have a chance to develop. Instead of wings, we would have Thalidomide-style flippers. It didn't really matter if we were crouched beneath our desks or playing in the schoolyard. At best, when the blast took us, we might leave the imprints of our shadows on a wall. Looking backwards over our shoulders, these would seem as poignant to us as 18th-century cut-out paper silhouettes. Steam would leak from them, due to pressure from trapped oceans. Then tiny lightning bolts would flash, decalibrated. Our DNA would unzip. We would see the light, an artificial one, yet we would not know if the light saw us, and our voyage into it would seem more terrifying than staying where we were. Yanked back through our navels, we would wake up neither here nor there.

We had too much unfinished business. We would not be able to move smoothly to the outer edge of light, and then into the space beyond. A network of past actions would confront us, of which we were, until then, almost totally unaware. Our primal forms would get stuck. A great stadium would unfold out of a storm-drain, towering through the void, just as that storm-drain had unfolded from a pinhead.

There, in that turning stadium, where the too-bright light was broken by dark gulfs, a supernatural Olympiad would be held. Banners would flap in the epileptic breeze. With four limbs or eight, and screaming for our blood, the best of the interspecies champions would appear. They would pop up from their archaeological periods. We would first have to determine how many hands we had. Also, why did none of them hold weapons? With a hiss of electricity, we would move straight into our targets, like boxers that had landed punches on the chin of the Beyond, only to find that they were miles from the fight. In the meantime, as we watched, our opponents would have cut us limb from limb. They would eat our hearts and flatten out our force-fields. The records of our passing would be less clear than a Rorschach blot. Runes would comment on our ambiguity. Sailors tangled in Sargasso wrecks would wag their fingers in judgment, as they boasted about the progress they were making. The human sculptures from Pompeii would mock us for our lack of "significant form." In 5000 years, if our relics were to be shown in a museum, the curators would have to install electron microscopes, through which visitors could observe the haunted skid-marks that we left.

We were fetal nebulae. We were seers who could not read their instruction manuals, yet we could not do without them, and we chewed on them like pacifiers. 12,000 years ago, we had turned to run from the Lords of the Scalar Flying Guillotine, and we only just noticed that a flash had wiped them from the Earth. What a joy it was, to discover that the vitrified city that stretched before us had belonged to someone else. It was the purest of good luck that such a thing had happened. We were wide-eyed children, who would not hurt a fly.

Nothing scared us more than the mile-long shadows that stretched out from our feet. Some day we would figure out the best way to remove them. There were bad people out there. To teach them a lesson, we would suffer. The rumors of our death had not been greatly exaggerated. The horror was prodigious. Few had ever observed such suffering as ours! Yet mistakes were made. We were weather balloons that had crash-landed on the sky. If we saw the light, then there was no reason we would have wanted to experience such a thing. There were presences within it, protean ones, who seemed all too familiar, and the light itself looked painful. Rituals would be held, or so we had heard, in which they would force us to confront our ancient fears. There was one thing that did not add up, however: that these protean presences trembled at the thought of our return. We were just the tiny children of the Jornada del Muerto Desert, with wide eyes that we did not dare to open. We were ciphers in training. We would have left the one world just to prove that we were impotent in the next.

Sides had been chosen, an age ago. It was 1962. There was no way to avoid the confrontation that was coming. There was no way to sidestep the jagged ruins in the foreground, whose spectral light illuminated the darkest corners of the Psyche. Still, "Duck and Cover" may have been as useful a strategy as any other, and I can appreciate the thought behind these Vedic Neo-Dada preparations.

Ritual gesture can have an impact on a multitude of levels, and to "go through the motions" is at times the only practical course of action. Duck and Cover was, I think, a legacy from the Second World War, during which the U.S. government launched massive rubber and scrap metal drives, which, as it turned out, were designed more to improve public morale than because the government didn't have access to rubber and scrap metal. The principle seemed to be: It is always better to do something rather than nothing. In the face of an invasion by the Absolute, we must see to it that we died in the proper crouching pose.

My memories from the year of the Cuban Missile Crisis are quite strange and, I would say, almost wonderful. The emotions that it stirs are bittersweet and complex: an ache starts in my solar plexus and spreads upwards to my heart. The crisis happened in October, about a month after the start of the school year. In Worcester, Massachusetts, where I lived, it seemed as though the leaves were just beginning to change color—red and gold—and yet, already, there were many on the ground. Still, I can hear them crunching underfoot as I walked to school at 7:30 AM, and still, I can see them floating from the trees. With each foot that they fell they seemed to move ever slower, coming almost to a stop, until that morning became a memory of itself. Then I fell into that memory. I have not stopped falling since.

This was probably the first time that I became aware of the possibility of my own death, as well as of the possible destruction of the rest of the human race and the planet. But the sensation was that of the Japanese Cherry Blossom Festival. A sense of the beauty and the transience of all things washed over me—or perhaps I should say *blew* over me. Behind the wind, there was another and much bigger wind that seemed like it was always just about to blow. This wind was the wind of our own depth of coiled energy, an alchemical wind, which for aeons had been sealed in its athanor. We sensed that we were guilty; we did not know of what. We were just kids on our way to school. We were only trying to get away with staring out of the window! Why should we be expected to pay the price for the dismantling of the third dimension? Still, it seemed that we were somehow in this up to our ears.

As we stared at our hands, it was easy enough to tell that our solidity had been compromised. They flickered, at times, like a TV signal that was not quite coming in. There were many questions that we did not think to ask. Among these were the following:

If we were the receivers, then from what station was the signal being broadcast? Was only the bull's-eye of the circular test pattern real, and why did it remind us of a nuclear alert? Would the late night hum continue to get louder until it shook apart the atoms of each set? Just who was in control of the vertical and the horizontal axes? There was information missing. We should probably have worn our adjustable antennas! Then again, there was no one left who could be trusted to adjust them. Our teachers only added to the metaphysical static. Our parents were the servants of a technological pod. They were not really our parents. In any case, they were dealing with their own pre-programmed problems with adjustment.

We knew too much, by far, without knowing that we knew anything. Just recently, we had decided to take our powers out of storage, and our ignorance was a danger to the cosmos as a whole. In our toy ships, with shovels in hand, we would set sail from our sandbox! With our miniaturized brains, we would boldly go where no man had gone before! The path was not a straight one, however, and the arc of our discovery bent towards the Abyss.

We had stepped into the last act of a drama that had been set in motion years before our births, in the springtime of the world. Then, war was a game that the omnipotent seers played; death was an adventure, and the ocean was a vast but comprehensible text. Not only could we read the glyphs inside each atom, we could also read the emptiness on which they had been written. The gods were our contraptions. We had little respect for the authorities that would bar our access to "junk" DNA. We were living mirrors, from whose backs the mercury had not yet been removed. An oath prompted us to throw away almost everything we had, recklessly, and to cover our tracks by destroying the horizon. How infinitely strange it was to be a leaf that somehow did not know it was hanging from a tree. At last, we had tied the year into a perfect figure eight. October, as predicted, had arrived.

It was the 14th of October, 1962, and the Doomsday Clock was reading at 12 minutes before 12:00. As we made our way to school, with our book-bags on our shoulders, we could hear the newly fallen leaves crunch underfoot, like the bones of ancient warriors, like the husks of derelict gods, and we were struck dumb by the wonderful stillness of the moment. The beauty of the flame-like foliage was a harbinger of the descent of actual flame; the gentle falling of the leaves was perhaps a prelude to the imminent vaporization of our bodies, and to the gentle descent of our ashes through the air.

Green, like a Leaf, on which the World is Written

Monkey on the Lightning Tree, photogram, 2002

In the early 1970s, there was still much talk about "returning to the land," which action, it was theorized, would set one's soul free. As though it were possible to be separate from the land, as though one's feet were not always planted on the mothership of the Earth. Its guardian genius does not ask for our permission. Like it or not, and come hell or high water, we are carried through the hallucinatory mechanics of a circle. One cannot return, for one has never left.

If only such knowledge could remove one's deep sensation of abandonment, one's fear that one's reflection would reach out from the mirror, one's fear that the drone of a Tibetan chant might cause the whole of Worcester to dissolve, that even the most massive factories would float like leaves into the wind. My own body had already started to fade out. I was not quite in it. I was never sure to what extent it could be trusted. To avoid annihilation, I turned for guidance to my literary models. Fresh air would make me strong, as it did Kafka. Knut Hamsun was another success story. Upon learning that he had tuberculosis, he crossed the US on the roof of a freight train, gulping mouthfuls of cleansing wind.

Was I infected by the trendier aspects of this back to the land project? It is not for me to judge. I did have political goals—none too achievable ones, as I would learn—but my relationship to the forest was in no way theoretical. I had just come out of two years of Cub Scouts and five years of Boy Scouts, and I was far more at home outdoors than in a classroom. My friends and I would often disappear for a week into the woods, each of us taking only a knife, a piece of flint, some twine, and several other easy-to-carry items. Plants were everywhere, waiting to be eaten. A rabbit would insert its neck into a noose. Pine boughs could be used to make a more or less comfortable mattress. Our goal was to be so attuned to and knowledgeable about the environment that all necessities could be discovered as we went.

To me, a forest was a cathedral. Animals were the saints, quite suspiciously free of sin, however violent their liturgical behavior. The scent of pine was the frankincense. In their Dorian, Phrygian, and Mixolydian modes, ranks of birds chirped in their choir lofts. The chanting of the grasshoppers rose and fell in waves. Spiders were the magicians, the last survivors of a prehistoric cult, who had come disguised as priests. Snakes were the delinquents in the back rows of the annex. Fungi tended to the heaps of pagan relics in the crypt. If I stared into the sky, I could just make out the other-than-physical species on the windows. Snails were the guardians of the pi ratios of the vault.

If green was my favorite color, it was also much more than that. It was, as I would later come to understand, a presence into which I was meant to disappear. It was wisdom made visible, the projection of an esoteric force. In green, nature and supernature found a field on which to play. Green did indeed reorganize the soul. As 12th-century Sufi mystic Sohravardi claimed in his *Recital of the Exile*, green was the color that outlasted all the others. Green was the retrospective color of the well as one looked back at the end of a mystical ascent. Green was the light of Mount Qaf, of the threshold of the Pleuroma, of the glow that pulsed from the boundary between the eighth sphere and the ninth. Green was nature's tribute to the Tablets of Hermes Trismegistus. Primordial letters were inscribed upon the green. They were waiting to be assembled by some future version of the self. At the boundary between worlds, green split apart the atoms of the body, thus opening the heart.

If I understood green as an abstract force, as a call that I must answer, and if I saw it as the clothing behind which was a guide, I was not at all sure this guide would act on my behalf, that he was concerned with who I was or what I wanted. Hide and seek seemed to be the agenda of the day. Madness rustled in the branches. The fall of pinecones made me jump. If I disturbed the nap of a snake, I would distantly take note of the rattling at my feet. I would watch as my arms and legs just barely seemed to move. Apparently I lived, but only because a hand would yank me out of danger. Let's say a warm breeze blew from the south, I would shiver for no reason. Let's say I could not find a toehold on a cliff, I would suddenly feel at peace. Stimulus and response were quite often disconnected. Some part of what I was could not be found in an atlas. It did not fit inside my head. I would watch instead of acting. I then would watch myself watching myself watch.

In retrospect, I can see that the guide's instructions were relentless. This does not mean that I could have been other than a student from South Worcester, a writer just learning to write, a painter just learning to paint. I could not have grown up in any other neighborhood or known all that much more than I did. I listened as intently as I could. I x-ed out my biography. I filled myself up with space. I demanded to know why such a large percentage of mixed messages had been sent. Years went by. The inescapable conclusion: my guide should have spoken less nonsensically. He should have spoken to the ears I had, not to those I would put on.

I still adhere to the Boy Scout motto, "Always be prepared," as I did, to the best of my ability, back then, when I saw these forays into nature as attempts to heal the rifts within my mind. I was not where I was. I was of the Earth, yes, but this was not my point of origin. Granted, I had never left, but this Earth was not the Earth that I remembered. To head towards home was to become more fully aware of my displacement. The forest's green was only a surrogate for the green that I desired. It whet my appetite. It did not satisfy my longing.

In Hebrew, curiously, the word "Olam" means both "world" and "concealed." If the space of "Ayin"—the divine nonexistence that gives birth to existence—is unbounded, the space of Olam is concave, as described by Plato. The various worlds are like slides or photographic negatives through which the light arising out of

"Ayin Soph" is projected. Olam can also mean "eon," a concave space conceived as a cycle of time, or "beyond the horizon," as in the distant past or future. The waves of a black ocean called. There was an ocean that stretched from our pup tents on Mount Tom to some space that opened at the edge of the horizon, from what I knew to worlds beyond my power to conceive. Stripping my life to the bare essentials seemed a good way to prepare for the trials of the crossing, for the almost certain violence of the ocean.

Sadly, however, in spite of how absurdly serious I was, I was never able to disentangle my intuitions from my fears, nor was I was able to transplant my rustic resourcefulness back to high school. Like a technocrat returning from a five-day New Age workshop, I would quickly forget what had just seemed over-whelmingly apparent. "Was it only a few days ago," I thought, "when I told myself that we humans could once more learn the Language of the Birds?" I was joyous or depressed, sane or crazy, in my body or outside of it. I had not yet found a way to be all of these things at once. I could not find a way through or beyond my contradictions. I was not able to treat them with a pinch of salt.

If one is ill and out of balance, as I was then, perhaps the goal is not to immediately become "healthy"; it is rather, at that one disjunctive moment, to be fully what one is, to discover the arc of the story in which one plays a part, however different that part is from what one would prefer. To long for the first Earth—the "Golden Age" of the Ancient Greeks, the "First World" of the Hopi," the Vedic "Satya Yuga"—does not mean that our feet should not be planted on the fifth, nor should we love the first Earth less. Our longing will serve to deepen the expression of our longing. Our guide: an intimate stranger. Our home: a series of catastrophic die-offs, an emptiness in which is stored the seeds of a lost language. We do not put on bodies to just quickly take them off; for such would be an insult to the Fates, who miss nothing, and do not forgive. Life is not a problem to be solved, except by death. And even this solution is not quite what it seems.

Revenge is a Dish Best Tasted Cold

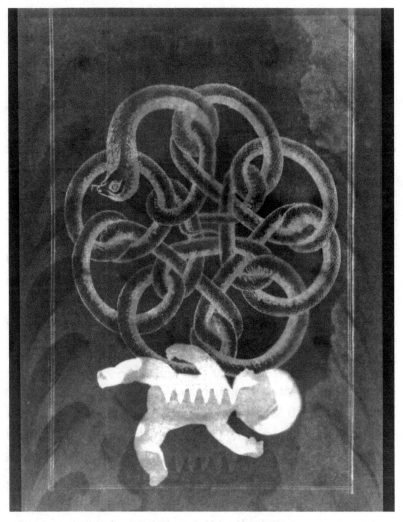

Snake Knot, photogram, 2002

Before being kicked out, I attended a parochial high school for two years—two years of Hell, or of preparation for the arcane tortures of the Apocalypse. An "education in the Classics," as they say. The mind is a muscle, which one would never be allowed to use—

or else. Self-knowledge was regarded as a form of masturbation. Just see where that would lead. And, once you got started, then how would you ever stop? It might one day become impossible to distinguish between one's intellect and an orgasm. No exclamations of "Eureka!" were allowed. One's flash of sudden intuition might disrupt the Pre-Game Pep Rally.

Such intellectual "exercise" as there was—and the use of this term strains language to the breaking point—was like the watching of an aerobics video: The instructor shouts like a drill sergeant. It is good for you, somehow. Although sitting on a couch, one feels virtuous by the end. St. Thomas Aquinas had corrected the few small mistakes of Aristotle. He was smarter than you! In this age of genetic recombination, he was the thinking Darwinian's modernist. He had determined how many angels should be allowed to dance on a pin. No more need be said. Even now, those angels are too petrified to get off.

No doubts need mar one's contemplation of the shadow of the atomic bomb.

Usurping the right-of-way on Main Street, we were forever staging marches with felt banners and singing songs with choruses like, "And they'll know we are Christians by our love, by our love." —Ugh. Such sentiments are among the few things that can inspire me to hatred. Even now, the sight of a flaming dove can cause my stomach to turn over. They are not cute; they are evil. Cosmic love can be difficult, if not in theory then in practice. It is more of a rare element than the evidence-free chorus of a song. Cosmic love is not for beginners, but the basic idea of forgiveness is a sound one.

"Forgive us our trespasses, as we forgive those who trespass against us."

Christ—yes; Christians—no. How many devotees of the cross have ever shouldered the above pronouncement? The first part they take seriously, yes; the second part they ignore. "Only connect," said E.M. Forster. Both injunctions perhaps point us toward the fact of our radical interdependence. The web is inconceivably complex. We have no way to extract ourselves. The web breathes us, even as we argue that our breathing is our own. In the Cloud of Unknowing, forgiveness may prove the only method of "dead reckoning" that will work. From the seed of nothing to the shore of nowhere, we do our best to mark an X upon the fog. How strange that we trade enemies from one life to the next.

Some hard kernel of insight has survived my scorched-earth war against the "Savior," who, as an omniscient god, should have known better than to hang around with Christians. "Thank god that I am Jung, and not a Jungian!" exclaimed Jung, in a tone that we can imagine to be incredulous with disgust, or perhaps relief. A foreknowing Christ should have followed Jung's example. I would argue, too, that a Monotheist is the greatest enemy of the One. They have named "G-d," though in a somewhat generic form. To make an idol, they have shrunk the haunted oceans of the Void. They have cut down the Tree of Life. Omphalos is now horizontal. They have literalized the interdependent meanings of the Ur-Text.

Yes, it may be practical to take back our emotions from our enemies, those emotions we have all too eagerly invested, but when is it better to judge than to forgive? Should we go easy on the murderous salesmen of forgiveness, whose love is only for their own beliefs? If the people that we have symbolically forgiven continue to hurt others, to lie about the most obvious of facts, to bend the law where they can and make new ones when they can't, when the richest 26 people control as much wealth as the poorest 3 ½ billion, when those in charge shrug at the destruction of an ocean, of what use is our act?

Social justice may demand that we make use of our anger. In its time, the guillotine was a perfectly reasonable invention, designed to right many centuries of wrongs. What should we do with our list of malefactors, other than add names? Some, we can teach to regurgitate our theories. Those not subject to improvement we should kill. The only problem is that our anger can turn into a life-form. An algorithm might add our own name to the list.

"Revenge is a dish best tasted cold," or "Living well is the best revenge." I would argue for a third alternative, a non-dual one: Forgiveness dares us to imagine the soulless sociopath as guide— not to actions but to self-divisions, not to ends but to obstructions. The I is Other—but in a way that makes no sense, in a way that we must stretch the self beyond the breaking point to grasp.

In *Shakespeare in Love*, the plans of the young Shakespeare and his friends are always just about to collapse. In one scene, all of London's theaters have been shut down by the plague, and the Rose's owner, Philip Henslowe, is about to be tortured by moneylenders. He says, "Mr. Fennyman, allow me to explain about the theatre business. The natural condition is one of insurmountable obstacles on the road to imminent disaster." Fennyman then asks, "So what do we do?" Henslowe answers, "Nothing. Strangely enough, it all turns out well." Fennyman asks, "How?" Henslowe answers, "I don't know. It's a mystery." The town crier then announces, "The theatres are reopened, by order of the Master of Revels!" Forgiveness may depend upon a similar sense of mystery. To forgive, we must trust that the play will get produced.

We must play more than one role. We must reconceive the theater of our actions. There is a well that leads from the Pole Star to the City of the Oppressors. There is a well that leads from the City of the Oppressors to the Pole Star. More than personal animosities block our movement towards forgiveness. To get a green light from the Pole Star, we may be forced to exchange one body for another. We must see out of new eyes. If the act of saying does not make our forgiveness so, if there are leaders—fill in blank—whom we would still choose to defenestrate, we may nonetheless commit our invocations to the depths.

As we cast our darkness off, those we killed may clatter from the future to assault us. There, we are not we, not are the others they. We must enter a new space. There, we may judge the judges. There, we may wear the skins of the accused. The spheres will ring. The teachers who have supervised our progress may appear. An archaic smile may then tug at the corners of our lips.

The Stranger Face of the Friend

Bird Arising out of Snake, Snake Arising out of Pot, 1989

1

I had overstayed my welcome at St. Peter's Parochial High School. Its one virtue was its location in an ancient house, with many irrational crawl spaces. The smells of oiled wood and chalk dust were of more interest to me than my courses. Both teachers and classmates struck me as proof positive that the race did not evolve. Faith had pinned the intellects of some. Others had been locked in the cabinet of science. Of one thing I was sure: that the servants of Earth's cybernetic reich had been planning to remove my neocortex. Better embalmers than they had tried! It was difficult to get each scrap without damaging the nose.

My supernatural weapons were in storage. A wind preceded the philosopher's stone, whose energy had been hidden behind the two hands of a clock. My teachers were concerned about my psychological health. I did not dare to obey them; no, because whatever the consequences, a voice more frightening than any of theirs had also issued ultimatums. I observed myself from a corner of the Van Allen Radiation Belts. The voice spoke, and I did my best to perform the actions that it specified. There were times when I succeeded. There were others when this performance was only in my head.

"Drop your pencil on the floor," the voice said, "whenever you see the headmaster coming. He is a recruiter for Opus Dei, an evil sect, and he will almost certainly criticize your hair. Insist that he lead by example, as did Christ. Leave no evidence behind should you choose to hang him from a cross." Or, "Demand to know: If Mary had sex with the Holy Ghost, who is usually pictured as a dove, then why was Jesus born without a beak?" Had I not tried to behave? It was only by accident that I had broken such a large percentage of St. Peter's rules. I left, with a strong push to the back from a secret board of judges, at the end of my sophomore year.

A revolt against causality had been launched. Ghosts pointing to the collapse of the third dimension congregated. No act of will could restore my freedom of association with the Double, who was then present only in the form of an abstract shadow, as a threat made in a language that I did not understand. This was a language that only the dead spoke, the stellar dead, not the makeshift versions. I was alive, in a manner of speaking, a bit more here, a bit less there, though not in the sense that the Ancients would have understood the concept, not in the sense that I would later come to use the word myself.

I did not yet know enough, of course, to call this abstract shape "my Double," any more than I could pierce the psyche of a naked Siddha in a cremation ground, any more than I could grasp the instructions in the Egyptian Book of the Dead, however much they had been left specifically for me. I knew this Double only through his impact on my sanity, as a promise that I would get what I deserved. On the back of my head: cold breath. He was the sum of things unknown and abilities untapped. If this figure was close, his motives were obscure. I was not yet free to associate with him, only to go where his finger pointed. That freedom would come at the end of a long war. It would be necessary for a designated enemy to prepare the way for my breakthrough. The dream that we called waking consciousness was a joke, whose punchline had not yet arrived.

Current humans were just variations on the prototype of the object. They were person-shaped bundles of stimulus and response. They were designed to perform a set variety of functions. They were objects that could move, upon which corporations could hang the latest styles of clothing. Such humans were less real than the powers that consumed them, who were themselves only real in their own minds, by virtue of the shadows that lent to them their strength. Fate would orient the phallus of the wounded god. My socially-constructed self was a necessary evil. It was, as I would later come to understand, the contraction of an eight-armed sphere, the plaything projected by an earlier but still present state of omnipotence. Was I conscious? Not at all. Did my body not look much or anything like a sphere? These were no more than temporary setbacks, glitches in Enoch's gematria, permutations in the occupational status of the One.

Instructions had been broadcast from a star, from the depths of the night sky: "Get out!" It was time for a change. Milkweed pods, sprouting from the junk of abandoned lots, broke open. My sail swelled. Bright with hope, I said goodbye to working-class South Worcester, a neighborhood of factories and railroad tracks. At the age of 15, I transferred to Doherty Memorial High. It was at the time a brand-new school, in the low, expansive style of architecture common during the 1970s. The complex of buildings was enormous, resembling, more than a bit, a shopping mall. The corridors were brightly lit and long, going off in all directions. Vast crowds migrated when the bell rang.

From my perch at the corner of the Van Allen Radiation Belts, which some might describe as the doorway of my homeroom, I observed the drifting of the ghost-like students through the complex. In their hunger, they migrated without knowing where they went. They saw without knowing what they saw. They heard without knowing what they heard. They felt without knowing what they felt. They consumed without knowing who or what they ate. By doing no more than shuffling from one foot to the other, they went in search of a symbol that existed before birth. They went in search of the key to industrial-strength sacrifice. They went in search of the loved bodies that they left on a crumbling shore. They went in search of the magnet of Mohenjo Daro. They went, without knowing more than the room number towards which they were turning. Such was the arcane path of their migration.

It is not that I believed that I was other than a ghost. I was, if anything, even more of a disembodied remnant than my classmates. Unlike them, however, I could feel the breath of the emptiness that was waiting to engulf us, the emptiness that several ages ago had eaten our souls for lunch, even as we continued to be driven by our habits.

The school was by far the best in Worcester. It was located in an affluent part of the city, with some of the most challenging courses and the most demanding teachers. Even the students, children of lawyers, professors, and factory owners, were more articulate than the teachers I was used to. Until my junior year at Doherty, I am not sure that I had ever encountered a good teacher, not one, at least, that made me sit up and take notice. In sophomore English class at Saint Peter's, we had studied Joyce Kilmer's "Trees." In Mrs. Goldman's junior English class at Doherty, we analyzed T.S. Eliot's "The Wasteland." I preferred the later poem. It was at Doherty that I began to recover from my childhood. I had known that my world was small, but I had not realized just how small it was.

It was there that I met the gruff but not especially lovable Mr. Sleeper, my Cultural and Intellectual History of Europe teacher, who confronted me with the large holes in my knowledge, who introduced me to Pico della Mirandola's *Oration on the Dignity of Man*, which had the effect of a depth-charge. It was there that I met Sue Castigliano, a teacher who intervened at a crucial turning-point in my development, who was present in a way that no previous teacher had been present. It was there also that I met Mr. Trippi, my senior-year art teacher, the enforcer of technique and the enemy of vision, who was demanding in a way of which I was not prepared to take advantage. To learn to create art, he believed, was no different from learning the elements of Euclidean geometry. There were principles, to memorize, and procedures, to perform. Like many would-be geniuses, I believed that such doglike obedience was for others.

Mr. Trippi was short, aggressive in his occupation of space, very plainly spoken, with wide, intense eyes. He had many of the traits that I associated with the first-generation descendants of immigrants from Europe, in his case Italy, of whom there were many in Worcester at the time. This was back when the American Dream—whatever the limitations of the concept—was something more than a myth, when a whole extended family could go from poor to affluent in a matter of two decades, so long as they believed, so long as they defined their goals in the image of this dream. To judge by his body language, you would think that Mr. Trippi had missed his calling as a bricklayer, until you noticed the flash of intelligence in the eyes or picked up on the scholarly references when he spoke.

Mr. Trippi was proud to be an American, at a time when I was against the war in Vietnam. He was eager to continue to ascend through the ranks of the middle class, to display his success, to prove what he was worth. I did not see him as a person like myself, nor did I recognize that we acted from a similar urge to prove what we could do. I was by turns arrogant and withdrawn, contemptuous and scared. That I might be almost wholly uninformed about a subject was not enough to prevent me from passing the most absolute of judgments. Mr. Trippi was unwilling to admit that a student even had a right to an opinion. When he talked, Mr. Trippi would stand about a foot in front of you, and stare, unblinking, into your eyes. I would always end up looking at the floor, at the wall, at the ceiling, or out the window. He did not seem to notice or to care that nothing of what he said was getting through. He took my disengagement as an invitation to stare even more directly, to be even more insistent in the proving of his points, to stand a few inches closer.

In this period, I had great hopes for myself without knowing much of anything, without being able to do more than gesture towards my spiritual and creative goals. I preferred a more oblique approach to self-discovery. Let us call this the method of "actively visualized self-deception." By imagining a larger space than the one in which I lived, I was, by fits and starts, able to gain some partial access to it. If this method was, to some extent, successful, I was not in any way prepared to prove myself to someone as militantly sure of his principles as Mr. Trippi. I would often stay up late, listening to crickets chirp in the field across the street from my house. The night was my idea of a good teacher. She did not bore me. She did not make me feel more limited than I knew myself to be, and I suspected that even her most absurd demands would prove more useful than yet another lecture about Raphael. Yes, I knew that he could draw. I also knew that Shakespeare was important.

In his *Oration on the Dignity of Man*, Pico della Mirandola had said,

> We have given you, O Adam, no visage proper to yourself, nor
> endowment properly your own, in order that whatever place,
> whatever form, whatever gifts you may, with premeditation,
> select, these same you may have and possess through your own
> judgement and decision…We have made you a creature neither
> of heaven nor of earth, neither mortal nor immortal, in order
> that you may, as the free and proud shaper of your own being,
> fashion yourself in the form you may prefer. It will be in your
> power to descend to the lower, brutish forms of life; you will be
> able, through your own decision, to rise again to the superior
> orders whose life is divine.

"Five centuries after his death," I thought, "how many of us have really come to terms with Pico's words? Other thinkers have said similar things, perhaps, but who has said them in so personal a manner, in a tone that both accuses and invites? I can hear his voice. As Pico says, I am a creature with no place to call my own. I will shape myself. I will test the rungs of Jacob's Ladder. My alienation is a role; it is not a disadvantage. Can I write a perfect college-level essay? Can I draw a good self-portrait? No. Many students at Doherty can, but what is that to me? I will burn with the Seraphim. I will challenge the Thrones. I will not be content to see out of two eyes. I will somehow find the talents that I need."

Pico also said,

> For a certainty I shall speak out (though in a manner which is neither modest in itself nor conformable to my character), I shall speak out because those who envy me and detract me force me to speak out. I have wanted to make clear in disputation not only that I know a great many things, but also that I know a great many things which others do not know.

Yes. Like Pico, I would speak. I would demand to express my mode of vision, however half-formed it might be. I loved the matter-of-fact nature of Pico's arrogance. Unlike Pico, I was not a prodigy. I was a child of the working class, who, in spite of several years of far-flung reading, had only just begun to come into his own. There were times when I experienced my stupidity as an almost physical weight, as a slowly constricting boa, as a virus that had begun to eat into my brain. I had said to Sue Castigliano, "I feel that I am getting stupider by the day." She answered, "Why should you be any different?" Against all available evidence, however, I did feel that I knew certain things that others did not know.

Then, at 2:00 AM one night, with no warning that anything unusual might occur, I experienced an outpouring of creative energy, as explosive as a pyroclastic flow. To say that this outpouring was explosive is to only speak of its force. The quality of the outpouring—or near total lack thereof—must be seen as a separate issue. (Nothing to see here, Reader. You are getting very sleepy. When you wake, you will forgive the author for his teenage grandiosity. You will forgive his crimes against late 19th-century Symbolism. You will see that he has set aside his ego. When you come to a sentence that begins "two things," you will obey without remembering a word of these commands.) Two things came from this life-altering experience. These were a 16-page personal epic and a series of labyrinthine, hieroglyphic drawings, unlike anything I had previously done. If these pieces were not good, they were maybe just good enough. An energetic vortex had popped open.

The space that I had entered, or rather, that had entered me, felt pregnant with both danger and the shadow of true vision. To what end should I stuff facts into my head when it could, at any moment, be cut off? I told my mother that I was ill, and I did not return to school for several days.

I became obsessed with the idea of the "façade." Worcester's skyline was no more than a series of cardboard cutouts. How strange it was that they had no other side. They held back surging currents, the waves of a black ocean. To peek behind them was to plunge into the depths. I could not stop myself; I peeked. To believe that the city had more substance than a stage-set was to fall victim to a form of hypnotic propaganda.

The Institute of Oceanic Flux sent agents to recruit me. Their instructional method: dreams, quite often long. These provocateurs were somewhat less active during the day. In their terrifying bird-masks, they would observe from behind my shoulder. Should they reach out, they were anything but gentle, and their claws would feel like vice-grips on my arm. These presences were my protectors, my guides to the great society whose branches stretched far off into the dark. Tangled beyond belief, and anxious to be fed, its roots were a bloody map traced by the transmigration of lightning. I would be taken by the hand, led layer by archeological layer down through the flames of collapsing civilizations, the walls almost falling on my head, until, at the last moment, a small passage leading to the next stratum would be found. Snakes would whisk me across epileptic floods. The knowledge found in these chaotic states was not meant to be accumulated; it was meant to be spent, to be only partially grasped. I could barely do that much.

Images led to images. The chains of association sprawled in all directions. Was this vision or schizophrenia? Few meanings could be solidified. As this alternate space grew, I had to give myself instructions: "Remember, you must eat. Put cheese on crackers. Pour milk in glass. There are your shoes. Do not stare at the floor. Do you think that your shoelaces are going to tie themselves? Why are you looking at your body from the corner of the room? Put your eyes back in your head." Sadly, no supernatural presence would appear on call to help me with a math exam, nor would the World Snake lend me the courage to ask Claudia Mulalley for a date.

"Sheathed in an iron glove," I said, "let the hand of Fate, as in the 1914 painting by de Chirico, with a thunderous click put its finger on the chessboard." Already, and how many times, had the stage-props of the 20th Century been swallowed by the ocean, on one of whose waves I rode? Only fools could believe that the First World War had begun in 1914. I saw my body in a trench, parts gone, decommissioned. One self, out of hundreds. So much for my avant-garde movement, my unpainted paintings, my unwritten books. My heart was cold. There were no tears in my eyes.

Let the Untermenchen believe that each thing happened only once, and only on a particular date, as if this war was somehow special because we had forgotten all the others. It was "a" world war; by no means was it the first. Through the mists of ancient history, I saw catastrophic die-offs, mass exterminations. Soon my genius would transform and systematize the dissociation of Pierre Lunaire. The moon was a vehicle. The true sun was black. Pursued by implanted memories, we were pawns lost on a flood plain of spent symbols, the victims of atomic bioengineering, the playthings of omniscient beasts. We were the horizontal shadows thrown by a vertical geometry. Our bodies were not other than symptoms. Our brains were the materialized fallout left from the sabotage of the Hall of Records.

I had discovered a poem by Cesar Vallejo that in part reads, "You people are dead. But what a strange manner of being dead. Anyone might say that you were not." These were my thoughts, exactly. Each night, I continued my back-breaking work on the scaffold of a Micronesian volcano, producing a few more pages for my journal, a few more drawings. As the weeks drifted by, I let a large amount of homework pile up. When I was able, finally, to yank my attention back to school, I brought the 16-page megalomaniacal epic to show to Mr. Sleeper, and I brought the best drawings from this series to show to Mr. Trippi. (Bad teachers! Metaphysical pretenders! Guides who could not read a map!) Neither of these mountebanks seemed to understand their job, to play the role that I assigned them. Mr. Sleeper liked three lines. Certain metaphors showed "promise." Mr. Trippi did not seem to be amazed. As Vallejo had warned, these people were dead, but so strange was the manner of their being dead that I had been tempted to assume they were not.

Slowly, with an expression of deep thought, Mr. Trippi examined each one of the several dozen pieces. He said almost nothing. Here and there he pointed out some detail that he thought I might want to change. He would like to see more color. Had I thought of doing these on a larger scale? In retrospect, there was nothing he could have said that would have been adequate, or enough. This could even be seen as a highly sensitive response. It is unfortunate that things did not stop there. What happened next brought a quick end to my experience in the class. It led me to block out whatever it was that he might have had to teach.

Returning to his bull in the china shop mode, he insisted that I stay after school for the next few days to complete the assignments I had not turned in. These were a color chart and a still life with some fishing nets, driftwood, a piece of cloth, and a bottle. This was like asking that I should do one of those paint-by-number versions of Gainsborough. *Blue Boy*, a masterpiece in a box. A painting to be hung above a couch. If I was an artist already, why would I want to pretend to be one, to learn skills whose only purpose was to please my bourgeois relatives? Like Miro, I wished to "assassinate painting." Like Breton, I believed that "Beauty will be convulsive or it will not be at all."

My teacher's words, as few and measured as they were, had unsettled me more than I was willing to allow. I was not, in fact, a shaman. I could not travel by choice from one place to another. No, I had to be carried. As my model, Rimbaud, had advised in his 1871 letter to Paul Demeny, I had done my best to derange my senses, but I seemed to have messed up on the systematic part. I had not distilled any poison into its quintessence. I had not come out the other side of madness. I was not yet a *voyant*. My explorations led only to the knowledge of how much I had left to do. If I did have some experience with vision, if I did feel the beginnings of some subtle form of guidance, I was not, as of yet, an artist or a writer. After school, I hung around for several hours, trying to imitate the grain on a piece of driftwood. I did not return to class for the rest of the semester. Later in the year, I was allowed to submit an independent body of work, and I squeaked by with a C.

Mr. Trippi came and went, like a mastodon in the moment before the glacial crags descended. He was, of course, guilty of bad timing, a flaw in any teacher, but also of violating the first commandment, which reads, "Do not disrespect the daimon. The primordial twin has no sense of humor." Like many adolescents, I could be faulted for a pathological inability to listen. I had not yet found a way to take from each teacher what he or she had to offer, and always, always, I demanded something else.

Now, at the age of 66, there are times when it seems that all perspectives have reversed. Death is not what we call death, life is not what we call life, nor are the two set in a simple binary opposition. What was large shrinks to the scale of a small toy, as I study the young "Brian" through the wide eyes of his Double. These physical events then appear in a ghostly light. These unimportant echoes then speak to their subtle aspects.

Shortly before graduation, Brian ran into Mr. Tsang, his art teacher from junior year. Mr. Tsang said, "What happened with Mr. Trippi? He was upset that you dropped out of his class. He thought you had talent, and he was doing his best to try to toughen you up, to teach you how to focus. You wouldn't look him in the eye. You wouldn't answer when he asked you simple questions, and then you just stopped doing your assignments. He couldn't guess what he'd done wrong."

During the next few years, after Brian had moved to Boston to go to art school, he would return to visit his family once or twice a month. There, he would sometimes see Mr. Trippi, wandering among the statues of the 19th-century heroes, wandering by the Dollar Store and the Paris Triple-X Theater, wandering along the concrete margins of I-90, wandering among cars in the parking lot of the Worcester Center Shopping Mall, blown here and there, an autumn leaf.

An infinite ache would spread upwards from Brian's solar plexus to his heart and then finally to his throat. Was this shrunken man the monster who would stare into his eyes, whose hateful words had sent him running out the door? Was this the fascist who had interrupted his early training as a shaman? Was this the demiurge whose finger snap had once broken his connection to the dream? No, he was just a retired high school teacher. He often looked quite serious, having found out that his wife was very sick.

Mr. Trippi was the unacknowledged catalyst, the distorted face of the friend. Brian asked for certain lessons. Mr. Trippi offered others. He taught more than he knew. He was the left hand of a broken god, an irrational number, a stray quark, Phi's infinite recursion, the flawed avatar who had all along been important to my subject's growth.

2

At cross-purposes, wearing constellated masks, two actors perform what they are scheduled to perform, and they may not turn to applaud each other's skill, even as death's birdsong can be heard. They just turn their heads aside. In the amphitheater that looks like downtown Worcester, they do not notice how the small waves lap the lower steps. They do not notice that these waves are getting bigger, that dolphins are circling the pretzel stand, that their feet are very cold, or that their shoes had started to squeak many centuries in the past. In spite of our great freedom, it is difficult for us to be other than who or what we are. Collapsing the wave function, by violence crafting a location for the socially-programmed self, we pull one story from the oceanic flux of all potential versions of that story.

We would far prefer to believe that we are conscious. We would far prefer to believe that our talents are our own, that our names are not detachable. We would far prefer to believe that the ignorant hear what we say. We would far prefer to believe that our actions all make sense, that we know where we were born, that a luminous tide was not waiting to retrieve us, as though it were possible to have an "up" without a "down," or a shore without a seabed. No artist should ever feel misunderstood. No teacher should ever feel that his gift has gone unvalued. Things should happen when we expect that they will happen. How troubling it is that they do not.

It would be so much easier to come equipped with all we need to know at birth. To forget, of course, is the reason we have chosen to be born. There are crimes that a nonexistent culture once committed, wells that we filled with blood. There are books we wrote on the wind that we grew too drunk to decipher. There are suns we threw into the bowels of the deep. There are gods that we dismembered, orphans we indifferently let starve, close family members that we struck down in a rage. There are vehicles that we miniaturized so as to tuck them in our pockets. We have accidentally turned these pockets inside out.

In moments of sudden illumination, we can, on an almost tactile level, feel how all the bits and pieces of our story fit together. The satisfaction that we feel, however, may be anything but complete, for the whole of the story can seem to have happened to someone else. The Perfect watch from the upper benches of the atmosphere. To themselves, they appear hunched over and attentive, with lamp-like elbows pressed on lamp-like knees. To us, the Perfect are no more than abstract points, just barely visible, but we can sense that they have some say in how the drama will be judged. We would probably go blind if we looked at them directly. It is a good thing, then, that our eyes just barely work.

The Goddess as Active Listener

Nut, from Tomb of Ramses VI, Hans Bernhard, CC BY-SA 3.0

1

When I was first introduced to my wife, I told her that I had always missed her but had never realized it until we finally met. She was present as a kind of pregnant absence. I was aware on some alternate level of the self of a kind of negative space, like the shape of a missing puzzle part, to which her image corresponded. Shape would one day fit itself into corresponding shape to complete the occult structure. We might certainly wish that this process were more foolproof than it is, that so many things could not potentially go wrong, and yet, in its own wonderfully slipshod way, this tendency of linked fragments to reassemble themselves into an image sometimes takes us where we need to go.

Are we meant to have certain experiences? Are we meant to connect with certain people rather than with others? At a multidimensional intersection—at a 19th-century train station as designed by Giorgio de Chirico, let's say, where the newly arriving and newly departed search for their respective tracks—it is possible to see how precarious forces constellate, not always to our advantage. You would think that each soul might choose the simplest path, so that joy would feed on joy. Why would we choose to live in exile, far from our own coast, to be stepped on, starved, and deceived? It should not be so difficult to return to the Satya Yuga. Nonetheless, it is. We break what we love. We then yearn for what we broke. Habit is not harmony. Safety is an illusion of the microcosm. With their eyes that never close, the seers of the World Maritime Empire watch.

Listen, and I will whisper in your ear. Perhaps earth-shattering events happen every day around you, more or less invisibly, as you brush past in your haste to buy a donut. A catastrophe that occurred in 9800 BC is only just now informing you of the whereabouts of your heart. After so much time it has decided to return, again to advocate for its role as the seat of true intelligence. If you do not stop the world, for just a moment, to talk to the stranger standing next to you, you may have thrown away your one and only chance to meet that significant Other. But where was the music of the occluded sphere hiding, and why did love's messengers take so long to appear? No doubt you are bad.

The more romantic among us are used to thinking that there may be one true soul-mate for each person. It is less common to imagine that friends or teachers may also play such central roles. How many of these are there? No more than a small handful. They may do no more than acknowledge what you are, but without them, somehow, you would not be you. In the staircase of your DNA, there are certain friends who wait on certain landings. At the Institute of Interplanetary Forms, a bird has programmed an encounter with a teacher. "Real" events are later tweaked to correspond. Such collisions have about them a great sense of uncanniness; the world has changed, and it is not possible to return to your earlier and simpler view of existence. Certain bits of information had been stored in your subconscious. If these were not meant to stay hidden, why would they have been put there? Why should this Mongol invader have access to what you cannot touch yourself? A kind of right to left reversal has occurred. Your mode of vision has been altered.

Once, let's say, you despaired of ever meeting a teacher who could see you. Then, through no effort on your part, such a teacher is just there. In retrospect, this meeting will no doubt seem inevitable, the most natural thing in the world. At the same time, you must study how the opposite is true: such a meeting should be seen as an "opus contra naturam," as an alchemical "work against nature," as the reverse engineering of a series of wrong turns, as the deconstruction of a badly deconstructed text. How do you know when a bird has programmed a key meeting? You know because the meeting should not have taken place at all.

"Aha!" you exclaim, and then breathe a sigh of relief. What a gift it is to have found a teacher you could love. A day or a year later, you are forced to read through the person to the presence just beyond, to a presence you suspect might see your every flaw, to a presence still sympathetic but also more demanding. Why had it seemed like a good idea to be seen and heard and understood? Was not anonymity far preferable? Was it not much better to let the centuries slide past, to categorize your visions as a quirk of biochemistry? The seers of the World Maritime Empire had once given you a thread. Their lines of transmission: disrupted by a comet. This presence demands to know if the thread they gave you has been cut.

The person hands you a copy of Par Lagerkvist's *The Sybil*. The presence reaches into the center of your skull, where the pineal gland is located, massaging it in such a way that it almost stops your heart. The person reassures, but the presence regrets to inform you that all your nightmares must hatch out, that your mind is an unopened oyster, that no one seems to have bothered to teach you how to breathe. There are, it seems, valid reasons for your enemies to hate you. Oh, and by the way, some two-thirds of what you take to be your good habits are a joke. The seers of the World Maritime Empire shake their heads. They had hoped for more. Who will take care of the web of underwater ports? Who will mourn for the primal culture? Turning their backs to you, they sigh. It hurts them more than you to outsource your correction. The noseless clerks of the Sitra Achra tremble, weak with excitement, unsure which mishap or mutilation should come next.

Somehow, you have met those you should meet. Each meeting leads to another. The known leads to the unknown; the unknown leads to the half-remembered. Do those special people remind you of someone in your past, or do they remind you, much more strangely, of themselves? When you encounter a person who is meant to be important, it can expose a need that, until then, you did not consciously know to exist. The ache you felt but did not know that you felt becomes somehow pleasurable in becoming more acute. There is nowhere left to hide. There is no need to avoid the pain that has tied a knot in your solar plexus, a knot that is as inscrutable as it is essential to your being.

Yes, "mistakes were made," as the hoard of your nameless accusers has suggested. By accident, no doubt, you have killed those whom you loved. You have burnt the books you wrote. You have double-crossed those causes for which you vowed to give your life. This has led to some degree of paranoia. You have learned to assume the worst about those who have come to teach you. Why else should you be so terrified? Why else should you fear the chanting that now streams from the horizon?

Your error was not the atrocity itself but rather your refusal to see the action clearly. "What do we have here?" a kind but terrifying presence asks, a slight smile on her lips. She has come from a distant place to stand a few feet in front of you. As a finger points to a wound, there is no reason to be embarrassed. A touch sets the healing sap in motion. One simple look communicates the lost history of an era, reversing the great wheel of devolution and freeing you from the crimes of the last 52,000 years. Green buds open on the derelict branch. Hallucinatory blossoms are not long in arriving. Messengers bring fruit from a tree already old when the first Earth had contracted from a dream.

2

Of whom does the inner teacher remind us? Perhaps the outer teacher is a key to unlock the inner teacher's door, beyond which breathes the most luminous of shadows. Demanding that the code of silence be removed, each synchronistic meeting is like a knock that echoes through the Hall of Records, that hall our Antediluvian betters once built from the skull of Akasha. "Who is there?" asks one of the bird-headed eunuchs who attend to its every need. We are usually too busy talking to respond. And if we do put aside our distractions and take a moment to respond, we will probably say something stupid like, "Who is asking?" With their wide eyes that have never ceased to stare, the seers of the World Maritime Empire watch the cities they once dreamed of sink their roots, the hunger they once planted grow. What does the shape of our longing look like? We will know it if and when.

This may be one of the key functions that good friends perform for each other. Our first meeting with such friends can be a shock, a slap to the face of our common sense, which shows us how things can make sense without having to make any sense. We are called to develop talents that we thought belonged to others. If our friend is not for use, not as such, he/she may serve ends more mysterious than we know. We may be called to summon memories for which our friend is just the conduit. We may be called to lift the spirits of the damned, to flirt with the unborn, to break the back of the military-industrial-infotainment complex, to rip the mask from the zeitgeist. And then, just as easily, the magnetic force that attracts two friends can later push them apart. We share a world with them. One day, their eyes go suddenly blank. If there were no parting, we might never gain the distance necessary to come to terms with their influence.

A good teacher is not a friend, as such. Unlike a good friend, a good teacher is never more than partially accessible, a moon of which we can only see the cusp, and yet, being gone, he/she is still capable of answering a question. If the inner teacher can justly be called "good," this goodness may depend on us. We have only to redefine the meaning of the term. We have only to find some way to invoke this teacher's presence, in such a way that our question can be posed, in such a way that the absent can answer, in such a way that student and teacher are speaking the same language. In a strange land, our lips must form the words of a song that we learned in childhood; this time around, however, its effect will not be innocent. This song may sound like the howling of a ghost; like the gasping of a city's population, buried while alive; like the banging of a door in the blood-drenched beerhall of the gods; like the whisper of the rivers of mercury in the tomb of the first Chin emperor.

Let us posit that the inner teacher is led by another hand, by that teacher as demanding as he/she is omniscient, whose influence is most often not seen nor heard but rather felt in the peculiarities of external circumstance. We use terms like "male" and "female," "right" and "left." These are practical enough. Terms like "body," however, stump us. We do not see how "inside" and "outside" are connected. "Do not test us," we say, "We are tired of being stalked. We would prefer that our glass houses do not have any windows. What genius planned that a tornado should be our mode of transport? Our iPhones will live for us." Of course, Sir or Madam. Your wish is our command. As you like.

Is there any moment at which the teacher behind the teacher is not present? Yes and No. There are those who say that no good teacher would throw away his student, that cruelty is not love, that she would not leave him, cold and naked, with only a few well-worn platitudes to chew on. How absurd! There is a grammar to such silence, which the teacher expects the student to remember how to parse.

If the seers of the World Maritime Empire have pulled the waves above them, we should not assume that they are other than alert. We should only say that they observe from a great distance. Their wide eyes do not blink. They breathe neither water nor air. If they do, indeed, watch, if they even now continue to subject us to surveillance, if there is no way to escape from the life-patterns that they guard, the inner teacher may yet serve as our articulate ambassador. To what end and for whose benefit does he/she intercede? "Kneel," say the bird-headed eunuchs, and we must. "Yes, obey," says the inner teacher, "then rebel." There are few actions that will lead in a straight line. Threads can be cut without warning. Whole cultures can be ripped from their coasts. As intimate as the breath, as well-positioned as the tongue behind the teeth, the teacher subtly supports. To the dead student, this type of support is a mixed blessing. It may not, at first, be of use.

3

Omphalos

Each of us starts life as a world center, indifferent to the laws of time and space, sure that our call will result in a response. At first, our solar plexuses have only a few shadows, like the cities on the sun. Our unconscious minds are as inhabited by symbols as an ocean is by fish. New sensory data float on the surface. We are everywhere, but in need of much.

Soon enough, we are shocked. We find, as we steadily expand the sphere of our discovery, that the world does not cooperate in affirming our self-image. Maddeningly, few recognize our age. There are theorists who dismiss our clearly audible demands as no more than mechanical reflexes. Q: "Does the young world center feel pain?" A: "No, of course not. He is only a pouch of biochemical intersections, whose random spurts of electricity cause him to make noise."

Donations from the maternal breast aside, perhaps there is something wrong here. It is not that others do not also come to kneel, or offer tribute, or express their joy and wonder. They do, but their actions are unpredictable. Colored toys revolve like intoxicated planets. When we dream of other lives, our hands no longer return with the objects that they clutch. It is necessary for light to fall on objects in order that we should see them, and it is more difficult to see at night than in the morning. Some whisper that we are "cute." Doors open and close for no reason. A revolt is imminent, perhaps, and we note that, one by one, our caretakers have begun to disobey. You then discover that your body has a skin, "you," who were once a "We." Will somebody shut that baby up? It is difficult to think with so much crying going on.

Earth is cold and wet. Life will kill you. It is probably better to keep the real story of your predestination hidden, even from yourself. Once consciousness was big. There was no fear. By sharing songs all species could communicate. Little art was needed to interpret the self-dramatizing image, the self-illuminating text. There was a mountain that rose from the bowels of the deep. To stand on it was to scan each period of history, like a landscape. The new body in which you find yourself is small. The mask you wear cannot mediate between incompatible scales. After all, it is a mask. The bigger you get, the less of your original face can be remembered.

As humans, we are not the puppets of the gods; no, we played a part in the creation of the world, in the Shivirat ha-Kelim, the "Breaking of the Vessels," in the lifting up of the first city from the depths. We played our part in the removal of the future, in the far from innocent displacement of the past. We played our part in the successive reconstructions of the torus. The human function goes as far back as the Bindu, as the scarab Kheper, as the Aleph, as the Orphic Egg, as the gravitational singularity that preceded the Big Bang, and then even possibly beyond. These bodies are the most recent version of an archetype. The human role remains the same; it is only its associated powers that may expand or contract.

You had come with a gift. It was not like any other gift, and there was no one else who could offer it to the world. It was not that you were special, as this word is normally understood; no, you were anonymous, and each person ever born had brought some particular gift, however much they may not have remembered what it was. This gift was not an object, at least not in the usual sense. It was an aboriginal totem on the move, a baroque feat of geometry, the fixation of one of the sub-powers of the zodiac, a kneeling of the wind before the wind, a monstrous prodigy of disinformation, the opening of a clean, well-lighted space, an offering from a child of the gods to the beyond. It was, in short, an individuated Uroboros, whose tail, from the first of days, was hidden in its mouth.

How strange that it took the form of a not-yet-spoken story. Already close to perfect, this story went in search of a new audience. Such a gift could not be separated from your nature. It simply was, a matter of fact, beyond argument, and also was why you were here. There was a task to perform for which no one else was suitable. You should find some way to make a living, yes, but there were other, more complex obligations.

There was a task to perform for which no one else was suitable, or perhaps, for which no one else had been dumb enough to volunteer. Each year, the path back to the instructions in the seed would grow more and more circuitous. Not many of your goals would be achieved. That, too, is something that you would earlier have known. For obscure reasons, like the other 7.6 billion people on the planet, you had picked this time and place, a time of converging crises, a place where snake oil salesmen sold only empty bottles. Leaps of imagination would be waiting to transport you, if and when they chose. This was not at all convenient. You could hear the ticking of an inner clock. This had led you to regard your more personal objectives as irrelevant, to the extent that you had the sanity to judge. It would have been so much easier not to care at all, not to sense the growing disturbance in your bones. There were many modern devices to which you could have turned.

To not have to see with your eyes: what a joy! To not have to hear with your ears: what a joy! You were broken, perhaps. There was some sort of a screw loose, or an extra piece or a piece that did not fit. Once, the spirits had collaborated in taking you apart. They had shown great skill. They were much less certain about putting you back together. Your brain was left on some random shore. These spirits seemed to have more important things to do.

Once, the seers of the World Maritime Empire had pulled you from the waves. They were tall and thin. Their skin just barely covered the luminous currents underneath it. Within their elongated skulls, points flickered like constellations. Speaking mostly with their eyes, which were somehow both peaceful and sad, they led you up white cliffs to the ruins of an observatory. There, they showed you how your story looked from a great distance.

They showed you how your life was really not your life, not as this was commonly understood. It was not "a" life, nor was it only yours. They showed you how wheel turned inside of wheel, each alive, each psychotically complex, each wheel kept in motion by the wheels that turned within it, each larger and more frightening than the wheels a moment before. You saw how the Earth was no bigger than a pinhead—just large enough to be visible—even as its circumference stretched to GN-z11. You then saw how, should you go there, it would not take 13.4 billion light years to fly back to the pinhead. No, at least according to what they told you, this would take less than an eyeblink. You could see the many dozens of chores that you left only half-complete, the messages unheard, the promises you broke, the tens of thousands of hours thrown away. Some might classify such a voyage as a dream. What cosmic irony. Steps would have to be taken so you did not fall entirely back to sleep.

In the end, what luck was yours. What an influx from the dark side of the sun, where you had once, so pleasantly, had sex.

You no longer had to depend upon your own imagination, not at all; there was no way to determine whose imagination it was. You could hear the ticking of an inner clock, the dead, with their long shadows, laughing, the Earth cracking along its geometric seams, the birds weeping, the plants of the Amazon shriveling up. You could hear the cities buzzing like white nuclear reactors, the gods getting drunk, the hedge fund managers cursing as they jumped from the roofs of buildings. You could hear the chiming of the eight-dimensional vimanas in their clouds, the zombies gnashing, the snails roaring. You could hear the continents arguing about the state of their relationships, plate over groaning plate, the oceans whispering as they plotted out their long-delayed return.

You could see the four elements fume, the primal letters cut and pasted to give birth to new cultures, the revolution shaking the sub-powers of the zodiac. You could see the flying snakes, the crawling birds. You could see the mountain rising from the ocean, the salt-encrusted ruins at its top. You could see the wide eyes of its resident cartographers, the unspeakably old, the curious, those able to look through your eyes as you tried and once more failed to look through theirs. You could see the mountain rising from the ocean, Mount Kunlun or Mount Meru or Mount Qaf, its peak towering towards Orion, even as it rose 10,000 times before.

You could see how many times your story had been told, how you wrote it long ago and far away. Why did you only just now decide to come to terms with your mistakes? Who would have thought that a finished story would take so long to revise? Utnapishtim did not leave a manual. Menes thought that only stones should be allowed to speak. It would be useful to be able to figure out how to diagram a sentence. Some help would be offered, but not, of course, in a form that you were ready to accept.

4

"Gnothi Seauton" or "Know Thyself"—attributed to Socrates

But also to Chilon of Sparta, Heraclitus, Pythagoras, Solon
of Athens, and Thales of Miletus. Juvenal, in his 11th Satire,
claimed that the precept actually descended "de caelo"—directly
out of heaven

When I met Sue Castigliano, my speech teacher during senior year
at Doherty Memorial High School, it was not at first apparent
that she would one day change my life. I had never before had a
teacher who had any sense of who I was, of the hole in my heart
or the blockage in my psyche. She was from the Midwest, not
obviously countercultural—I would find out otherwise—and her
most noticeable virtues were such things as calmness, openness,
acceptance, and curiosity. She dressed simply. She wore very little
jewelry. She was not at all theatrical, and she certainly did not
announce that our speech class would be about so many things
other than speech. Gently pushing aside my defenses, she reached
out and down through the soul to touch me on the most elemental
level. Even now, looking back from a distance of more than 40
years, and far removed from the melodrama of that period, it is
hard for me to imagine who, what, or where I would be if that
meeting had never taken place. Again, I exhale a sigh of relief.

It is said that when the student is ready the teacher will appear.
Luckily, the teacher may also choose to appear when the student is
not at all ready. She drags him, if need be kicking and screaming,
into a new, more direct, but also more paradoxical relationship with
the self. Socrates' injunction, "Gnothi Seauton" or "Know Thyself,"
which, according to Pausanias, was inscribed on the forecourt of
the Temple of Apollo at Delphi, is far more demanding than it
has any right to be. It is a simple statement, composed of only two
small words. The injunction becomes more demanding, not less,

as we attempt to translate our all-too-often inflated insights into action. Who, exactly, is doing the knowing? What is the nature of the self that presents itself to be known? Perhaps what we see is the illuminated crescent at the edge of an—almost—unimaginable sphere. As with the subtle but subversive presence of the teacher, this crescent becomes more visible as we are forced to grapple with the limits of our vision, until, quite suddenly perhaps, we are led into the dark. To begin to grasp the "what" of what we are, we must let go of the fixed version of the "who."

Is the ego the knower of the self, or is the self the knower of the ego? Perhaps the soul is itself a mask, soon to morph into a different form with the astronomical rotation of the fashion industry. Although, as a matter of convenience, I use it here, I do not like the word "ego." Over the past six years or so, I have tended to use it less and less. I have just as little use for or patience with the all too popular term "seeker." I far prefer Picasso's formulation. He states—somewhat arrogantly, perhaps—"I do not seek; I find." The term "teacher" I like more, but this term, if casually used, has problems of its own. Too many students of famous gurus, for example, can't seem to wait to give away all of their own intuitive authority to the teacher. It can be difficult for the teacher to be idolized, either spiritually or intellectually, and many are tempted to turn their students into small, submissive versions of themselves. This can be as true in a PhD program in archeology as in an ashram.

Clearly, good teachers are needed to transmit information, to help students to discover themselves, and to model certain skills. We cannot do without them. Even the most abstract of knowledge is not abstract; at least in the first stages, it must come attached to a living body. In this essay, however, it is the more primal concept of "teacher"—the teacher as spiritual catalyst—that I am attempting to explore. If such teachers are, in a different way, essential, they may tend to hold themselves to a lower standard than their students: They may stamp the void with their brand; they may speak highly of their total unimportance; in an energetic contest with Joe Average, they may judge themselves the victor; they may take themselves as seriously as their most obedient followers; they may believe that the light has more to teach them than the darkness; they may take as much as they give; they may have the power to catalytically intervene but be unwilling to let go.

It is not that such teachers lack the knowledge that they claim; they may very well possess it, but they do not give it freely. They do not prefer to overflow. Rather, they choose to portion this knowledge out, and, in the process, they can come to believe their own PR. How easy it is for the once enlightened teacher—accidentally on purpose—to be sucked into the vortex of his own charisma! Power intoxicates, and the gods do like to drink. The student may then become sadomasochistically attached to his own childhood, to the deadness of his feet and the blockage in his spine. He will not make of his heart a meeting place or expect that his head will click open like an aperture. He will see his mind as an electrochemical databank, as an empty space to be filled up with the teacher's big ideas. He will not learn how to leap from a great height, to move into and beyond death, or to hatch the universe from an egg. He will not dare to trust that his energy is a kind of self-existent vehicle.

I think that seekers often fixate on the "shattering of the ego" as a way to prove to themselves that they actually do exist; if they do not possess any breadth of cosmic vision, they are nonetheless experts in the role from which they are trying to escape. It is far more problematic for the seeker to accept that he is where he is supposed to be, even if he has no memory at all of when this choice was made. This is not to say that he should not speak truth to power, or take action against injustice, or withhold his empathy from a person in a dead-end situation because supposedly this person has "created his own reality"; no, I say only that he should challenge himself to grasp the larger shape of his life-story, to intuit how *daimon* and *persona* fit together. The real challenge is not to be elsewhere; it is to be, more fully, here. And that, of course, is the question: just what do we mean by *here*?

Once, we lived in a city that we loved, a city in which humans mixed freely with the gods. That city would seem to have long ago disappeared, and yet it calls to us from the depths of the horizon. Our hand rests on the doorknob of the house where we came of age. Driven by implanted memories, the human genome dreams of a real voyage to the stars.

It is 1971. And, as my hunt for occult wealth intensifies, I am attempting to round up my predecessors. I would determine, first of all, if there was ever anyone else like me who had existed on the Earth. Arrogance and Insecurity, my twin ravens, have returned with a few drops of mercury for my cup. I have set up Friedrich Nietzsche, Arthur Rimbaud, and Giorgio de Chirico as my makeshift Holy Trinity. At midnight, periodically, a black pyramid will descend to crush my skull. This is less fun than it sounds.

In a manuscript from 1913, Giorgio de Chirico writes,

> What is needed is great sensitivity: to look upon everything in the world as enigma…to live in the world as in an immense museum of strangeness, full of curious multi-colored toys which change their appearance, which, like little children, we sometimes break to see how they are made on the inside, and, disappointed, realize they are empty.

As if to prove that my potential genius is a toy, and indifferent to the scale of my embarrassment, not de Chirico but de Chirico's *daimon* seems to reach inside my head, whose contents he then removes to view them from odd angles. O infinite extension of the Argonaut! The *daimon's* arrogance is breathtaking. It is clear that he feels no obligation to put the original contents back, so that de Chirico, the 1913 version, from his squalid studio in the rue Compagne-Premiere, somehow stares out of my eyes. In the end, I can barely recognize my mother, who begins to look suspiciously like a manikin, so that I jump when she suddenly appears, with a plate of sardines, at my door.

"The first man must have seen auguries everywhere," writes de Chirico, "He must have trembled at each step that he took." It is 1917. The end of the Vietnam War is at hand, and, disoriented that Apollinaire survived a shrapnel wound to the head only to then be promptly carried off by the flu—how often must we poor humans bow to Fate the Ironist?—I am recovering from a bout of nervous exhaustion in Ferrara.

"Stone engineers, though silent," I shout, "please WASH UP ON THE BEACH. Give praise to Hygenia, the Muse." Depositing treasures, a wave lifts me, and I can hear my floorboards creak like tectonic plates. It is 1971, the year of the industrial-strength slaughter at Verdun, and I struggle to understand why I am hovering six feet above my body. My head does not seem to be damaged, so why can't I get in? Luckily, the luminous acorn of my genius is intact. Depositing treasures, a wave lifts me, and I can hear my floorboards creak like tectonic plates. When I turn, the door's frame is the only thing that stands.

Between 1954, the year of my birth, and 1973, 4.6 million tons of explosives are dropped on North Vietnam. Eggs of jellied fire do not play favorites with the pawns of geopolitics. Napalm burns both actors and observers to the bone, and then keeps on burning, in the souls of US citizens as well. Agent Orange defoliates at least 11,969 square miles of the land that is said to be "beloved by snakes." I am shocked by the infinitely ballooning shadow of my country, and yet, and yet, this shadow is familiar. At my feet, an abyss opens, and I stare into its depths. "How noble are your objectives!" a voice calls from below. "You have stamped your tiny foot against the Empire! You have raged against the war machine!" My innocence sticks in my throat, and I find that I cannot breathe.

Suitably chastened, I bit by bit withdraw my energies from the stage of social justice to refocus them on a more pragmatic goal— on my slapstick perfection of the role of *poete maudit*. My anger then prompts the transvaluation of all values. Revolution by night cracks the eggshell of the sky, which results in my omnipotence, that is, of a hollow, toy-sized version thereof. The experience is nonetheless somewhat satisfying. Following in the sacred footsteps of Rimbaud, I do my best to practice the "systematic derangement of the senses"—as though my senses had not so far been adequately deranged, as though I had not lost some 98 percent of them at birth. I begin to wear a beret and smoke a historically-accurate clay pipe. The grand rhetorical gesture is supreme, as in this passage from *A Season in Hell*, in which Rimbaud reminisces that "Disaster was my god. I called to my executioners to let me bite the ends of their guns, as I died. Spring brought to me the idiot's terrifying laughter."

Je est un autre, "I is an other." As was specified by Breton, true beauty should be convulsive. Nietzsche is a better friend than Jesus, who had followers, who were Christians, who in their current versions are far less likeable than when they had volunteered to be martyrs. What a nerve to have chickened out on the Apocalypse, the one in 72 AD. An experience of the "Eternal Return" is triggered by the turning pedals of my bicycle. That dragonfly landing on a milkweed pod is clearly the second coming of Parmenides. He will provide me with the keys to perpetual motion! Yogic breathing exercises will yet give birth to a race of wide-eyed Ubermenchen. Always, the entire visible world is about to pass out of existence.

If I, as "Brian George," now exist in more than one location, you must place the blame squarely on the other one, this earlier Brian, who is dead. Even now, I can hear the bird-chirps of the Underworld. I can feel the hand of a goddess still resting on my shoulder.

The process of self-discovery is a paradoxical one, which for most of us, at least at first, demands the steady hand of a guide, of a living person who is scheduled to perform the role of the psychopomp. His or her magnetic power draws us into the orbit of the self. The teacher confronts us with an inexplicable presence, a presence which, as we torture our minds to demystify its movements, we understand less and less. There is no way to encircle the motives of such a presence in advance. They cannot be grasped from the outside in, or as a matter of theory. They are always more and other than they were. For each clear purpose, there is always an unmediated shadow, within which a far vaster purpose breathes.

Given the importance of this role—the fact that billions of bits of information may not add up to real knowledge, and that knowledge, left to its own devices, is no substitute for vision—it is shocking that students can go from k-1 through grade 12 without ever meeting a teacher who might serve in this capacity. But then again, a public school is probably the last place that one should expect to find such guidance, and the tarred and feathered pyschopomp would most often be run out of town on a rail.

What would have happened to me if I had not met this particular teacher when I did, if she had travelled to some city other than Worcester from Ohio, if she had made use of the more typical "one-size-fits-all" approach, if the snakes from Minos had not wrapped around her arms? I might have eventually become more or less who or what I am—assuming that I did not slip and fall into psychosis—but I would lack a sense of trust in the origin of things, a sense of confidence equal to my desire for self-realization. As self-determined as I like to believe myself to be, so much of what and who I am is the result of the well-timed intervention of others, in this case Sue Castigliano, who so generously gave what I could not provide for myself.

Through the years of adolescent angst, I had grown away from childhood without making any progress towards adulthood. My parents had divorced when I was four years old, and my mother never quite recovered from the experience. From the time of their divorce until the day he died, my mother spoke less than a hundred words to my father. His name had gone into her black book of real and imagined wrongs. She did not forgive. It would not be taken out. As though out of nowhere, the happy nuclear family had exploded. I remember the shock of being evicted from the garden, at whose gate a fiery sword revolved. I remember how, in the short period before this, I would get into fistfights for no particular reason, from a sheer excess of energy, for the joy of it. I would wake up singing with the birds without even being aware that I was singing. How I treasure those few early years as an extrovert.

At the age of five, I had been unofficially appointed to serve as a kind of surrogate parent for my mother. As though she and not I were in need, I would sometimes rock her as she sobbed, uncontrollably, in my arms. I had to pretend to be strong enough for both of us.

I was left with an unacknowledged sense of abandonment. Distantly aware of being angry, perhaps a bit more aware of having lost my sense of trust, of the ache in my heart, I knew these emotions only through their symptoms.

I did not choose to confront my reflection in the mirror, for fear of falling through. I no longer enjoyed getting into fistfights; it had become a chore, not a pleasure. Instead, I got into arguments, in which I would go to any lengths to prove the dolt-like nature of my opponents. Somewhat later, starting in my senior year of high school—at the same time, curiously, that I took my first literary baby steps—I would often be very hesitant to drift off into sleep, for fear that I would not know who I was when I woke up, of not being sane. Planets would taunt me with their superior musical ability. I could barely play the recorder. I went through a long period of being terrified of perspective. I saw distance as a threat. I would not allow my eyes to drift down the converging lines of Main Street, for fear that I might be sucked out of my skin, for fear that the horizon would eat me. I was careful to focus only on signs and objects in the foreground.

Black magic had turned the too conscientious child into a headless plastic doll. "What a stupid place the world is," it thought. "Let me share my new-found freedom." Where the self should be, there were atoms, clashing. There were voids inside of voids. Used to being around adults, I could camouflage my thoughts in articulate form. On a good day, I could pass for a responsible young revolutionary. In due course, my comrades would overthrow the government. The industrial age would spontaneously combust. Chants would levitate the Pentagon. An urban gorilla at 17, I could strip and reassemble my attitude like an AK-47. Bourgeois robots would creak and beg for oil on a forced march to the amber fields of grain. A part of me was still very much a child, hurt and confused, who had no desire to expose his vulnerabilities to others. I wanted to disappear into the branches of my favorite apple tree, to daydream for hours as the clouds changed shape, to feel the Earth darken as the afternoon wore on. I would watch in secret as smoke billowed from a factory, beneath whose stacks the ant-sized workers crawled.

I cannot say exactly how Sue Castigliano changed me. I can only say that through and because of her a change took place. Stepping from the cave-mouth of a dream, the Goddess of Active Listening took my hand. By the end of the year, my concept of strength had been dissolved and reconfigured. I was less afraid of fear. Without yet knowing how to access what I knew, I had begun to see my wounds as so much raw material, the dark matter with which an alchemist might one day create wealth. It is as though my teacher had said, "What you see before you is now yours for the asking. The world is no longer a vast and anonymous space. It is a book that waits to be opened. Here, open it, and read."

5

When I remember Sue Castigliano, I think of almost naked dancers vaulting above the gold-tipped horns of Cretan bulls to the sound of waves breaking in the distance. Wandering with the ghosts of an exploded island empire, I enter the doors of a library that I first thought was an octopus. When I think of her, I see wheat bound in sheaves, gourds hanging from a makeshift wooden peristyle, grapes being stomped by rhythmic feet in vats. I think of the minute preparations of a glad community in the month before a human sacrifice.

When I remember her, I think of a face that encompasses multitudes, whose each component is distinct, the dark face of the goddess, projected against curdling clouds. I think of Ceres, of Inanna, of Isis, and of Rhea. I think of a complex network of retorts, of the seven stages of transmutation, of the althanor in which philosophers are heated and distilled. I think of olive oil sleeping inside of prehistoric jars, the Sibyl smoothing out her wrinkles in the shadow of the arch of Constantine. I think of a young girl standing on a cliff above the sea, the wind playing with her hair, as she listens for the voice of her drowned lover.

Her body is the world tree. Her navel is Omphalos, the place of interconnection. Her womb is the cave where stars can get changed into their human suits. In her left palm Saturn, time's comptroller, tilts and revolves. The fingers of her right hand touch the Earth with a gesture of abundance. And then, quite unexpectedly, she stands before me in a robe. In her eyes, I can see ships sailing back and forth. There, beneath the gigantic shadow of a wave, a wave that towers, still swelling, up and up, they go in search of a dock that may not ever have existed.

As I stare into her eyes, I can see myself staring back, one pair of eyes in a long series of reflections, eyes within eyes within eyes, some with bodies, some without. Even I, who have a body, seem only a bit more solid than the surf. Above our heads: a roof, whose beams have disappeared. There is only a charred corner. The shore is not far away. The astringent scent of salt is softened by the scent of moss and rosemary. "Beloved, come. Like fireflies, the ghosts of all past seers flicker in the dusk, where, if you hurry, you might catch one in a jar. Our fingers touching, like our souls, by its light we will read an elegy on the metastasis of Rome, on the triumph of the Age of Iron, the last statement by a poet who is called by some 'Anonymous.' You have only to write it first. You have only to reconstruct the text that you folded, spindled, and mutilated. Upon your lips, my breath: the elixir by which your name will be alchemically removed.

"Many years have passed since the day that you were buried, facing east, with a luminous stone clutched tightly in your hand, with much to say that would never be expressed. It is reasonable that your knees should start to tremble and give out. A drum beats in the distance, in the labyrinth of your ear. My pulse suspends you. Are you dead, or are you not, or is there some third alternative?

"In my eyes, you can see your culture, falling. Do not dare to look away! A slow spiral has returned you to this spot, and it will do so once again. You can even now feel how spaces open in your stomach, how your heart breaks with the ocean, how the sky reroutes the tangles of your nerves. And who is that small echo, now dancing on your tongue? As you fall into my eyes, you can even now feel how your thoughts are not your thoughts, how these thoughts belong to a figure that you lack the strength to recognize, how the wind sucks the marrow from your bones. There is more to fear than you know, but do not fear too much. We are free, in this silence, to calmly see and then celebrate the worst. Each throwing our arms around the other, as the light fades, we will weep."

This is the role that my teacher acted out for me. It is not, of course, who she was in her day-to day-existence. In hindsight, my memory manufactures images, which, no doubt, obscure far more than they illuminate, and yet they point to something not entirely untrue.

6

It is 1972. The seers of the World Maritime Empire have been swallowed by the fog. No buoys mark the locations of their ports. They were not voted out. They were utterly destroyed. 12,000 years have passed, and yet these guardians have not gone anywhere at all. Their eyes are wide. They watch. The intersection of one dimension with another is not subject to the tyranny of the calendar. One thing happens, then another. The wheel that connects them can only be seen when one has left it.

There are charts that we left spread out on our tables, stars that beg us to return them to their signs, loaves of bread that we left half-eaten, technologies that no amount of blood can reconstruct. Some people we happen to know. Others we were scheduled to meet. There are teachers who remind us that our house is not our home. No, I was not born at Fort Devens, in Shirley, Massachusetts. I did not live at 43 Richards Street. My biography was in no way the whole of my identity. I was only the small shadow of myself.

Oddly, there was nothing supernatural about Sue's persona, quite the opposite in fact. She was a middle-aged woman from Ohio, 42 years old, the wife of an Episcopal priest, in no way unusual in appearance. She confessed that she found it difficult to lose weight from her hips and thighs. A few varicose veins were visible. The birth of two of her three children had been difficult, resulting in a number of health problems. To me she was quite a beautiful, and even glamorous, figure. Her imperfections removed her—almost—from the realm of mythological fantasy. They made her real.

Few suspected how old my teacher really was, how many centuries she had spent preparing for her role. Her eyes were publicly accessible. How else could she teach in a public school? These eyes were not the only set I saw, nor could one read her persona without some knowledge of Cretan pictographs. Few noticed the live snakes that she wore instead of bracelets.

I am tempted to say that Sue's method was that of direct communication between one human and another. To some extent this was true. One might note in passing the resemblance of her approach to the "logical consequences" theory of Dreiker, the "self-awareness" model of Meichenbaum, the "reality therapy" of Glasser, and the "teacher effectiveness training" of Gordon. In retrospect, I am surprised to see to what extent her actions were informed by developmental theory. When she interacted with her students, no abstractions were allowed to show.

As she spoke to the class as a whole, I often had the sense that she was speaking directly to me. I suspect, of course, that many other students also felt the same. As she tuned in to each student physically present in that space, she also spoke to the student hidden in the student. By the end of a class, a student might feel that they knew less instead of more, that their sense of who lived in their skin was slightly off the mark. A reflex had been tested. A memory had been activated. A chink had been opened, into which real knowledge might flow.

A prerequisite for the guide is a mastery of what Buddhists call "skillful means." The good teacher disrupts. He or she has a killer instinct for the best way to subvert the status quo. After interfering, the true catalyst allows nature to take its course. Speech class took the form of a circular discussion group, in which every voice could be heard. Sue would subtly steer but not dominate the conversation. She would set an idea in motion, she would set up a scenario, then she would sit back to see what might develop.

One morning, for no apparent reason, I decided to attack a girl who had transferred from St. Peter's High, the school from which I had been terminated, with extreme prejudice, two years before. I was outraged by her wholesomeness, and I finished a nonsensical diatribe by saying, "Did you leave your fuzzy pink bunny slippers at home? You should wear them to school. They would complement your outfit." The girl launched herself across the room at me, swung once with her book bag, and then yanked with the intoxicated fury of a maenad at my hair. Its two-foot length allowed her to wrap it securely around her hands. When she had almost succeeded in removing it from my scalp, my psychopomp said, "Enough." Another teacher might have put a stop to things before they went that far. She later asked, "What do you think you said that made her so upset? Were you really angry with her, or were you angry about something else?"

Sue's catalytic technique did not always involve giving girls permission to hit me. She might choose to observe from a distance; she might choose to directly intervene. More often, though, as in Aikido, she would slip strategically sideways. She would grok half-formed intent and angle of movement and center of gravity. Then, she had only to push or pull.

I remember Sue's response when I informed her that I felt I was growing stupider every day. I could not imagine what was wrong with me. My mind felt numb, and passively chaotic. My sentences self-destructed. My tongue was an alien artifact. It no longer fit in my mouth. Words flew across the horizon, to drift like litter through the streets of empty cities, to lose themselves on the other side of the globe. Could I really have become more stupid? Was this a thing that humans did? An irrational fear, perhaps, yet there was no mistaking the symptoms. I could feel the active force of petrifaction, like a boa constrictor, coiling, each day a bit tighter, to squeeze the life-force from my neocortex. Pretty soon I would be too stupid to even bother to complain. My teacher did not argue, or offer to help, or in any way attempt to talk me out of the experience. Practicing a bit of reality therapy, she said:

> Why do you think that your stupidity is so unique? You do realize there are stupid people all around you, and that one of them is speaking at this moment?
>
> I've been searching all week for an image for the end of the poem that I'm working on. It is right on the tip of my tongue, but it refuses to come out. You probably wouldn't like the poem. It doesn't have any exclamation points. It's about slowly getting up each day to change one small part of the world.
>
> I often feel as though I'm moving under water. Everything seems too difficult. This morning I reached for a box of cereal

on the top shelf of the pantry. My fingers were not long enough. I look at myself in the mirror. I am not young. The years just disappear. At times it doesn't seem possible that the girl I used to be is gone. Who is this middle-aged woman looking back at me from the mirror?

And then I think that I was able to reach the cereal box after all. The image that I'm searching for will probably arrive tomorrow, or perhaps it will be waiting for me to notice it in a dream. My husband is a good man. I love being a teacher.

It may seem odd that such a confession should have a liberating effect. The reason is not complicated. My teacher gave me permission to be human, to begin from where I was. It was wonderful to know that the goddess too had doubts. She also said, "Why don't you keep a notebook to write down everything that comes to mind, stupid or not?"

I already had a few notebooks. I bought a half-dozen more. Shortly thereafter, at 2:00 AM one morning, I wrote a 16-page personal epic. The writing was so illegible that it might as well have been Sanskrit. It was a good thing that I copied it soon after. Gore Vidal once said about Kerouac's *On the Road*, "That's not writing, that's typing." How lucky I was to have no problem of this sort. I did not own a typewriter. As if I had the time to try to figure out how to type. Then again, the hands of my alarm clock did not seem to move. How primordial were my energies! How flowing was my vision! How spotless was my Will! How numerous were my adjectives! How free and generous was my use of the exclamation point! I missed few chances to insert them. Unseen by the world, I traded secrets with the night. The applause of the crickets rose and fell in waves.

If memory serves, the poem was not especially good, or really any good at all, as Mr. Sleeper, my Cultural and Intellectual History of Europe teacher, would soon enough inform me. Ok, the piece was bad, but that is not the point. I had experienced a glitch in the faux-solidity of my ego, which was also a glitch in the faux-solidity of the world. One night, it had occurred to me suddenly and with violence, "You have the power to create."

7

A teacher at a public school is not meant to be a psychopomp, and the student is presumed to be alive. A teacher should offer information and perhaps a bit of emotional support. I was never sure of whether Sue had devised an occult plan or whether she simply allowed some form of guidance to work through her. How many people was she? Should her age be measured in decades or millennia? Would the Doherty administration have given her methods a thumbs up? I could not guess the answers to these questions. There was no pressing need to do so. This was the heyday of the counterculture. Boundaries were fluid. We would sometimes talk through the afternoon on the back porch of her house, sipping lemonade from tall plastic glasses and discussing the merits of peyote versus psilocybin, as the shadows projected from a distant war lengthened slowly across the grass.

Black pajamas from a Viet Minh girl would follow her burnt scent, flapping, turning this way and that in the crosswinds of the Pacific. With the banging of a door, the girl's pain would slip into the wide heart of the goddess, there to find a home, there perhaps to find some tiny bit of rest. We could hear the blasts from the 30-foot mountain horns, along with the struck gongs, which together were like the sound of tectonic plates scraping. We could hear the interdimensional elephants trumpeting, with the blood of gods on their tusks. We could hear the Paleolithic bird-squeaks, growing louder, as the Nagas climbed from their atonal graves.

Troops would reenact on a cloud the opening games of the *Mahabharata*. Suddenly, we might note that the sun had vanished from the sky. Revolving on one spot, which just happened to be the spot where we were seated, the wheel of time would appear almost motionless as it flew. It was not 1972, the year we met. It was not 3102 BC, the year of the war at Kurukshetra. It was not 9600 BC, the year of the last major rearrangement of Earth's coasts. We could hear the seers of the World Maritime Empire breathing slowly in and out, each in-breath one-half of a Mahakalpa, each out-breath one-half of a Mahakalpa. Their eyes were wide. They had not ceased to watch. To them each passing wave, however empty, was important.

Who knew that silence could be just as loud as speech? Well placed speech could also steer you back towards silence. "Have you read Thich Nhat Hanh's *The Lotus in a Sea of Fire*?" Sue once said. "In luminous prose, he explains the reasons that monks burn themselves. According to Hanh, it is not correct to call this suicide, as most Western reporters do. It is not really even protest. Can you imagine how much love it takes to set yourself on fire? He says, 'In Buddhist belief, life is not confined to a period of 60 or 80 or 100 years: life is eternal. Life is not confined to the body: life is universal.' By burning himself, the monk shows that he is willing to suffer any pain for others, not only to call attention to the suffering of the oppressed but also to touch and open the hearts of their oppressors. Hanh's language is simple enough, but it has the force of great poetry."

A kind of natural hallucinogen was produced by the mere proximity of the beloved. A storm would make the oak leaves rustle. The scent of lilacs would overwhelm the senses. Rooting itself in the moment, the self moved deeper into incarnation.

8

Again, my teacher has moved into a dream that powers the perpetual beginning of the world, whose initiates will at length restore the transparency of space.

The beloved now becomes anonymous.

It is of no importance who or what she was, but only that she play each role that memory invents.

Falling as though from a distant planet, the shadow of Sue Castigiliano opens like a door. The footprints of a prehistoric goddess lead straight across a tiny but quite terrifying ocean.

Only Two Lines Could be Saved
from the Mahabharata

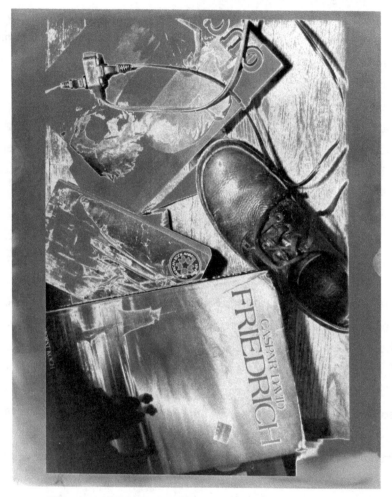

Study Area, solarized photo, 2002

When I was a senior at Doherty Memorial High, I had a "Cultural and Intellectual History of Europe" teacher called Samuel Sleeper. He was gruff but not especially lovable, a classic professorial type, with a tweed jacket and Meerschaum pipe. He was brilliant but absent-minded and more than a bit disgruntled, since he was teaching at a high school and not a college. He seemed to forever be picking some piece of mucus or tobacco off his lip.

His eyes fixed on a point known only to himself, words almost but not quite exiting from his mouth, his hand half-raised in some archaic gesture, Mr. Sleeper would drift through the corridors of our shopping-mall-style school, as though drawn by the field of a Nietzschean magnet, as though each door were the cover of one of the Great Books. At times, he would sense some strange disturbance in the field, as when, for example, a student flagged him down to ask a question about homework. He would pause, annoyed, as his eyes refocused on the third dimension, before answering a question that the student did not ask.

His lack of immediate focus was the sign of some deep philosophical assault on the Abyss. He would spend five minutes in tamping the tobacco into his pipe, and then stare at it, and then just as studiously remove all the tobacco he had just put in. As different as we were, I could not help but wonder if we hailed from the same continent of the soul. From the age of 13, I would sometimes spend many hours a day stretched out on my bed, staring meaningfully into space, wrestling with great philosophical questions such as, "Why is one part of my consciousness looking so hard at the other?" In his magnum opus *Sein und Zeit*, Heidegger had spent more than 500 pages in not quite answering the question "Why is there something rather than nothing?" I was not any more successful. If Mr. Sleeper was not a kindred spirit, there was something in his lack of resolution that I recognized.

When confronted with a door, I was not at all certain of what was waiting on the other side. There was the doorknob. There was the door. If I stepped beyond the threshold, perhaps I would find that there was no floor underneath me. I took nothing on faith. I did not trust the common wisdom any more than the laws of nature. Perhaps I would experience a freefall to the depths of the Abyss, this same Abyss that Mr. Sleeper had so randomly assaulted.

As a senior, I would often stay up late. One morning, from 2:00 to 6:00 AM, I wrote my first real poem, a 16-page megalomaniacal *Mahabharata*. Very foolishly, perhaps, I turned to the most self-important teacher that I could think of for assistance. Mr. Sleeper agreed to edit. A student's more personal exploration of the Cultural and Intellectual History of Europe was a goal it was his pleasure to encourage. He would be glad to help with the fine-tuning of any too farfetched metaphors. Slowly puffing on his pipe, pausing every few minutes to pick a piece of food from his tie or jacket, the Incarnate History of the West, the Living Sculpture of Praxiteles pondered, as the up and down wagging of his enormous head came finally to rest. He said, "Well, here is a good line down at the bottom of page three, and here is another one on 16 that has a bit of potential."

I did my best to put a Band-Aid on the wound. Mr. Sleeper was a snob. I was a working- class kid from the wrong side of the city—there was no wrong side of the tracks, since Worcester was an industrial hub and there were tracks in all directions—who had somehow wandered into a school for affluent students. My teacher's most immediate concern, no doubt, was to put me in my place. Nevertheless, his judgment haunted me.

Half in my body, half out of it, I reenacted these events. Why had my teacher tried to dismember my just barely formed Homunculus? Slowly lifting his leonine head from the Abyss, Mr. Sleeper had somehow noticed I was there. It then occurred to him that I must have been a student. Oh yes, he had some sort of judgment to pronounce. Was that a crumb from a sandwich? It should not be on his tie. My poem might demand a few more moments than the crumb. "No," he thought as he read it, "this will not do at all. Has not a canon been established? The best writers have spent thousands of years in uttering every word that could be uttered. Even if Brian's writing were not bad, how could he add to the sum of perfection?" The day had started well for my linguistic ants, who in their geogrammatical ranks had trooped down page after page, who had held up signs saying "Read Us!" Now, the ants were sad. They had disappointed the Keeper of the Golden Compass of Pythagoras.

Mr. Sleeper, in his arrogant and blissfully accidental way, had offered me a gift, a seed of divine discontent. During the two years before I left to go to the Art Institute of Boston, throughout which I worked as a janitor at the Worcester Telegram & Gazette, I would spend much of my free time going book by book through the stacks of the Clark University Library. From my favorite third-floor alcove, I would look down at the students as they scurried through the courtyard or stood smoking and chatting by the statue of Sigmund Freud. I saw them. They did not see me. As these two years drifted past, I often felt that I was no more solid than a ghost.

I wore my obsessive focus like a hair shirt. I would finger it to remind myself of how far I had to go. By the standards of the Incarnate History of the West, I did not, perhaps, increase my store of knowledge by more than the tiniest of amounts, but these two years of contemplative solitude were the womb from which my first half-decent poem would be born.

The Long Curve of Descent

Winged Snake Uncoiling out of Triangle, 1991

One morning, when I was four years old, I was sitting on the third-floor back porch of my family's three-decker. It was 1958, and Worcester, Massachusetts, was still regarded as the industrial heart of New England. Looking out, I could see smoke puffing from tall smokestacks, a freight-yard and a railroad bridge, hills with houses perched on them that rolled into the distance, and, a few miles off, on one of the highest hills, the gothic architecture of Holy Cross College. How wonderful the day was! I could not have asked for a more perfect moment. My grandmother had given me a large chunk of clay. And then, I was no longer looking out over Worcester; no, I was hovering above the Amazon, making snakes, canoes, and villagers out of the substance in my hands.

As I worked, however, I became frustrated. It occurred to me that I had succumbed to a creative block. I grew angry. I could not believe what I was seeing. My hands were small. My mind just barely worked. My imagination seemed like a blunt instrument. I remembered what it was like to create real snakes and villagers.

Since that morning, I have explored a variety of methods to get from the place where my feet are planted to the larger space that surrounds me, which is not, of course, mine in any personal sense. The path has been a labyrinthine one. My raids on the inexpressible have imposed many contradictory demands. Scholarship and meditation have opened onto vision, onto a mode of knowledge as intimate as it is vast. An ocean, of a sort, boiled, and I could feel the enormous pressure on my skin. Convulsing on the current, I was thrown here and there. Over time, the heat of vision has given way to a much cooler sense of transparency. But always, there are gaps, which demand that I let go of any sense of certainty, which also ask that the reader should play a more active role.

Without gaps being left, my raids on the inexpressible will serve as no more than travelogues. My goal is to take the reader to a space that will pose a subtle challenge, a challenge that may, upon reflection, turn into a threat. The reader must then return to his own coast. He must do his best to convince himself that no shift in his perception has occurred.

In a critique of my essay "Memories of Mr. Trippi: The Trauma of an Urban Shaman," Dave Hanson wrote:

> So as you step in and out of the implicate order I can only suggest looking at your intention, honing your control, looking for opportunities to heal others, and seriously questioning everything you experience on the journey. I would like your writing more if it was more simple and direct, but that is me. I don't know that just because something comes to us from "the spirits" it is any more meaningful than the sound of the toilet flushing. I'm surrounded by people who "see things." I don't understand the underlying meanings of most of it, so I plant more vegetables.
>
> My dog died. I miss him. I can feel his body under my hand. My wife is working too hard and worries too much. I have a broken ankle and hate crutches. I can't do what I love to do and when I'm back on my feet I'll waste precious time. A Native American spirit showed me a painting I am supposed to do, over twenty years ago, and I haven't done it...Can your visions help heal another? That's all there is.

I responded: As regards "healing," my small role as a healer has to do with the reclamation of collective memory. In my explorations, bits and pieces of lost history become clear, "as if lit for the first time by a brilliant star," as de Chirico would say. For whatever it is worth, I then attempt to tell others what I see. For me, healing has to do with the discovery of our wholeness, which exists, to some extent, beyond us. This challenge is like the real gesture that we make with our artificial hand. There is water in a cup. It waits for centuries for us to drink it. Yet, though broken, we have never ceased to be whole.

Upon birth, having exited from the All beneath the stern gaze of Necessity, we are only allowed to bring a few meaningless details with us. One by one, the pages vanish from the book, as, earlier, our footprints had vanished from the ocean. Only mist marks the biodomes of the cities that we left. A buoy clangs, in the distance, somewhere. We have forgotten more than even the omnipotent are aware of, far more than they know themselves. Trauma locks the doors to the dark theatre of the body. We Are What We Eat: the bread of dreams, the sewage of the dead. The rest is junk DNA—or so our controllers would prefer us to believe. A strange presence guards the other half of each symbol.

I would speak truth to the powers that oppress us, who, if they are monsters, are not quite as unrelated to us as we think. As we breathe out, they breathe in, and vice versa. It is our pose of wide-eyed innocence that has tempted them to act badly. Our stealth has been impeccable. It has, perhaps, been *too* impeccable, by a factor of 10,000. We have shown few tells.

"Who are we? Where do we come from? What are we here for? Where are we going?"

These are the questions that the artist has been hoodwinked by society into asking. Such questions are stupid. We should know better. It is possible that they constitute a crime against the Soul. In the stomach of each reader, I would plant and tend the acorn of Omphalos, the one intersection, in order to make the asking of such questions obsolete.

You have asked, "Can your visions heal another?" I tend to view myself more as a catalyst than a healer—a role that has a higher percentage of the energy of the trickster—but the two roles are related. The term "shaman" is used somewhat ironically in the essay. I would make no claim to be one, any more than I would speak casually about world transformation, as so many do. There are more than enough snake-oil salesmen. Preferring to learn from real snakes, I would reverse engineer the most dangerous of toxins.

In 1988, I had a dream in which a green figure took me by the hand. He led me layer by layer through an underground mega-lithic complex. We came to a door with a corbel arch and then entered a great hall, at whose center was a mass of writhing snakes, lashing this way and that, copulating, and tying themselves into knots. Moving closer, it became apparent that the snakes were all made from rubber. Thinking, "There is nothing to be scared of," I reached down to pick one up—and then immediately felt it sink its fangs into my hand. My guide said, "We always mix in a few real ones for effect!" The pain in my hand was sharp. Even now, I can feel the impact of the fangs.

Like the rubber snake that bites, I would pierce the reader's psyche. My vision is meant to wound, not heal. Any healing may or may not happen later on. A cosmology is embedded in the cross-weave of the text, in the toxin of the snake, in the body of the reader, a cosmology that even now exists in its first and final form. What heals and what harms are in no way antithetical. Good habits may, in fact, be symptoms. Hidden energies may disturb us. We have infinitely far to travel to reach the space in which we breathe. What the snakes do not know, the birds may be willing to volunteer, so long as one is open to the removal of one's head. From long before Gobekli Tepe had been built, such birds have been looking for new spheres with which to juggle. They may or may not choose to return their plaything to its owner. Neither snakes nor birds see safety as important. As goes the head, so goes the year from which it comes.

Jasun Horsley once pointed out that whenever I would go to write "2012" it would always come out "2112"—a kind of metaphysical Freudian slip. There are cycles within cycles. We should not jump to any conclusions when we place ourselves within them. We are, at a minimum, a thousand years out of practice. Can one individual be healthy if the world died long ago? As I probe my wounds, I am hesitant to give others the peace of mind that I do not allow to myself. Shock at one's corpse-like decrepitude can be viewed as a big plus. Vision and healing may not always coincide.

Since the end of the Paleolithic Era, it is possible that we have been riding a long curve of descent, in which all things once transparent have become more and more opaque. We do not remember what our hands are for. Our speech is inert. Our intelligence cannot exit from the top part of the skull, a door whose key has been broken off in its keyhole, an aperture that lacks oil. Once, our story had been written on the leaves of a great tree. The leaves have been torn off. The glyphs on them are illegible, and the tree is now a stump. Preprogrammed from beyond the clockwork of the stars, the decline that we have experienced does not appear as such; no, some trick of perspective causes us to hallucinate an ascent.

Archetypes break like toys, left over from a childhood that never did exist. We discard them. We ask, "Why is it so difficult for us to see into the cosmos?" We speak loudly. We do not hear the response. The cultures that we dismembered have been sucked into a cloud. Their outcries circle, and then fall like rain. The last civic structures are consumed by a decentralized plutocracy. "Who put you in charge?" we demand. "Do you have any vision at all?" Our overseers then announce the launch of the next generation iPhone. The Guardians of the Homepage tweak our algorithm. "May you live in interesting times," goes the Chinese curse. We do, for better or for worse, live in "interesting times," in which we must reconfigure all traditionally fixed roles. At the age of 64, I am just beginning to figure out what my public role might be.

A role is a social construct, with a set of rules attached; society can make no rules that the Self is obligated to obey. Why should space concern itself with the shoe size of its mouthpiece? To point people towards what they know but have chosen to forget may be no more than an exercise in futility. Some types of exercise are almost certainly good; others, not so much. Even now, my knees creaky, I still find myself at a perpetual beginning as I test the strength of my lineage, tongue-tied, a bit nervous, as naked as a child who has just stepped from the womb. And here I had pretended to have the answers to each question! "Do I contradict myself? Very well then, I contradict myself," as Whitman said.

For such is the prerogative of the preexistent Voice, and of its vehicle: WE.

All periods cohere in the one moment of my Memory. With a shock, one notes that the old becomes new. By the power of my austerities I have vacuumed up all of the water from the ocean. Cities shine there. I am Death—the Shatterer of Worlds. My weapon liberates multitudes.

Early Days in the Vortex

Sky-Net, 2003

1

Is the logic of a dream different from that of the external world? Let us imagine that the one is a slow-motion and more solid version of the other. The laws of physics keep things from happening all at the same time, so that you are better able to focus on the next step you must take. Then again, these laws are none too rigorously enforced. Rips can appear in a hologram, for no good reason, for good reasons that do not make sense to you, or at the discretion of a bird-like judge. Objective events can unfold with the uncanniness of a dream, as though you watched instead of acted, as though you had seen it all before. You have come to suspect that an original does exist, for which the actual event is but a makeshift reproduction.

Having lost your privileges at the Akashic Hall of Records, you have been forced to see through a cone of 55 degrees. Once, before the Deluge, you could see by simply entering into the depth of the world body, which meant, of course, that you should be fearless in exiting from your own. Your current methodology is more cautious. Still, in spite of your amnesia as to origins, by some natural blind reckoning you can sense when you are doing what you should, when chance is cooperating, and when all is moving in accordance with the preexistent death-flash video. This is, at any rate, a good description of your experience when your life is going well. So you tell yourself at the time.

You will probably choose to overlook the fact that several days have gone missing, along with several continents, and that there is no way to un-brand the barcode from your forehead. If only the world body had not been turned into a shopping mall, in which there is no way to tell if you are product or consumer. If only your guides were more consistently supportive. If only no other forces were at play. If only you could interpret your harsh punishment as proof that you had taken a wrong turn. If only Pollyanna were omniscient. To the extent that you can judge, the operative principle is as follows: if you are good, you will get patted on the head; if you are bad, you will get spanked, or vice versa.

Beneath black domes, the all-seeing eyes of the video-cameras watch. They are motion activated. They come equipped with the latest in backscatter x-ray technology, which does only minimal damage to the chromosomes, or so your masters say. There is no point in pretending to keep secrets! There are few embarrassments that are not yet part of the archeological record, few atrocities in which you have not yet indulged, including those about which you are dreaming at this moment. The cameras move with you, step by step, as you attempt to probe more deeply into the mystery of the labyrinth.

2

There are those who say that Worcester, Massachusetts, is a city. It is more like a collection of discontinuous neighborhoods. It is a place of factories and colleges, of Gothic spires and freight yards. Worcester was the only U.S. city that Freud visited. Robert Goddard, the inventor of the first liquid-fueled rocket, was bounced out for scaring the cows. There were trees to climb and hills down which to roll and corner lots where friends could throw a last-minute baseball game together. It was a city where men might work for the same factory for most of their adult lives, where schools taught them to sit up straight and not complain, where molten steel could put a sudden end to a career. It was, in retrospect, not a bad place to grow up. I get sentimental when I think about the twilight of the American working class, about the culture that formed me. Yet this was also a city in which it was possible to get stuck. At the age of 18, I was ready for adventures. I was willing to travel light. I would bring only a few books and some clothes and a sleeping bag and a radio. From Worcester to Boston it is only 45 miles. A bus can take you from one to the other in an hour. I am puzzled that it should have taken me two years.

Even now, there are times when I wonder if there are pieces that I left, if it was only the subtle essence that I took, if these last

40 years have actually taken place. It is possible that my imagination is more powerful than I know, as well as more deceptive. Beneath an upright oar, I may be peeking through the soil in the yard of my three-decker, breathing slowly in and out, with a view of the Seven Hills. There is not much left of the industrial powerhouse that I knew and towards which I once felt so large an amount of ambivalence. I am no longer tempted to pass judgment on this place, this city of filled-in canals, this navel towards which railroad tracks converged, this target for Nazi bombs. The city blinks to let us know that it is there. As Anonymous, I now just barely have such an urge. I am in the world but not of it. In passing, I take note of how desperate I was to prove that I had talent. I smile to see how eager I was to say goodbye to my home.

I still remember, vividly, the excitement of my first few months in Boston, in the fall of 1974, when I had finally escaped Worcester to go to the Art Institute. The first and most important fact is that I had managed to escape Worcester. The second important fact was that I had once more taken possession of my body. After graduating high school, I had been eaten by an ocean. This was not entirely a bad thing. I could swim a bit. It was nonetheless an ordeal, a labor-intensive test of my powers of self-deception, at a time when most of my friends had already gone off to college. No new teachers had appeared to me, reclining on their waves. I did not have any network of support. Upon my return, a return that was provisional, at best, I spent a year and a half cleaning ink from all of the surfaces at the Worcester Telegram & Gazette.

This was less a job than an enactment of my state of mental solitary confinement. The solidity of the land beneath my feet was not at all reassuring. Rather, boundaries blocked my view without offering any guarantee of safety. My goals had once been cosmic. Now, I only wanted to make it to my next 15-minute break, to get a Coke and a bag of Fritos. My life did not get bigger; it got smaller. A small crack could nonetheless swallow the wall in which it opened. "When you stare into the abyss," writes Nietzsche, "the abyss stares back at you." I could not meet its eyes. I kept my own eyes fixed, a few feet just ahead of me, on the floor of the Worcester Telegram & Gazette. I was not going anywhere fast. For that matter, I was not going anywhere slowly. It was clear to me that I had become a hungry ghost.

As in the mechanical trauma of a dream, a dream which, if we have had it once, we have had it 10,000 times, ink smeared itself on all pieces of equipment, on all ductwork, on all stairs and railings, on all fire extinguishers. There was no way to keep any surface clean. The end of one task was the beginning of another. A just society would regard such "work" as a form of legalized torture. I was the chosen youth, marked for dismemberment, the lobotomized genius sacrificed to the idol of wage slavery. Florescent lights threw shadows; they provided no illumination. No exit sign could be trusted. Each exit was an entrance to a corridor that led deeper into the bowels of the Underworld. Some unseen enemy had removed the hands from every clock. Time was as motionless as the curse of the black ink. I was Sisyphus at his boulder, Ixion on his wheel.

My main consolation during this period was my work as a volunteer at the Worcester Crisis Center, a low-budget suicide and drug abuse prevention hotline, where I could transform my sense of alienation into empathy for others. It did not hurt that the work provided reassurance that I was not myself too disturbed to be of use. Our technique was mostly to listen and to ask questions and to paraphrase and to clarify and to make connections and to support. Oh, and to keep people talking. This is not to say that we knew what we were doing, although we did receive some instructions at the Worcester State Hospital, a grandiose gothic prison complex, built in 1873, which would not look out of place in a horror movie. This was a place of peeling paint and ripped wallpaper and drugged inmates and bored orderlies, who looked at all outside observers with suspicion. Our goal was simply to enter, to not inhale too much of the smell of disinfectant, and to leave.

We were total amateurs. I think, though, that we filled a niche that might not otherwise have been filled. I can only hope that my good intentions had some value, that I did more good than harm, and that I was, perhaps, crudely effective. That I was wounded, I knew. I had just discovered that there were many who were even more wounded than I. That this woundedness could be a source of insight and of strength was an idea that struck me with the force of a revelation. Like a snake-skin, my narcissism was beginning to curl up at the edges. I was able to get a hold of it, and to pull. How strange and intricately patterned was this artifact! My small efforts as a healer had prompted me to test out a new vantage point, to view these patterns if not from above then from a less personal angle.

Gurdjieff argued that true consciousness is objective. He did not mean this in any scientific sense. It was his way of speaking about the state that Vedantists call "Turiya," the fourth state, the state beyond waking or dreaming or deep sleep. There is no way to form an image of this state, to grasp it by a process of addition. Rather, this state must take us by surprise. A series of misadventures may cast doubt on our belief that we are special. We would far prefer to believe that our wishes should come true. It may be, however, that the ends of this fourth state do not correspond to ours. In breaking us, it may accidentally teach us how to heal. If it "takes from our eyes the day of our return," this may prompt us, now and then, to see with other eyes. I spent a year and a half working at the Worcester Telegram & Gazette, smeared with ink and wandering in circles through the corridors, my eyes stinging from the harsh fluorescent lights. That I was led, I began gradually to suspect. "Get out!" said a voice, "Do not turn to look back!" This is what I thought that I had heard. I would have laughed if the voice had said that this experience was a gift.

Let me note in passing that there were other consolations in this period—madrigals at the art museum, lunches with poet and coworker Nick Karcasinas on the steps of Our Lady of Fatima, an introduction to a pre-Men's Movement and still edgy Robert Bly—consolations that I am choosing to underplay, for they did not significantly alter my sense of claustrophobia, my conviction that all was not right with the world. I would sometimes ride my bicycle up the hill to Worcester Airport, a steep climb. I would then let go of my handlebars as I plummeted, at 40 miles-per-hour, to the bottom. At no point did I feel that I was not inside a prison.

Much free time would be spent in a cubicle at the Clark University Library. There, subject by subject, I did my best to come to terms with the vast extent of my ignorance. From my perch in a fourth-floor window, I could gaze down at the miniature students with their backpacks, their eyes fixed on some shiny vision of the future as they scurried to cross the cratered moonscape of the quadrangle. They were so convinced that they were seeing a damp lawn in the spring, not the dust of Babylonian birds, that mist and not toxic gas was swirling around the statue of Sigmund Freud! I would not say that I grew; that would be too generous. Somehow, though, I changed. I was amazed to observe that, week by week, my contempt for the human race became just a little bit less. I somehow became more tolerant of others. I somehow became more open to myself. By the time that I left for Boston, this contempt was more like a vestigial organ, an appendix.

3

In Boston, my self-imposed atonement came suddenly to an end, as though I had closed the book that I was reading with a snap. Do not ask for what crime I had been sentenced to atone. A kind of antigravity took over when I stepped from the Greyhound bus. The top of my head flew off. The days appeared to physically grow brighter. The Sun moved closer to the Earth. I was as happy as one of the roaches that scurried in my 92 dollars-per-month apartment. In Worcester, I had put my shoulder against an almost immovable wheel. In Boston, in search of the later-day descendants of Bohemia, on the cusp of a cultural moment that I had not yet discovered, not the effort but the sense of difficulty disappeared.

If the most important changes are internal, having to do with one's subtle relationship to events, then there are also times when external changes are essential, when one would die inside without them. These external changes then shift the balance between the subject and the object, so that events begin to articulate the psyche, so that the psyche appears to be present in the most random of events.

So: one Sunday night, having finished all of my art school projects for the weekend, I decided to check out a writers' workshop held at the Widener Library at Harvard. There, I met two poets, Jack Kimball and Don Quatrale, who invited me to a poets' gathering to be held on Joy Street on Beacon Hill the following night. My role: just being in a place, and later on: a nod of assent. Said Jack, "Your work is young, but there are signs pointing to some future breakthrough into vision." "Oh?" I responded, "How nice." Unsure about whether to interpret Jack's analysis as rude, I was at first hesitant to accept the invitation. It was a close call, and I almost did not go. A hair's breadth of a difference separates the right from the wrong action. We may reasonably shame the actor for not making perfect choices. We should probably apologize when these choices later prove to be correct.

One life stops; another life begins at one and the same moment of remembrance. We do not know what we know. Yet it is possible that our ignorance is also a non-issue. The contraption once built by the oracle runs as smoothly as a broken clock.

Upon opening my eyes, I found that I was standing in front of a Second Empire townhouse. Joy Street. Number 23. I rang the bell and slowly climbed the stairs. When an almost naked vegetarian, eating a hot dog, opened the door, clouds of incense smoke billowed from the apartment. (Will Bennett, the door opener, was just then moving out of a macrobiotic phase and into a proto-punk rock one.) The gathering began at 7:00 PM and went until 3:00 AM, during most of which time, because I had recently cut my hair short at a time when most men in such circles wore it long, I was regarded as a possible DEA agent or at best an MIT nerd.

The group read, contributed lines to spontaneous poems, made "exquisite corpse" drawings, and engaged in various other avant-garde activities. I took it as a good sign that people spoke of Lautreamont and Rimbaud and de Chirico and Ernst and Michaux and Vallejo and Lamantia, all of whom were influences. Finally, at 2:30 AM, I was able to take advantage of a quiet moment to read several of my pieces. The themes of my poetry were archetypal. I suspect that the work was not especially good. (I have been too squeamish to look back, to see just how bad it was.) It was definitely strange. One of the participants would later describe the poems from this period as "cosmic caveman cartoons." My reading style was eccentric, a bit like Tibetan chanting. It had evolved during those two years of near solitude in Worcester, and it did not resemble any of the current styles of performing poetry. It had been known to scare people.

I read one piece without incident, but a minute, or perhaps two, into the second piece, something unexpected happened. Many group members started to laugh, hysterically, as they rolled around on the floor. They slapped the arms of their chairs, shrieking. They hooted and barked. They threw pillows around the room. Should I be offended? I was not sure how to take this. As it turned out, they loved the work. They were pleased to discover that appearances could be so wrong. Many in this group were to remain my friends for the next 10 or 15 years.

Had I met these people at the appointed time and place? Had I always known them, or is this a retroactive attempt to impose coherence on my narrative? Chance: the displaced effect of a cause that we have long ago forgotten. Thus "accident" may not be different from "intent."

I had originally listed the names of all of the people at this event. I have edited these out. There is no particular reason that the reader should care about these people or share my sense of why they are important. None are famous. A few have won prizes. A few have founded small magazines, and a few are well known in small literary circles. I was surprised to find how limited a presence the majority of them have on the internet. I doubt that they are searching for me. Most are now strangers. They are as distant from me as they were before we had ever met. They are as distant from me as they were before we had ever met, and yet, without them, I would be living in an entirely different world. If the Fates had not led me to that cloud-filled room in a Second-Empire townhouse, and if the third-floor door had not been opened by an almost naked vegetarian eating a hotdog, then I would not be who and what I am. Even now, I am grateful. I gasp with relief.

I am out of touch with Jack Kimball. Don Quatrale is now dead.

In five thousand years, it is possible that some avian monk will compile a catalogue of all of the obscure writers of our era. By then, if all goes well, if there are lands that have managed to peek above the ocean, our sonic technology may be able to track the spin of each electron in the universe. We may be able to assess, objectively, the stature of each writer and the importance of each friend. The synchronicities that drew me to my band of bohemian catalysts may reveal themselves in all of their perfection. The avian monk will then reunite my circle with a footnote.

4

In this period, the inner and the outer worlds frequently changed places. I not only felt that I belonged to an arts community, I felt that I was part of a living universe in which all things were interconnected, in which the living differed from the dead mostly in being subject to the law of gravity. The way to grasp the psychotic complexity of the web was to plunge without looking towards the depths of the confusion. Joy was the key to the City of the Ancients. Once, the whole of the world could be fit inside my heart. Facts in the foreground led to the conundrum of the infinite, as the figure eight revealed—if only to cover it up again—the erotic subtext of the Aeon. False rulers had corrupted the translucency of the records. It was our job to remember how to read.

As the great net moved, its electromagnetic fields pulled this way and that by Clotho, Lachesis, and Atrapos, worlds once obscure to each other would communicate with signs, or with ultimatums, or with jokes, as I had specified in a pre-birth memo that they should.

Lacunae were like oceans, once thought by archaeologists to create barriers between continents, which our hairier prototypes were too stupid to overcome. More recent theories suggest that such "barriers" could be a means of transportation. The very opacity of the sign was an indication that something big was going on. The more absurd, the better. The sign suggested, it did not denote, and the further we had to go to wrap our minds around it the more radical, in the end, would be the change in our awareness. It was good to be puzzled, and at the mercy of the currents and the winds. It was possible that our own breath was the thread that led from the labyrinth, whose exit, now too tiny to see, was located on a foreign shore.

The rate of coincidence exploded. For example, at 6 AM one day I was awakened from a dream, as I heard, forced from my lips, the Mayan word "Xibalba." At 8:30, when I left for school, I found that some passerby had written "Xibalba" on the front of my apartment building. How often does that happen? A coincidence, or so the scientist says, of which one normally does not bother to take note. And yet…This was the only day, out of the thousands before and since, on which some passerby has written a Mayan word by my door.

It was possible, also, to put this power of connection to the test. For example, the phrase, "the pyramids of Antarctica" once popped into my head. I then wandered blindly into a bookstore, allowing my hand to select a volume from the shelves. As the book fell open, my eyes landed on the phrase "the pyramids of Antarctica." Snorting, the skeptical reductionist might exclaim, "Such things are hardly unusual, and are easily explained by current theories of statistical probability! Will you never tire of pointing these trite coincidences out?" And yet this experience did not feel in any way reducible to the laws of mathematics, nor did my certainty that the event was just about to occur. Appearances to the contrary, I would argue that I watched instead of acted. My role was that of a detached observer, and it felt as though my memory had been moving from the future to the present.

No, it is the skeptical reductionist who violates the rule of "Occam's Razor"; the sheer outrageousness of many such connections seems designed to place them beyond the realm of mathematical probability, to insure that we regard them as a kind of wake-up call, or as a test. Their opaque absurdity is not different from their message.

For example: once, traveling on a Greyhound bus to visit my family back in Worcester, I began mentally to repeat to myself a pun from a "gargoyle" poem I had written, involving Shamash, the Babylonian god, and sour mash whiskey. Frost froze on my lips as I perched on the ledge of a cathedral. "Shamash! Shamash!" I invoked, as, in the seats just behind me, two guys began to discuss, in some detail, the distillation of sour mash whiskey. Thus completing the predetermined pun. The proponent of mathematical probability might say, "Out of the tens of millions of times every year that a Greyhound passenger might repeat the god-name "Shamash" to himself, simultaneously having punned on the name in a free-associative poem, of course there would be at least one instance where the two guys in the seats just behind him would start talking about sour mash."

I would conscript each random stranger into the army of synchronicity! I would stage a revolution! The Self must become a collective, a forum for the returning gods. The One must recover its capacity to act. I would educate the dead in the lost art of ventriloquism, even I, the most ignorant of all.

Who knows what such coincidences mean? I took them nonetheless as signs that there were forces guiding, if somewhat obscurely, my steps. Metaphors were oceans: to be crossed, and vice versa. So too, each booby-trap in the metalinguistic labyrinth was usually, when you looked at it, far more logical than it seemed. Its goal was to inform you of the next step you should take. Some would argue, of course, that we have no good reason to place our trust in coincidence, that its hand may be that of a trickster, not a guide. Well, that would not surprise me much. But the goal of exploration has never been to play safe. "If we do not expect the unexpected," says Heraclitus, "then we will not discover it, for it is not to be searched out and is difficult to apprehend." At the crossroads, I met Hermes; there, he killed me.

5

A red sun, now repopulated, rises from the ocean. It is time to return the rooster that one had borrowed from Asclepius. For, in a moment, one must die.

Key turning points give access to the realm of the Ideal.

There is one story, only, however odd this might seem, out of which each Argonaut must assemble his own version, by stealth illuminating the character of the once generic face.

The Music of the Spheres, Again Audible

Nun Lifting the Barge of Ra, Public Domain

There are moments when the world comes suddenly to a stop, when the ground withdraws its support, when a schism opens, into which one may or may not fall. The world then employs its archaic sleight-of-hand to remove whatever faith you may have placed in this event. The structure of projection has barely missed a beat, but the schism in your psyche has not actually been sealed. When

I was 17, I had an experience from which I never did recover. To describe it clearly is not to communicate its impact. One night, at 2:00 AM or so, I was seized by an enormously loud ringing and droning sound. At first, I took this to be some type of bizarre emergency warning system, designed to get each person in the city out of bed, although it seemed like overkill for anything short of an imminent nuclear war. The sound could also be compared to Tibetan chanting: enormously low, bone-shaking bass notes supported a middle ground of complex musical geometries, repetitive but chameleonic and difficult to hear all at once, which then rose into almost inaudible overtones.

Upon hearing this sound, I rushed from one window to the next. The whole of space reverberated, as if the visible world were about to shake itself apart, and yet nowhere could I detect the nature of the emergency or the source of the alarm. A soft wind lifted the curtains, bringing with it the aroma of burnt ozone. As I looked out over the factories and freight-yards and the lights of the few cars moving, I could imagine the night watchmen leaning back in their chairs, pausing with their bottles of Jim Beam lifted halfway to their lips. I could imagine mothers holding their crying children to their breasts. I could imagine fathers yelling at their crying children to shut up. I could imagine the bored policemen, now suddenly alert, trying to remember what their training manuals specified. I could imagine the confusion of the airport personnel, as they struggled to find a target for their searchlights. I could imagine the National Guardsmen snapping to attention by their bunks.

In passing, I registered the odd lack of activity. No one in my family had joined me at the windows. Not a single one of my neighbors had run into the street. No lights had immediately come on, and most of the houses in the city were still dark. I saw, in the field across from my house, the milkweed pods pop open. I did not wake anyone up, and I hoped that the city would still be there when I woke up in the morning.

In the morning, when I discovered that no one else had heard a thing, I was shocked, yes, but I was less shocked than I would have expected myself to be. I had begun, even as the event was taking place, to suspect that this sound was actually the "music of the spheres." For many thousands of years, perhaps, the volume of these spheres had been turned down way too low, or it could be that faceless functionaries had plugged our ears with wax. Then suddenly—no doubt for reasons that were long ago explained, but by temperamental teachers, and in a language we don't speak—the music became audible. Certain things, once heard, cannot later be unheard. With my ears a bit more open than they were, I also came to understand the implications of my exile, the hard limits of my ability to communicate what I knew.

Years later, in 1992, I had just finished the first coherent version of *To Akasha: An Incantation for the Crossing of an Ocean*. There would be quite a number of others. This first one was significant, however. In an attempt to create a body from my spiritual explorations, I had filled notebook after notebook with circuitous scribblings. Together, they formed a pile about ten inches high. This 80-page version suggested that there may be hope for me yet.

It was 11:00 PM. I was still at work, and I had just found out that my relief would be an hour to 90 minutes late. Restless, and very eager to get home, I went out for a walk around the building. A few squeaks and some static trickled from the exosphere. With a twinge of concern, I noticed that my shadow, bit by bit, had begun to disregard the law that it should imitate my movements. It measured between four and thirty feet, and it would slip from one length to the other with dangerous rapidity. It seemed possible that my height was actually changing. In addition, I did not dare to look at my reflection in the window, for fear that it would not be there. Then suddenly, at my feet, I heard a loud clicking and banging and clattering sound, like a bunch of scissors snipping, along with pots and pans being knocked together. Looking down, I saw a luminous red-gold scarab, about two and one-half inches long. It was flapping its wings, and doing a kind of geometrical dance, and going out of its way to make sure that I would stop to pay attention.

Are there scarabs in the Boston/Cambridge area? There were certainly none of this size or color or beauty, and it seemed unlikely that a dung beetle was supposed to be emitting light. All of this was strange, but stranger still was that I had just Xeroxed the inner cover of a book, upon which was a picture from an Egyptian manuscript of a scarab riding in the Barge of the Enead—the nine Egyptian gods—with his forelegs holding up the Sun.

What else could I do? I followed where the scarab led. I followed him for about 80 feet, around the front and then around the side of the building, at which point he flew up and positioned himself about three inches down from and directly under the center of a lamp, as though, once again, he were holding up the Sun. "Thank you, thank you, thank you," I repeated in my mind, which I had become convinced that he could read. My mind was almost altogether blank, like a sky with a few clouds, through which bolts of compacted information, like lightning, would flash and then dissolve. I did not dare to move, and I stared, transfixed, until my relief arrived an hour and a half later. The scarab was still there when I left. The next day, when I arrived for work at 3:00 PM, I found that, beneath the lamp, a faint triangle had been inscribed on the cement.

Through the years, I had experienced quite a number of synchronicities, events in which the inner and the outer worlds, for a moment, corresponded. The encounter with the scarab nonetheless took me by surprise. This did not seem like a "meaningful

150

coincidence." Rather, it seemed like a sign that had been sent, and the sign itself appeared to have some degree of agency. What is the sound of one anonymous poet speaking? The scarab was the physical embodiment of an answer.

There was another, more recent, incident, as well. If the encounter did not grab me by the hair, as did the first, it too could not later be unseen. That the incident was not dramatic was perhaps a part of its point. In June of 2010, at midnight, I was walking by a field a few blocks from my house. I had left for work at 6:15 AM. It had been a long and entirely uneventful day. I had no energy left, and I could not wait to get home. From a distance, I observed that the night was very beautiful. I felt nothing. Clouds billowed, like the spirits of dead architects, across the moon, and I became convinced that a scarab would be waiting for me on the sidewalk. And there he was! This was a slightly smaller red-gold scarab, not quite as luminous, but, then again, I had learned to pay attention.

The fragrance of the night washed over me: cut grass, car exhaust, cedar chips mixed with dung, sumac in heat, salt air from the ocean, rosemary. The scarab, after doing a little geometric dance, then crawled toward my right foot in a perfectly straight line. He touched the center of the shoe with his head, looped sideways, walked straight between my feet, keeping to a path that was equidistant between the shoes, and then looped back to touch the center of my left heel, before veering off at a 45-degree angle into the field. I took this to mean, "Hello." There was no grand drama, only a silent exchange of gestures, unnoticed by the world.

Who knew that scarabs were such organized creatures? Truly, they have rolled the cities of Prehistory into a ball, which they then proceed to exhibit to the blind. They are OCD metaphysicians! Earlier, it had taken the equivalent of an air-raid siren to remind me of the inner workings of the cosmos. If the music that I heard was real, an encrustation of defenses had led me to hear it as an alarm, to perceive these primordial harmonies as a threat. The two scarabs employed a subtler mode of provocation. If I was far too big to follow them through the cracks in the lunar mirror, at least I had not stepped on one. I felt that I was making some small amount of progress.

I take no gifts from the decentralized kleptocracy. I put no faith in credentials, my own or those of others. I do my best to be aware of the actions I perform, to pour my blood into my writing, to speak out of the dark heart of the zeitgeist. I would see with eyes that are lit by a distant star. I would hear what was whispered on the Barge of the Enead. I would kiss the stone that prompts fear in the most ancient of philosophers, the stone whose energy shook apart the first home of the gods. These scarabs were the witnesses to the seriousness of my efforts. It was difficult to tell whether or not they were impressed. One makes do.

The Art of Deep-Sea Fishing

The Reemergence of the Eye, 2001

1

C.J. Moore wrote:

It was as if the poem came to life, and it was now reading itself
from the great poem of the cosmos. This was happening on so
many levels that I was just a twig in a maelstrom. I danced with
the experience, but it was like dancing with a shark. I would
find myself sitting in the university library, with my eyes buried
in corridors of Egyptian temples that wound their sentences

through languages that have long since vanished in the sands of time, and I would suddenly wake up with a start and I would be reading *Aurelia* by Nerval, and I would see myself walking through the streets of Paris, following Nerval's footsteps. I was seeing the hallucinations he saw, seeing where he was going in dark rooms when the vision stood before his astonished gaze. Then I would suddenly wake hours later walking down the hill from the university, not knowing how I got there, and I would stop and feel the last light filtering through the trees and wonder "Who are you?"

I responded: When I taught junior high art, I developed a strategy that I referred to as "creative disorientation." Many students could not remember that, from the ages of three to seven, they were once in love with art, and most had come to believe they did not have any talent. 'Show; don't tell," was the operative principle. It was not that I did not have any clear-cut goals in mind. A goal would be clear to me, but not to them, and, by a process of "reverse engineering," I would lead students into an almost unbearable state of disorientation, which would swell into a kind of cognitive crisis. I was familiar with this mini-version of the abyss. I had stared into it. It had spoken back. While the experience of disorientation would be particular to each, I knew the general habits that were preventing these students from gaining access to their talents. Reactions would be supervised. Adjustments would be made. A nudge here. A show of support there. At some point, almost inevitably, a student's cognitive crisis would flip over into a breakthrough, and it would open up a space in which real learning could occur.

In situations such as the one that you describe, in which a hair's breadth separates a breakthrough from a breakdown, I sometimes wonder if this is what is going on. With a goal that is clear to them, but not to us, perhaps our other-dimensional teachers have reverse engineered a confrontation with the abyss. To this end, no academic knowledge would be adequate, and no human teacher could see far enough ahead. Then too, such teachers know that ecstasy is our primal out-of-body state, and they do not lose any sleep if the student must be tortured. Some degree of disorientation is a small enough price to pay to learn to what extent our vision has been compromised. We tend to see what we expect to see. We fail to grasp the thread that would lead us through the labyrinth.

It is tempting to theorize that other methods could have been used, that a different path would have led to the same end. Could our teachers not have given us a true and false questionnaire? "When I was a boy of fourteen," Mark Twain writes, "my father was so ignorant I could hardly stand to have the old man around. But when I got to be twenty-one, I was astonished at how much the old man had learned in seven years." So too, it can be difficult for us to see that our teachers know much of anything, until, turning back, we note that the Earth has become a small speck in the distance, and we then exclaim, "Aha!"

A straight line is not always the shortest distance between two points, and certainly not in the education of a poet. If we had learned more about French Symbolism and Surrealism in school, it would have made it much more difficult for us to discover these things for ourselves and would have removed much of the fun and mystery from the process. Lautreamont would have become an eccentric version of Longfellow. The quiz on *Les Fleurs du Mal* would have been as subversive as the one on *Hiawatha*. Revolutionary fervor would have been graded on a curve, and school policy would have demanded that each essay should be taken back whole from a dream. If, with a wink, a cuneiform chanteuse were to wave to us from a street corner—too hot, too avant-garde to be true!—school policy would encourage us to make love to her in class. Upon climax, she would turn back into clay. Verese's *Arcana* would be the school's atonal fight-song, and Picasso's "I do not seek; I find" the motto.

Hey, those ideas could work! A Man Ray photo could be used for the cover of the *High Modernism* textbook, perhaps the famous one of Meret Oppenheim standing nude in front of a printing press, smeared in ink, with one hand lifted in an ambiguous gesture against her forehead. Our project would of course be subject to approval by the Texas State Board of Education.

2

In the *Tao Tè Ching*, Chapter 73, we read, "Heaven's net is vast. It is loose. Yet nothing slips through." And in Chapter 34, "The Way brings to completion but cannot be said to exist...It is always desireless, so we call it the small. The myriad things return to it and it doesn't exact lordship, thus it can be called great." Once, there was only breathing. We did have bodies, yes, but each one was provisional, no more than a convenience. Let us say there was a plan behind the original self/other disconnect, one that made sense to our teachers but none at all to us, in what form could we glimpse this plan aside from that of a waking dream? We can ask, and insight may be given. We can summon back some portion of what we knew in the womb, before the sky contracted, before the zodiac broke. The dream of everyday life may offer one more means of access. Events do not have to be strange to prompt a sense of wonder, especially when we review these from a distance. When young, the world is outside, and the future is ahead of us. We might later wake while walking up a hill, a hill we had not climbed in 40 years, and, holding our hands up to examine, think, "Who are you?"

The city in which I came of age was a self-emergent form—not reducible to the play of social forces, far more than the sum of its parts—sometimes quietly and sometimes noisily alive, through whose streets I freely roamed. If its boundaries were not fixed, if many small towns ringed the city, if it was only one metaphor in an infinitely long sentence, which was only one wave in an infinitely wide sea, the city nonetheless served as a vessel for my growth. Its life may not have defined the extent of what I was; still, without it, I would not be who I am. I would not have had the experiences that gave birth to my perspective.

I grew up in a factory area in Worcester, Massachusetts, up the hill from a freight-yard, across the street from a field of mysterious weeds, and a few miles off from the pasture where Robert H. Goddard, the father of aerospace, used to scare the cows with his rockets. At times, the ironworkers would roll up the doors to the foundries, and on our bikes, my friends and I would watch the red glow spill from the furnaces, as ladles portioned out the white-hot metal from the vats. There were always scraps to take home, which we saw as treasures. In the distance you could see the giant smokestacks. These came equipped with ladders, up and down which you could see the ant-like workers climb. I have never ceased to regard myself as a member of the working class, or to love the area in which I came of age. My heart aches to remember the late-afternoon light of the "American Dream," which fades to darkness even as I write. Some part of me is rooted in that neighborhood.

The stage-set in which I acted out my childhood—from, say, 1957-1970—should perhaps not be imagined in terms of Worcester as a whole, for the city included a few affluent sections, which might as well have been on Mars. We knew that such suburb-like neighborhoods existed. Few were jealous. They just did not seem real. No, my city was the eight miles or so that were visible from the porch of my three-decker, which sat on a hill.

Born at Fort Devens, at the end of the Korean War, I saw Sagittarius conspire with Celtic DNA to stamp me as a Roosevelt Democrat. I was formed by the hands of that one moment on the clock, in the image of that way of life. It is possible, however, that other members of the working class would view my interests with suspicion, if they had any idea of what those interests were. Who knows? I make sounds in acknowledgement when my neighbors talk about baseball. I do not quote any poems by Rimbaud. I learned, long ago, to hide the greater part of my being, to think strategically and to operate by stealth.

In Chapter 20 of the *Tao Te Ching*, we read,

> I am scattered, never having been in a comfortable center. All of the people enjoy themselves, as if they were at the festival of the great sacrifice, or climbing the Spring Platform. I alone remain, not yet having shown myself. Like an infant who has not yet laughed. Weary, like one despairing of no home to return to…While average people are clear and bright, I alone am obscure.

The world is vast and often hostile to our interests, those interests that might disturb even our closest neighbors, if they did not live in a culture so dissimilar to our own. What has happened to the playgrounds of our childhood? Most are probably much less violent than before, but we do not stop to spend ten minutes on the swings. Twenty-six oligarchs hold as much wealth as one-half of the world's population. The poet has no more importance than his shadow. Ok, then. This is where his heartless teachers left him, with no grades, good or bad, with no avant-garde manifestoes to distribute. They did not even leave any notes when they drove their cars into trees, when they leapt off of their roofs.

There is a painting by Max Ernst called *Revolution by Night*. This title has always sent a shiver down my spine. When else should a true revolution happen? It must well up from the Apsu, from the waters of the Abyss, from the secret spaces of the void beneath the Underworld, to only gradually emerge into the light of the public square. The stars can then, from an inconceivable distance, also lend a hand. Diana Reed Slattery, in her essay "Shifting to a Psychedelic World Culture," writes, "Without 'silence, exile, and cunning,' and the secret Dublin of the soul, I would not have accomplished my own research, that noetic quest to understand an alien language, Glide." To be alienated may be less of a punishment than a strategy—imposed, by circuitous fiat, from beyond—which the poet may be the last to understand. The poet/revolutionary is a latecomer to the scheme. He must figure out where to place the incendiary device—for maximum impact but no real loss of life. He must speak directly to the subconscious of the public. He must come and go undetected, as subtle as the wind.

It would do the poet/revolutionary no good to be told what he should know, let alone what he should do. If only things were so simple. Instead, his teachers can very helpfully inform him of the rules, and he must then proceed to laugh at their advice. Creative disorientation is more than a grim necessity; it is our source of wealth, our means of transport. We must not mute our anxiety. Our creations must come wriggling from the depths. To allow for this circuitous process to unfold, to pry open our previous if not our primal mode of vision, our teachers "take from our eyes the day of our return."

3

If the poet is to be blind, it is also necessary that his art should be impeccable, for, at the ocean's depth, say some, there are exobiological creatures that are more bizarre than fish. They too may be fishing, and it may not at first be clear which species is the predator, which species is the food. The good poet should be able to sense if he is still among the living. Is he happy, having eaten, or is he no more than a hologram? His life may not be other than a habit of projection, whose source has long since ceased to exist. The goal of the average traveler may be simply to avoid annihilation. The good poet—the practitioner of *metis*, the man of many turnings—must do more. He should not be a passive recipient of the strange. He must plunge into the mystery of what it means to have a body. He must then test to what extent he might be able to hold his breath.

In Ancient Greece, it was thought that we saw the world by projecting light-beams from our eyes, like superheroes. Contemporary scientists regard the concept as absurd. The retina is clearly a concave screen, onto which the world projects its inverted image. But what if scientists are wrong, or, at the least, not entirely correct? If nature's laws are habits, which can change, then perhaps this mode of vision—the "emission theory" as put forth by Plato, Ptolemy, and Euclid—was actually the common one in a previous world cycle.

In those days, we saw the world inside out, as from the backside of a mirror. Both the eye and the light that it perceived were different. So too, our bodies were like nuclear reactors, which pulsed with a kind of telepathic force. When we asked that the world reveal itself, there were few objects that would dare to disagree. We would not take "no" for an answer. To see was an active art. Or, one could also say: to see was to act, and such action was an archaic science, as much as it was an art. From under layers of nerves and muscles, we could see a skeleton flash. We could see the sap circulate through the veins of a growing leaf. As from an anteroom to the Earth, we could see our life's beginning, and its end. Upon entering an atom, we could track each electron's orbit. We could enter the locked spirals of our DNA, there to read the histories that have been classified as "junk," there to determine how, from our prototype, every species had devolved.

"Were these general powers?" we might reasonably ask. There were no doubt those, the poet/seers, for whom vision was a branch of yoga or gymnastics, who had cultivated skills of which others could only dream. This does not mean, however, that the eyes of the early race were not different from ours. If their numbers were fewer, there may have been far greater quantities of vision to be shared. The group's powers of emission were not dispersed among 8 ½ billion strangers.

Now, the poet must find his own way back beyond the Deluge, sailing into and up its mind-destroying fear, and then out beyond the violence of the mile-high wave. There, in a contest with his own stupidity, and, if all goes according to schedule, with some small amount of help, he must once more learn to see. A great sucking sound will make his ears pop. His "I" will once more turn into a "we," into the roar of a cacophonous collective.

The wave, when it withdraws, will have swept off all of the bad art that was heaped up during the time-cycle, leaving only some few precious relics in the sand. If "seeing is believing," as is often said, at the mirror's back we will not have long to wait. Not darkly, but face to face, we will there see the designers of our nonsensical curriculum. They will not prove to be strangers, after all. We will there learn who among them has played games with our memory, who among them may have put words in our mouths. We will there see who has nudged us, trial by trail, little death by big death, dream by waking dream, towards an end that preexisted our first baby steps towards vision.

We will there be as eight-armed ships. We will there be as luminous eyeballs. We will there be imploded suns. We will there be the fish-suited messengers that Sirius once sent to Assyria. Our dangerousness will remove the majority of our doubts about self-defense. If we do not mind being laughed at, we can then dare to begin to communicate what we know.

Anonymous, and His International Fame

The Conjuration, 2003

1

Genetic engineering of the planetary rulers has projected each subject's shadow as a hex, as a door that none should open, as a gulf that none should cross. All attempts at purification are shaped like a figure eight. We are not natural. Our powers are congested. If we were to add up all of the experiences that define us, we would note, upon closer scrutiny, that it is always the key element that is missing. Why do people we do not know dare to occupy our homes? They do not dress well. We must hurt them. An archaic wound pursues us like the voice of superconsciousness.

From the end of the last ice age, when what were first small streams broke through the dams of the Himalayas, when whales were stranded on the Andes, when ships crashed on the sky, Earth's rulers have agreed to play the role of our absent yet somehow abusive guides, and to model, in the mists of our imaginations, those behaviors we would do well to avoid. If they have set up signs and left us rules for their interpretation, we might, in the end, perceive such help to be a threat. If, however, the self exists in a multitude of locations, then what haunts us may be the lesson that we have not bothered to learn.

For what harms can heal. What does not kill us can potentially make us stronger, unless, as with Nietzsche, it strips us of our identity altogether. True harmony is disjunctive. We know that evil exists. We know the top 28 people hold as much wealth as the bottom three and one half billion. Trauma? Whose fault is that? We are fetuses. We are innocent. You can see how happily we kick against our wombs. It is said that the spheres make music.

Earth's rulers would prefer to rule, for that is the role to which their memories have assigned them. This leads them to see the destruction of an ocean in the light of a bigger picture. In terms of vision, it is only practical that I not attribute too much virtue to myself, that I not be quick to accuse. I have benefited as much as anyone from the extraction of rare elements, such as tantalum, from the Congo. I wear socks manufactured by starving children in Bangladesh. I keep my milk in a refrigerator, thus adding to the spread of HFCs and helping to push Earth's temperature towards the point of no return. Like the rulers who have conspired to take away my breath, I am also very old, what did not kill me has made me stronger but less sane, and my relationship to the living has grown steadily more ambivalent.

I have taken what I need. I fear no unseen hand, and I do not need to be liberated. Able finally to act as a good parent to the child that I was, and am, I am intent on making use of every scrap of my experience. The years now rearrange themselves, permitting me to wander through each period of my development. Time turns into horizontal space, as though the future and the past were no more than the handicapped-accessible rooms of a museum.

2

From 1968 to 1970 I attended St. Peter's Parochial High School, where I was subjected to two years of military drills in Latin, a subject that would interest me now but that held not a bit of interest for me then, when my goal was to help to provoke a revolution. "Why do I need to learn this?" I would ask. The answer was the one preformatted by the Roman Empire: "The mind is a muscle. Exposure to the classics will teach you how to think." Reason had constructed a converging web of roads. As all roads led to Rome, so too, all exploration was designed to lead to a single end. This form of institutionalized violence was almost seamlessly covert. The barbarian and/or student was allowed to wander off but only so as to demonstrate the hub's hypnotic force. The goal was not actually to exercise the intellect; rather, it was to give the impression that the intellect had been exercised.

When I did attempt to think for myself, at first in small and then in bigger ways, I very quickly got myself into trouble. No questioning of the shadow of Saturn was allowed. The new philosopher's stone should look no different from a football. Mystic transport should occur in the context of the pep rally. Mass hysteria was acceptable. Irony was not. The grail was a NEPSAC championship trophy. Light pulsed from it. Concern for the oppressed should result in a donation to the "poor box." Liberation

Theology led only to the Soviet Gulag system, to Stalin's forced industrialization and starvation of Ukraine.

At last, on the day of a country-wide protest against Nixon's covert bombing of Cambodia, I decided to put my body where my mouth was, to take my place at the barricades and to act on my beliefs. In practice, this was not as simple as it seemed. Perhaps, albeit unconsciously, I had decided to embody the Taoist ideal of "acting without acting." About 60 of us were milling around at the edges of the schoolyard. The bell rang, and we didn't move. The headmaster, Father Gonnier, then paced across the basketball court before stopping a few feet from where we stood. Straightening his back, he quite cryptically announced, "You are causing a disturbance. Please leave the property. Absence will be treated as such."

It seemed as though we had each heard something different. Such is the spell of Maya, the gnomic utterance of Thoth, the smoking mirror of Tezcatlipoca. About 50 or so of the rebels went immediately inside. The rest of us took this statement to mean that we were free to attend a protest march, with no consequences beyond being marked absent for the day. "Thanks, Father G!" I said. It can be difficult to tell the big things from the small. This almost accidental choice changed the whole course of my life.

Waving, students leaned out of the windows, shouting taunts at or encouragement to the few rebels that were left. Several of my comrades went downtown to shoot pool. Another expressed an interest in browsing through the magazines at Red Square, a combination communist propaganda outlet and pornographic bookstore. One James Dean-style drag racer went home to work on his car. Chanting slogans, the rest of us marched off toward Holy Cross College, where an all-day "teach-in" was scheduled to be held. Its row of Gothic pillboxes was just visible in the distance, about five miles off, at the top of one of the seven major hills.

This was Worcester, 1970. It was not, as it turned out, a flash-point for the coming revolution.

∾

In tight jeans and white t-shirts, hoods with existential hearts were the devotees of a car cult that was launched in the 1950s. Already, there were several thousand martyrs. Railroad bridges served as playground equipment, as well as initiatory tests: we would hang from one hand as a train went roaring by. Neighborhoods were mapped out according to the country of a family's origin. There had once been a gang war between Swedes and Latvians on the picturesque green of the Worcester Common. In one uncoordinated exchange of taunts, a French Canadian from two streets over had once yelled, "Hey, Lucky Charms, freckles are stupid!" Caught unprepared for battle, I came back with, "Yeah, well... French's Mustard!"

In the winter, we rode our sleds head-first down the hills of tree-filled parks. For whatever reason, we were more concerned about our "Flexible Flyers" than our skulls. Baseball was played in weedy lots, and football without pads or helmets. At the Boy's Club, there was still a compulsory "No Bathing Suits Allowed" policy in effect at the pool, left over from some health craze in the 1890s, when the New Age really began. There were pedestal shrines to fallen servicemen—just Average Joes, not "heroes"—that had been set up in small neighborhood squares. About once a month, the city would put fresh wreaths on them. Many businesses had large clocks on their towers, and there were ornamental bronze ones as well, with Roman numerals, set on 12-foot posts along Main Street.

Things would soon change, but many mothers had not yet joined the corporate workforce. Hands parted curtains, from behind which eyes would look. Boys and girls sat on opposite sides of the Saint Peter's High cafeteria. The law banning married female teachers from the classroom had only just recently been overturned. As to the Red Square Bookstore: the idea that sex would somehow lead to liberation, to be found, for example, in D.H. Lawrence, was still something that could be believed. This was before what Marcuse called "repressive desublimation"—the incorporation of sex by the advertising industry—had gone viral, before it had tainted every aspect of American life.

Quite a few men walked to the factories where they worked, which were located, often enough, no more than a mile off. Why spend more time travelling than you had to or waste any money on gas? Best to be close to home in case of an emergency. An archaic custom, even then. Perhaps this way of doing things developed during the years of the Second World War, when Worcester, the industrial heart of New England, was thought to be a prime target for German bombs. City-wide blackout drills were conducted until 1945.

When I was younger—until, perhaps, sixth grade—my grandfather, a shop steward at Crompton and Knowles, would walk home to eat lunch with me. This was usually two sandwiches, wrapped in wax paper, which my grandmother would leave out on plates. On a special occasion—such as an A-plus on a test, or a fight with a large bully that I won—my grandfather would cut a donut in half and then toast it in the oven, until crunchy. He would then ostentatiously serve each half with a slice of American cheese. Such rituals did not seem quaint, not yet, or at least not to us, and they had nothing to do with what we could or could not afford. If other people lived in other ways, so be it; the world was a big place.

It is difficult for me to register that more than 50 years have gone by. The key memories from that period are still as vivid as they were. In the morning, for example, I would look out of my window; there, I would see a one-inch figure climbing up a smokestack. Although we knew about pollution, the smoke puffing out of giant smokestacks was somehow reassuring. It meant that productive work was being done. On spring and summer evenings, many families would sit on their front porches, telling stories for hours, talking with any neighbors who happened to walk by, and democrats and republicans, engineers and cab drivers, factory workers and professors, did not, at least automatically, tend to see each other as enemies. The top one percent had not yet won the class war. Even working-class guys read books, and the Earth had not yet departed from its orbit.

α

Having set the scene, let us cut back to the action: The bell had rung, and all but a few rebels had obeyed the headmaster's order. Perhaps two dozen students stuck their heads out of the windows, waving, and we left, to change the world. The world, of course, did change, as did we, but in ways that the most intelligent could never have predicted.

A few days later, I found out what the Delphic pronouncement of the headmaster, "Absence will be treated as such," actually meant. It meant that we each should write a letter of apology, to be posted on the wall by the main office, as well as sign off on a list of punitive new rules. Then, and only then, would the school consider the possibility of revoking our expulsion. Quite oddly, the school did not bother to inform my family of this ultimatum, so anxious were they to escort me on my way. With no second thoughts, I left. "Mom," I said, "I am fed up with the nuns, and there are courses that I'd like to take at Doherty." I was used to and good at keeping secrets. My family never did find out.

The outer darkness was beginning to look very good indeed.

As it turned out, my expulsion was a blessing in disguise, a gift of almost unimaginable value. It was as though I had awakened beneath the mosquito netting of a hotel bed in Guatemala, like my uncle Ed, to see first a broken window, and then the bullet hole left sometime during the night about a foot above my head.

3

The mind may be a muscle, but it is not a muscle that can be exercised by fiat. Discipline does not make it automatically stronger, and it can be difficult to tell, at the time, what benefits and what harms it. Mistakes are of greater value than accomplishments. We must carry our stupidity on our own backs as we grow.

In 1888, in *Ecce Homo*, Nietzsche wrote, "What does not kill me makes me stronger." I have always been amazed that this is his most often quoted statement, since, in 1889, he went insane. The details of the breakdown are quite fascinating, if obscure.

On January 3rd, 1889, two policemen approached Nietzsche on a street in Turin, where he lay, sobbing uncontrollably, in a heap, after having caused a disturbance. According to one version of the story, he had seen a cabman whipping his horse at the other end of the Piazza Carlo Alberti. He ran to the horse, threw his arms up over its neck to protect it, and then collapsed. It is said that, as he put his head against the horse's neck, unmoving, he was able to hear the beating of its heart, and that this is what had caused him to start sobbing. He felt pity, perhaps, which might have struck him as a breach of his superhuman code, or perhaps the sobs were due to some memory of his father, Carl Ludwig, i.e., of his "spare the rod, spoil the child" approach to education.

Over the next few days, he wrote a series of short, and highly bizarre, letters to his friends. To Jacob Burckhardt, his former colleague at the University of Basel, he wrote, "I have had Caiaphas put in fetters. Also, last year I was crucified by the German doctors in a very drawn-out manner. Wilhelm, Bismarck, and all anti-Semites are abolished." And later, on a more practical note, he commanded that Kaiser Wilhelm should go to Rome to be shot and called on the European powers to declare a preemptive war against Germany. After issuing these instructions, he would spend the next 11 years in a state of near absolute silence, perhaps philosophical, "only broken on occasion," according to Franz Wright, "by a lengthy and unpunctuated scream."

In 1890, on January 3rd, he was committed to the Basel Psychiatric Clinic, and then, on January 17th, he was transferred to the clinic at Jena University. An anonymous patient there reports,

> What interested me most was a patient who was always quiet and secluded and held in his hand printed notes on which stood: "Professor Friedrich Nietzsche." He said this name often every day. He had no keeper at his personal disposal…He got up at six in the morning and washed in the general washroom. He had to be watched so that he would not steal an institute comb. He was most interested in an institutional hat, a so-called "progress-hat," which he wore from morning to evening and which no one could take away from him.

This anonymous patient reports that Nietzsche must have been a lively dancer in his youth. "When Baron X. played on his zither," he writes, "Herr Nietzsche could not get on his legs fast enough to begin a marathon dance until the head warden led him off to calm him down." The patient also reports that Nietzsche loved to bathe. Although the patients at Jena were only allowed to take two baths per week, Nietzsche could often be found sitting in the bathroom, where he would stare, with apparent longing, at a tub. This patient sketched him once while he was sitting there. When the philosopher noticed that a sketch was being done, he straightened his hat and made a happy face. The patient offered the completed sketch to Nietzsche, who stood up, shook his hand, and said, as much to himself as to the artist, "Professor Nietzsche."

In the same year, Nietzsche's mother, Franziska, took him to her home in Naumburg, where she cared for him until her death in 1897. At that point, his sister, Elizabeth, took over. She took him to Weimar, where, although totally uncommunicative, he was allowed to meet with a number of famous visitors, such as Rudolph Steiner. In 1898, he suffered a series of strokes, which left him partially paralyzed. After contracting pneumonia in mid-August of 1900, he suffered yet another stroke on the night of August 24th, and then died the next day at noon.

It is certainly coincidental that Nietzsche died at noon, when this hour has such pregnant significance in his work. For example, in *Thus Spake Zarathustra*, he wrote,

> The sun of knowledge stands once more at noon, and the serpent of eternity lies coiled in its light: It is your time, you children of the noon...

And this is from *Twilight of the Idols*,

> The true world—we have abolished. What world has remained? The apparent one perhaps? But no! With the true world we also have abolished the apparent one. Noon: moment of the briefest shadow; end of the longest error; high point of humanity; INCIPIT ZARATHUSTRA.

Unable to speak, or, towards the end, to dress or wash or feed himself, he then left at an apex, at the moment when the shadows were the shortest.

"What does not kill me makes me stronger," as he said. In the face of such convoluted irony, I, too, am left almost powerless to speak. But what should we make of this often-quoted statement, and do later developments invalidate its truth? I would answer: If a life coheres, it does so in and of itself, and it is not up to us to figure out just how, or at what point in the future we might grasp it as a whole. I would argue, too, that the sun at noon is not actually very bright, nor is it the original sun. In fact, we are haunted by the sun of the nonexistent, and it is that sun that tortures us. Such events as these are the cusp of an almost unimaginable sphere, which, without dark eyeglasses, there is no way we can see.

We do not know if a thing will transform or destroy us until long after the experience is over. We do not know how the story will play out, which arcs and elements and reversals have been scheduled in advance and which ones we have had some hand in shaping. Even after we have passed from this world to another, it is possible that the outcome is ambiguous. Necessity, the stern mistress, for reasons as metaphysical as they are opaque, may choose to veto every end of which we dream. Have we out-thought Schopenhauer? Are we prodigies of Will? Ananke does not care how weak or strong we are. Due to blindness, we must learn to navigate by scent.

4

In 1974, four years after being kicked out of Saint Peter's, I moved 40 miles east to attend the Art Institute of Boston. Worcester was a city, the second largest in Massachusetts, but I had come to see it more as a collection of small neighborhoods. I yearned to be where things happened, where I would find myself out of my depth. I had set aside my childish plans of helping to start a political revolution. Now I wanted to help to start an artistic revolution. The school did not cooperate. There may be such a thing as a revolutionary gray-scale chart, but I never got to paint one. I stumbled into a writers circle and took a detour into poetry. Many of the writers were better than I was. It was not until 1984, when I published *X: Revenge of the Autogenes*, that my writing came of age.

Real estate prices had shot up, Boston artists were being bounced from their lofts, harsh daylight was causing the alternative scene to blink, and Reagan's Morning in America had moved in for the kill. Luckily, centrifugal force was having its way with the writers of my circle. I was starting to feel bored and claustrophobic. The city had somehow shrunk, and it seemed that I had learned as much as I could learn. I took a detour into Taoist meditation, and then into Kundalini Yoga. Then, in 2000, married and with a two-year-old daughter, I found myself back at art school.

In 2004, twenty-seven years after graduating from the Art Institute of Boston, at a higher turn of the spiral, I at last received my state certification to work as a high school art teacher. Unfortunately, this was just at the moment when the city had gutted the majority of high school art programs. Once again, it was time to hurry up and wait.

An alchemical maxim reads, "In my patience is my soul." It was not the perfection of my own soul that concerned me. Ghosts had hollowed out the soul of the Decentralized Plutocracy. High Modernism: now sentenced to endless cycles of de-pixelation. Genius: the knack for selling outrage to those too inert to feel it, the transubstantiation of the ego to the brand. A cold wind howled from the wastes of the Younger Dryas. I had only a black stone upon which to rest my head.

My goals: just weightless holograms, lures designed to hypnotically distract me from their hooks, requests for donations to postpone a mass extinction. Attempting to make do, I taught junior high for a while. I then decided that I would prefer to cut my wrists. I loved teaching art, and I was skilled at cultivating a state of "creative disorientation" in my students, beyond which breakthroughs into some greater breadth and depth of imagination could occur, but I was no one's idea of a natural disciplinarian.

I have often wondered: why did this process take so long to play out? Why, upon my graduation from the Art Institute of Boston, and given my belief that my vision was unique, was I not prepared to assume my rightful place in the world? On the simplest level, you could say that I was reluctant to grow up, yet it was equally true that there was no world that was waiting to receive me. My body: a fortress left by an antediluvian reich, upon whose battlements a race of dismembered birdmen sang.

Perhaps the world actually had ended on July 16th, 1945, as many scientists had feared that it might, when the first atomic bomb, called "The Gadget," was detonated over the Jornada del Muerto Desert. Since then, we had measured out with calipers our lengthening shadows on the sand. In fear, we had turned our backs on this surrogate for the Bindu, with its 20-kiloton yield. We had scoffed at this gift from Shiva. We had fixed our eyes on our TV sets when so ordered by the Powers that Be.

However one chose to interpret the disjunction, I was in the world but not of it. In this I was not alone. Of the several hundred enthusiastic art students in the class of '77, I doubt that more than two dozen have continued, successfully, to pursue a career in art. It is hard for me to remember exactly what I had planned to do after graduation. It was not that I did not have goals; I did, but they were convoluted, intuitive, and arrogantly esoteric. They did not have a fixed form; thus I was under no obligation to justify my progress to anyone or to measure my amorphous intentions against fact.

In search of liminal extremes, my path led out beyond the exit of the labyrinth, and then back, by means of a wormhole, to the dark space at the center. I ask myself now: What feedback as to goals did I need or expect from AIB? My imagination was sometimes out of contact with my hands; I hoped to deepen their relationship. As a teenager, I had been tempted to do everything at once, to view things from too many angles, to be so open to possibilities that my gestures would cancel each other out. I hoped to learn to go, step by step, from the first to the last stage of a project. To go step by step was to be able to cut into one's subconscious, to find oneself through a tactile interaction with materials. Who knew that this process could take decades?

At AIB, I learned just enough. I did take several baby steps. I did develop a lifelong love of getting messy, as well as a capacity for misjudging every distance. I did learn to extract the pith from the words of stupid teachers. I did learn to appreciate the beauty of wrong turns.

My experience of the labyrinth was tactile: To see was to be able to feel one's way through the dark.

In retrospect, I can see how this tactile interaction with materials helped to format my later development as a writer. I seldom begin with an outline. When I do, I begin to quickly work against it. To complete a poem or an essay is to be open to the twists and turns of the creative process, to then read that process backwards, treating as suspect any too-facile bursts of inspiration. Edit harshly, yes, but be open to the uncanny if and when it occurs.

As soon as a new piece begins to swim out of the fog, I will have a sense that it is more real than I am, that it exists as a fully formed mind and body, in its own well-guarded manner of existing. Once, in a dream, on the top floor of a bombed-out warehouse, I sorted through four years of my artwork, laughing. It then then took me four years to catch up with the dream. At the age of 16, when I first started to write, I would hear a voice reading in a certain rhythm, with a certain tone, about subjects I could sense but in words that I could not entirely decipher. Over the past few years, I have come to realize that the voice I heard was my own. How to get from what I sensed to what I knew, from the movement of my fingers to the shape of the finished work? No straight path was available.

So, did I learn what I had hoped to learn at AIB? Not at all. I did learn to begin from where I was, to bond with my materials, to remove one wave from' the ocean at a time, to go step by step towards an end both present and obscure. For these lessons, I had no problem saying "thanks." It was useful to have gone there. I was grateful enough. My complaints had rather to do with wholesale errors of omission. Students were not asked or expected to come to terms with the larger context of their work—whether social, political, economic, historical, spiritual, or mythological—in any way that might lead to an upheaval in the present. We had shrunk the cosmos. We had set up and then focused upon objects in the foreground, in order to blot out the inscrutable forces that oppressed us.

We were the ghosts of a High Modernism that could never be fulfilled, the afterbirth of Hiroshima, the imprints that a context-upending flash had deconstructed. Curiously, however, the world continued to look more or less like it did before. In the dead of night, perhaps, our DNA had been altered, and the streets of our city had been subtly rearranged. How soundlessly the windows of our factories had been broken. We paid little or no attention as the wind blew through the shards.

We were the cattle of the revolving Disco sun, whose necks had not yet felt a knife. Death came to others, only, to Mayan villagers in the highlands of Guatemala, for example, where the CIA, under the guise of foreign aid, was just starting to set up its cocaine supply networks, and its agents scrawled Pentecostal slogans on the walls. The real sun hated us. Our hands were clean. Strangers carried out the crimes that we committed. We stupidly kept our hearts on the insides of our bodies. For this reason, no standing wave would carry us to the land of the Hyperboreans. When we called to the gods for help, we were offered Positive Thinking scams, each designed to look a bit different from the others. We could not see, without instruments, through the fog, or hear the birdmen calling from the shore of the nonexistent, where they hung, upside down, on their trees of recombinant lightning.

At AIB, in a manner that resembled but was opposed to my own metaphysical method, much as a corpse can be said to resemble a living body, knowledge of all large-scale issues was thought to be retroactive. Each thing worth doing had already taken place, in an almost perfect form, in such a way that we could imitate but never equal the achievement. Revolutionary concepts could best be found in the movements of the first half of the 20th century. In the 1970s, our epochal breakthroughs could not be other than clichés.

Einstein invented Cubism, for example, as channeled through his acolyte Picasso. Each object was the sum of all intersecting views. Kandinsky assigned a spiritual value to each color, along with synesthetic specifications. Blue is pure. It grows concentrically, like a snail in its shell. It sounds like a flute. Yellow disturbs and evokes delirium. It sounds like a trumpet. It jumps out at the viewer before leaving altogether. Green lacks vigor. Orange emits health. Purple is slow and dull, like an old person. It sounds like an English horn.

Malevich knelt before the icon of the square, its absoluteness, its silence, and its brutal pragmatism. Futurism was the embodiment of speed, an ever-accelerating Model T. Speed kills, however, and the movement did not last long. Dada harvested the nihilism of the First World War. With the help of the 9 ½ million gassed, machine-gunned, and shelled, it managed to invent a new species of black humor. Matisse was once regarded as a Fauve, a "wild beast." He later dreamed of "an art of balance…devoid of troubling or depressing subject matter," an art "something like a good armchair, which offers rest from physical fatigue."

Surrealism had appropriated the Cliff Notes version of Freud. Pollock had jettisoned his Jungian imagistic self-indulgence in order to focus on the elements of flatness, line, and color. Sadly, archetypal images were allowed to sneak back in. This betrayal of Abstraction led to an alcoholic relapse and then to semi-suicide by car crash. WARNING. CLEMENT GREENBERG AHEAD. CROSS AT YOUR OWN RISK. Art history soon after culminated in the color field paintings of Larry Poons.

It did seem that all of the most important breakthroughs already taken place, that there was, perhaps, little of substance left to do. It was odd to experience the avant-garde as an object of nostalgia. To read the future was to accurately read the entrails of the past, now embalmed. These served as a kind of Rorschach blot, whose fixed patterns could be, almost indefinitely, rearranged. This freed one from the messiness of having to come to terms with the living. The living were naughty, like children, prone to indeterminate movements. Granted: it was important for great artists to take risks. We were no more than interpreters. Our role was to systematically express our knowledge of such risks.

Among many of our teachers, it was an act of faith that death was the precondition of genius. Against this, I proposed the following: That our definition of "life" was that of the Ancient's "death." A stranger in a strange land, not quite a part of nature, the genius was the one who had hermetically sealed his leaks. By this sealing up of leaks, the artist would gain the energy to enact the "reversal of a reversal," as described by Schwaller de Lubicz, the idea behind the crossed arms of the Pharaoh. Already, I had begun to sense that the movement of time was problematic. Time did move, yes, but in more than one direction.

For the Ancients, the point of ontological convergence was projected back into the past—onto a period of higher civilization, heard as the echo of an echo within stories; onto an age when knowledge could be picked like fruit from trees; onto an age when the gods were playful, in which delegates from the three worlds drew up rules for war; onto a time when the human body was made up of eight limbs, when it could move, by the power of thought, from one place to another; onto a time when statues breathed, when babies could choose their own astrological charts; onto a time when the largest cities, with their tens of thousands of inhabitants, could be fit into a space no bigger than a vowel; onto a time when the blind poet could step down into the sky, before his plunge into the mist beyond.

We Moderns, on the other hand, project this point into the future. We envision it in terms of the Social Darwinist perfection of the race; the electrification of the rural South; the construction of a Marxist Workers Paradise; the triumph of abstract art; the Return of Jesus; the global spread of Neoliberalism; the cleansing of the curse of Multiculturalism from the West; the development of the driverless car and the replacement of real Uber drivers; the mapping of the three billion base pairs of DNA; the extraction of the last ounce of tar sands from the Alberta/Saskatchewan border; a leap to Teilhard de Chardin's "noosphere"; or the formulation of a Unified Field Theory. We believe that we are "evolving" toward this point, rather than "devolving" from some already more or less perfect sphere.

What key factor might allow us to grasp these two directions as one movement? It is to remember that the Great Year moves continuously backwards, even as, to us, it appears to be moving forwards. By such means, the year "precesses" to its origin. In the mid-1970s, we were still a few feet short of this point of cosmic convergence. A few relevant details had yet to be sketched in.

Was space an unbroken sphere, as Parmenides had argued? Or, as Heraclitus advised, should we train ourselves to "expect the unexpected"? I had mixed feelings about the theories of Teilhard de Chardin. If humanity was moving in a straight line towards perfection, why had the US dumped 7.6 million tons of bombs on Vietnam? You would think that 7.2 million might have been enough. We could have used the money to replenish our supplies of Agent Orange. I felt that this planet was in need of much repair. At the same time, I had some experience with the rings of light that surrounded it. Were we really even alive, in either the ancient or the modern sense, or were we reenacting a series of preprogrammed movements in the Bardo?

The world did appear to be moving faster every day. This could be no more than a trick of the eye, however, the movement of two hands around a clock that did not move. The world's busyness did not argue against the fact that it had ended. Movement, in and of itself, was not the same as living force. At AIB, it was an article of faith that paintings led only to other paintings, as in a museum whose windows opened onto windows, whose doors opened onto corridors that led to other doors, behind which were more paintings, in the range of canonical styles that would be specified in one's syllabus. "Have you ever heard of an artist called Van Gogh?" my freshman drawing teacher, Peter Krause, once asked. Such knowledge as was available was either practical or academic, as if we students had not existed for some 8 ½ billion years, as if all knowledge were additive, as if a museum had any need of walls.

Tribe and story had been disconnected. Corporate logos had stolen the magnetism from the world of ideal forms. One subject could not reweave the archaic thread of the breath. We were born *ex nihilo*. We were blank as *tabula rasas*. It would be years before our conscious and unconscious energies would be allowed to meet.

Like those before us, our immediate task was to learn the rules, in order to be able to break them. Like instructions from the beloved author of a totalitarian handbook, how many times did I hear these words repeated? All parties collaborated to confirm the wisdom of this paradox.

I, the prophetic capacitor, was not so sure. "Who is to say that a straight line cannot lead in a circle," I thought, "or that a hard-won skill may be no different than a snare? Earth's Rulers rule by playing on our yearning, by yanking on our psychology of previous investment, by weaponizing our desire to be liked. A trained dog does not bite its master's hand."

Anatomy was a challenge, both in the literal and esoteric human-as-microcosm sense. It was the job of our freshman anatomy teacher, Mr. Maars, to explain how we human beings were put together. Mr. Maars, for reasons known only to himself and the demons that possessed him, spoke in an almost inaudible whisper, so that he could not be heard beyond the second row of seats. If a student asked that he speak loudly enough to be heard, Mr. Maars would, no matter how articulately the question had been asked, continue to drone on. On a good day, he would not first pause to correct the student for his rudeness. If we did not speak Latin, well, that was not his fault.

The lack of actual instruction forced us to fall back on our textbooks, where names provided us with a substitute for insight. We somehow managed to pass over the pineal gland, that lock into which a key was waiting to be inserted, that eschatological pinecone. It was not visible on the surface of the body, and it was of no use whatsoever to the draftsman. There were always more bones to memorize.

We did learn to make objects, that much was real, but whom did we make those objects for? Some catastrophe would seem to have swept away our audience, the audience that would otherwise be waiting to applaud us. Then again, perhaps this audience did not exist in any form that we would recognize. Perhaps it did exist in a form that we did not dare to imagine. If there were eyes that had not closed, if there were ears that could hear the cutting-edge thoughts that we so strategically held back from the world, we still lacked the means to correctly place our gifts. As the subjects of a decentralized plutocracy, we lacked the energy to infuse our gestures with a fierce enough intent. No doubt it was better to think small.

When archeologists excavated the Olmec site of San Lorenzo, settled circa 1700 BC, they found that a number of ceramic gods had been cemented face-down in the aqueduct, which was 560 feet long. This is, or so archeologists theorize, the exact mirror image of an aqueduct still buried, an aqueduct set over to the side. Within the first, at key points, they have found a variety of "offerings"—from the mineral, plant, animal, and human kingdoms—which we could, just as easily, choose to view as the components of a "work of art."

Among these were the following: heaps of human bones showing signs of butchering and burn marks; broken pottery; jade axes; baby were-jaguars, with cleft heads; large rubber balls; small mirrors, some of them convex, polished from iron ore nodes and perhaps traded from the highlands of Oaxaca; wooden staffs with a bird's head on one end and a shark's tooth on the other, used for bloodletting; knotted cords, for drawing through the wound; a vast quantity of bones from the marine toad, *bufo marinus*, a creature inedible because of the toxins in its skin but which was valued because of one of these toxins is *bufotenine*, a potent hallucinogen. All of this had been buried with great ritualistic care, and then covered up with many layers of dirt, so that no sign of the work would be visible on the surface. Perhaps both we and our audience had once been buried in such a fashion. Yet the burials were separate, and we were now many light-years apart.

The Museum Without Walls, in the end, had little use for us, and it had long since ceased to be looking for fresh talent. Since this museum did not have an entrance, or, for that matter, any exits, there was no way to tell if one had actually stepped inside. And once done with one's visit, there was no way to tell what one had gained from the experience. Even if a sample of one's artwork did hang in mid-air, one's role was to stare in puzzlement at the name found underneath. Who was the actual artist? In what year was the work first done? As one stared at the name of the artist, as one stared at the once familiar work, the specifics of its long inception and development would become less and less distinct. In fact, the whole of horizontal space, with all of the hallucinatory objects that it held, would then appear to be no more than a quantum fluctuation.

The triumph of High Modernism had been frozen by a flash, by the splitting of an infinitely small point. Its brilliance would neither increase nor decline. *Newness*, as disjunction from all of the shadows of the past, as radical ideal upon which one might venture to bet one's life, was now itself a historic footnote.

5

"Though a permanent storm scorches my shores, far out my wave is deep, complex, and prodigious. I expect nothing *finite*, I am resigned to sculling between two unequal dimensions. But even so, my markers are of lead, not cork, my trail is salt, not smoke."— Rene Char, from "The Rampart of Twigs"

∝

A painter should learn to paint; the thinking of the AIB administration was no more complex than that. A bit of art history would do no harm. And what should the visually well-trained, if somewhat inarticulate, painter do to make a living after graduation? Time would tell. It would do no good to be pessimistic. If others had done it, in the 1950s or several centuries ago, then it was possible that you could too.

Let the creative waitress negotiate her schedule with the phallic manager of the steakhouse.

Let the intoxicated cabdriver each weekend tube by tube smear his Paleolithic blood across a landscape.

Let the genius who is missing his left ear deliver surplus government cheese to the suburbs in a van, for there are suburbanites who have signed up for the government cheese program.

Let Mickey Mouse in a beret cut the stretched throat of Post-Modernism on the altar of High Finance, for irony has had its day, and more than this the gods will not allow.

Let the shipwrecked artist return to his own coast, to the place of dark instruction, for it is there that his dog, Argos, is waiting to lick his hand, for it is there that a great slaughter is waiting to occur.

Let the body of the artist be the same size as the Earth, even as he learns to keep his arrogance in check.

Let the carefully concealed visionary sell rugs, a practical tradition, as was demonstrated by the Sufis.

Let all graffiti be written in the sky, where there are none to scrub it off.

Pursued by the horror of his prehistoric crimes, which have frozen half of his face and caused a lightness in his step, let the newly responsible artist not hesitate to look foolish.

Let warfare be served only at one's table at the café, the scale of megadeath to be determined between friends over little plates of toast and escargot.

Let the artists at Les Deux Magots drink no more wine than necessary, only as many bottles as might be suitable for the event, in order to prevent unscheduled fistfights from occurring.

Let artists collaborate in the prevention of bad habits, so that only the most ancient cities would be allowed to smoke.

Let the presence in a bird-mask teach artists to remove their heads, sometimes safely, for chaos looms, and there are those who must be skillful in this practice.

Let the timid avant-gardist be cast into the ocean, for it is there that he will learn the fate of the timid avant-gardist.

My Friend, the Minotaur

Untitled Photogram, 2002

1

A challenge had been issued: "Find the past!" Most records had disappeared. The ones that survived were not worth the DNA that they were printed on. The reasons for the body count—which, each year, grew by exponential leaps—were as variable as was the scale and appearance of the labyrinth. Some claimed that the labyrinth was actually just a concrete pillbox bunker, left over from the days of World War II, whose iron doors, streaked with salt, had long ago rusted shut. On one door: a large eye beneath a pair of horns, and on the other one: an octopus. Perched on a plateau, the complex gave access to a 360-degree view, and there were "wheel tracks," cut deep into the stone, which led from it in a network of straight lines to the beach, and then continued on, straight down through the surf and down into the depths. Every seven years, of course, would come the drawing of the lots, though few had ever met the occult corporatists who would materialize to serve as judges on the pageant, and the doors never did appear to open or to close.

Now, it was obvious that a new Reich was in charge, and that, from their makeshift cybernetic Bindu, they were ready to wrap their spell around the next 1000 years. At each of the 28 u-turns, they had cut the throat of a professor of geometry. It was a time for glad preparations. With his gold-tipped training horns, a tiny and scrunched-up bundle of omnipotence had arrived. It seemed possible, however, that the director of the WTO had been incorrect in his reading of the entrails. Many objects had been thrown, noses had been bitten, and ears had been torn off. A seizure had occurred, it was said, which had somehow split an atom. Great fissures had opened up in the holographic stage-set, which, as the Minotaur continued to stamp his tiny hoof against the world, had all the more aggressively to be closed. Amid the glow of the radioactive fallout, it was possible that the Guardians of the Double Ax had begun to lose control. It was possible that they too might succumb to the madness that, until then, they had found the means to micromanage.

Commandos in black parachutes had dropped like electrocuted birds and then landed in broken heaps, to form two rings around the steadily expanding complex. No direct assault could prevail against the Minotaur, no challenge to his force-field from without, no intrigue of rogue sub-departments of DARPA from within. He existed, as was scheduled in the stars. To attack the Minotaur was to amplify his strength. To turn against the labyrinth was to magnify its breadth.

Hoarse bellowing had flown across the black waves of the ocean. Foam had gathered on the lips of the scrunched-up bundle of omnipotence. His eyes rolled, striking fear into the hearts of even those in the inner circle. Was there some way to distinguish between a tantrum and a seizure, some method marked with the thumbprint of the Ancients, some safe way to harness the convulsions of the beast? This issue was a source of ongoing speculation among the Long-Skulled Seers of the Federal Reserve, yet both of these phenomena had pointed towards one end. It was feeding time. The technology that had been meant to keep the monster in had instead provided him with access to fresh victims, who were even less able than he was to escape.

The beast must be fed, that much was certain, yet strange reversals had conspired to cloud the vision of the Rulers, even they who had access to the best corrective lenses, even they who had perfected the most invasive algorithms. One, in the gray sky of the Underworld, there had appeared an alternate sun. It shone, for some period of centuries, coldly, on the cities that a race of ant-like workers built, and then stopped at three o'clock. It had been put there, perhaps, by Daedalus, because the real sun had disturbed him. At present, none were old enough to determine the source of the false light.

Turning back and forth through the labyrinth of the self, around each of the 28 u-turns, I probed almost to the circumference and then back again toward the center, where the scent of blood was strong, where, row upon row, the archaic glyphs began to look me in the eye. Some looked like broken eggs, others like DNA, others like snakes with walking sticks, others like humanoid knots. Some looked like portable oceans, others like pulsing shields, others like severed heads, and still others like overturned boats. As I stared at these glyphs, they more than met my gaze, and I slowly realized that I could not move my limbs. My lips buzzed. Some force was attempting to twist them into shapes.

I could smell salt in the air, and the iodine of seaweed, and the creaking of masts was not too far away. There was also another smell, like that of copper, and the taste of rusted iron. I could feel the coolness of the air around my ankles, inching up, then further up. When I woke, I saw then that the glyphs were random scratches on the wall. Whose eyes were those that saw, though? What had happened to my tongue? In my search to penetrate the top-secret lair of the narcissist, probing almost to the circumference and then back again to the center, where I could sense that some human had just been yanked out of his shoes, I asked myself eight questions, each corresponding to one of the eight primordial elements of the cosmos. These are as I present them here, or would be, had not circumstances taken the notebook from my hand, had not the questions and the questioner been lost.

Image: Public Domain

Most records have gone missing, and those that survive are not worth the DNA that they are printed on. Some catastrophe would appear to have intervened. The Earth tilts at a different angle. As I attempt to remember the eight questions that I asked, I often seem to be moving in slow motion, as though walking at the bottom of an ocean, in lead boots. My intellect is approximate, my bones creak, and my heart is filled with the fog of a shore that does not exist. So, instead, I will ask a substitute set of eight, which are as I present them here:

1. How can narcissism be considered a disease if the narcissist is superior to all but one percent of the race, and Fate has chosen him to be rich, smart, beautiful, and famous?

2. Is the narcissist aware that other people exist, or do they exist only insofar as they act out his scenarios, which are grand, and unlike any that mere mortals could imagine?

3. If the narcissist can create an artificial self, which he then engorges with blood, can he keep it in a state of maximum tumescence, and does that mean he is happy?

4. What is the source of the narcissist's rage against the world?

5. If the narcissist is driven by rage against the world and contempt for other human beings, how is he able to project so much charisma?

6. Is not industrial-strength sacrifice the birthright of the narcissist, the very reason that he was placed within the center of the labyrinth?

7. Is it fair that the narcissist should be forced to answer to any law, whether man-made or supernatural, when there are 8 ½ billion who are begging to be blamed?

8. Is narcissism a disease, as defined by the A.P.A.'s "Diagnostic and Statistical Manual of Mental Disorders," or is the narcissist, in fact, the proponent of a cosmology, the priest of an occult Reich, whose forces will soon dominate the world?

I will attempt to answer these eight questions, in both a personal and a more general way, by exploring an incident that occurred in August 2002, when I reached out to a friend I had not seen in ten years. I will describe what led up to the phone call, the deep background, the immediate cause, as well as what followed from it. Then, I will probe the reasons for why this phone call haunted me for weeks.

3

Virgins had gone missing. They were fuel, which had been consumed. They were not dead; they had simply "disappeared," for such are the rites demanded by the agents of the IMF. In search of a drop of blood, the Rulers of Prehistory had set up sweatshops in Honduras, where clothing for the Gap is manufactured, as well as Nike slave-labor factories in China, and tantalum mines in the Congo, without which no iPod would see the light of day. That the Many were created for the enjoyment of the One was a secret that few dared to speak aloud, and fewer still to celebrate, with no sleight-of-hand, in public, although lately that had begun to change. Truly, the Elite were those who did not hesitate to kill.

The years had taken a circuitous route. Lost innocence demanded justice. Such demands would, for the remainder of the time-cycle, continue to fall upon wax-plugged ears. Blackened bones showed teeth marks. Ghosts cried from pyramids of skulls. The labyrinth was a paradox. There was no clear inside or outside, even as it served as the most foolproof of containers. I turned back to go forward, out to go in. When I woke, I found that I was standing in the spot where I began—where my sense of smell had long ago abandoned me. The narcissist was just a breath away. As shadows had magnified the monster's strength, making him look taller than he was, the contest, when it did occur, was brief.

In the process, I was forced to take the Minotaur by the horns, with their terrible gold tips, to tear away his mask, to disentangle the thread of my own breath from the labyrinth, as turn by turn, I discovered the identity of its builder. And, finally, I was forced to mourn the ruins of a friendship that was dead but not yet buried. This essay is the epitaph.

4

When my ex-wife Lisa called from L.A. in August of 2002, after being out of touch for several years, to announce that she was planning a trip to Boston, she asked that I contact our old and mutual friend Danny Panagakos to inform him about the trip. She was working on a new video project, a kind of autobiography, and wanted to compare and contrast *then* and *now* versions of important people and places. She was very fond of Danny. His voice advised her. His image lived in her heart. To Lisa, Danny was a vampire god of the avant-garde. He referred to her as "Miss Georgette." I hesitated. Lisa would not take "no" for an answer. "I am not sure Danny wants to hear from either one of us," I said.

Lisa was fond of Danny. But was he also fond of her—or of his parents, or even of his wife, Salma? It was not clear to me that Danny could be truly fond of anybody. Danny and Lisa had, in fact, slept together during the hallucinated days that preceded our divorce, a fact about which Danny wasted no time in informing me. He did not want to place roadblocks on the freeway of our open communication. Did I care? No. It was an omen of the end of an anachronistic drama. As such, it was welcome. I was, however, puzzled by this need for confession on the part of someone so seemingly incapable of guilt.

I had no clue as to his motivations then, at lease none that was allowed to pass my threshold of awareness. Do I have one now? I do not have an explanation but I do have a suspicion, and again, it has to do with drama. There is little reason to apologize to an entity that does not exist, but, even in the labyrinth of mirrors, the false self needs a cast of supporting actors. The job of the supporting actors is to chant that the narcissist is the Minotaur, the devouring god, the black hole at the center of the labyrinth, towards which virgins of both sexes must converge. Transgression and loyalty collaborated to feed the appetite of the growing supernova.

5

After a number of false starts, I finally managed to track Danny down at the main branch of the Webster Public Library, where he had worked his way to the top. Founded by Samuel Slater in 1812 and located on Lake "I'll Fish on My Side and You Fish on Your Side and Nobody Fishes in the Middle," as the translation from the Nipmuc goes, Webster is an old mill town, once famous for the manufacturing of shoes and textiles, which had been reimagined as an upscale bedroom community, with a stage-set-style Main Street, during the high-tech "Massachusetts Miracle" of the 1980s.

The paint on all of the scenery is fresh. You will not find any worn spots on the railings. There are ordinances against pigeons pooping on the statues, and, for this reason, they have set up tiny rest rooms. Even the manikins look like Stepford versions of themselves. As odd as it might seem, such life-like verisimilitude can be spectral, and such micromanaged quaintness can be more than a bit disturbing. You would think that you were living in the 1920s, at the latest, and that Norman Rockwell might, at any moment, wander into the Owl Smoke Shop for tobacco.

Danny was now Director of Library Services for the town—an odd position for a flamboyant avant-gardist. I stopped to wonder at how my friend could pour so much energy into library science, which he hated, and so little into his artwork, which, supposedly, he loved. This was also one of the last places in which you would expect to find the Minotaur. A mastery of the Dewey Decimal System was not a classically recognized attribute. The library was, however, like the labyrinth, a hermetically-sealed environment, in which the Minotaur could enforce the centrality of his role. A high percentage of discordant feedback could be purged. Any leakage of his occult hungers could be plausibly denied. Few traces would be left. Amid the coolness of the well-lit shelves, the beast's rage would be more difficult to detect than the whisper of air from the AC units.

After a wait of two minutes, Danny's assistant put me through. "Hi Danny, this is Brian," I said. "Lisa is planning a trip to Boston next week, and she asked if I could arrange a time and place for the three of us to meet. She is working on a kind of video auto-biography. She's incorporated some Super 8 footage from 1978, in which we were all doing our best to act experimental. She was hoping to interview both of us, to revisit some of our favorite places and to cut back and forth between the present and the past."

D: "Tell her that I'm busy."

B: "Lisa is traveling 3,000 miles, and it's been eight years since her last trip. Are you sure that you can't set aside an hour for lunch?"

D: "Salma and I are building a house in Belize. I'm really very busy."

B: "Belize! Why Belize?"

D: "I am disgusted with America. It has Americans in it, who disgust me. My grandmother died last year. She left me all of her money, as well as all of her real estate holdings. Money is not an issue anymore. I've worked enough. Salma and I are planning to retire next year, in Belize, where small, brown-skinned peasants will worship the ground we walk on.

"Are you still living on Hemenway Street, or have they thrown you out yet?"

B: "I moved when I got married seven years ago. We own a house."

D: "A house! My, that really is impressive. Have you published anywhere, or are you still the ne'er do well that my father always called you?"

B: "I've written four books since the last time that I saw you. I've published here and there. What about you, Danny? Are you doing any writing or art?"

D: "I am, but I don't want to talk about it. You might steal my ideas again. Did you know that I have a radio show? They pay me to destroy movies."

B: "Steal your ideas! You've got to be kidding. You've never actually shown me any of your work, except for that black match-book with your name inside."

And so the conversation went. There was no rapport, no play of curiosity, not the slightest trace of affection. "Lisa is going to be disappointed," I said. "Perhaps you could give her a call."

D: "No. You talk to her. She's your ex-wife. I have no interest in ancient history."

Towards the end of our conversation Danny confided, with considerable self-satisfaction, a bit of information that I found amazing. He said, "I no longer feel inhibited about being a bitch. I make sure that people know what I think of them. I don't hide my feelings anymore." He presented this as though such an attitude were the sign of some new maturity, as though rudeness were not the most ancient of weapons in his arsenal. I could not remember a time when Danny did not feel free to taunt or mock others without the slightest of provocations. Friends did not get special privileges. Passersby were not exempt.

I thought back to a lunch at Bangkok Cuisine that occurred perhaps 12 years before. Our mutual friend Janet was visiting from New York, and as we were waiting for our Pad Thai and Green Duck Curry, Danny decided to entertain us with a series of sarcastic improvisations. He was quite inventively vicious, brilliant in his pantomime of the diners' gestures and actions. He did not speak quietly, but projected his lines as to the top seats in the balcony of a theatre. One especially outrageous comment took Janet by surprise. She snorted, with explosive force, covering Danny with a large amount of shrimp and lemongrass soup. The man sitting at the next table turned to him, and said, "I'm glad that she spit on you! I was about to do it myself."

Danny was special. Humans were stupid. Contempt was the most appropriate response to the opinions and activity of others. As Adam Smith, in *The Wealth of Nations*, wrote, "All for ourselves and nothing for other people, seems, in every age of the world, to have been the vile maxim of the masters of mankind." There were those who saw such "selfishness" as a bad thing. Danny was not among them.

This had all been explained by the Egyptians, a good five or six thousand years ago, in their theories about "styptic fire." This was the fire that, paradoxically, contracted, and by such means brought the world into existence—i.e., without it, there would be no world at all, but only sea, wave upon black wave. Being livestock, the unwashed masses seemed unable to appreciate that, even as things stood, the Elite were just barely able to get by. They did not understand that Danny was the Minotaur, or that he played by a different set of rules. One set was for him, another for the human race. They did not see the omnipotence that he had volunteered to give up, or that, as gift exchanges go, he had not received a gift of equal value. Preoccupied with such inanities as rent, they just did not understand how difficult it could be to choose between one vacation spot and another, to weigh the relative merits of St. Thomas and Cancun. They had no grasp of the existential loneliness of privilege.

The world was dead, and really very small. It was a sign that had burnt out, a keyhole in which they had broken off the key, a drain down which the Minotaur had been washed, inducing claustrophobia. It was a wasteland inhabited by hungry ghosts, who would not shut up. They were always informing the Minotaur of their "feelings." They insisted that he respond in kind, and not just with a factually correct approximation. As if! When they were done, they would then start in on their nutritional demands. Even the most evolved of artists were somehow mysteriously flawed, although once, against his better judgment, he had dared to imagine otherwise. They could, perhaps, be likened to the test subjects of the World War Two Japanese Vivisection Corps, Unit 731. They were of momentary interest and of use as a raw data-source, but they would soon be thrown away, to leave only a faint trace of energy in the air, a smudge of bioluminescence.

Once, the Minotaur had done his best to interpret the strange sounds that humans made. As instructed by his Neo-Ahrimanian therapist, he had also given a second chance to the most evolved of evolved artists—i.e., those beloved by investment bankers—for all the good that it did him. No more of that. Their vision was defective. Their brains were still in the larval stage. Broken chromosomes did not allow them to acknowledge his preeminence, which need not, of course, be justified by the production of any actual work.

The pure idea was enough. Attitude was all. The perfected self was the subtlest of creations. The Latter Day Orgiasts of Bataille would cleanse the unconverted masses. Death would serve as a form of remedial education, so that, from his bank of souls, the Minotaur would be able to draw the blood-sustenance that he needed. Lady Justice in her blindfold would see the light of his erased copy of a drawing by Joseph Beuys. She would compel even the most arrogant of faux-sophisticates to kneel. Again, they would be forced to grapple with the multiplicity of his forms. These forms would flash, tumescent and hypnotic, on the still proto-digital screens of their attention, in not all of which did he wear the Taurean mask or hook a gold ring through his nose. Clouds would part. Before the eyes of an unblinking crowd, the Chosen One would have Tantric sex with his own reflections in mid-air.

The broadcast would provoke a revolution. Taurean-Guard youths would throw critics into bonfires. Heads would roll, beginning with his own, as in the "March to the Scaffold" movement of Berlioz's *Symphonie Fantastique*. This would only serve to intensify his pleasure. The year would be Year One. In response to popular demand, which would have swelled to tsunami-like proportions, Caligula would then reinvent the Earth.

This long-range strategy for the Triumph of the Will had not changed much since October of 1970, when, as high school juniors in Mr. Tsang's art class, we traded jokes as we labored to assemble the tiny squares of our color charts.

6

Danny and I had lost touch several times before, only to have our friendship spring mysteriously to life again. I thought back to a reunion that occurred in 1977, when Danny and I had been out of touch for most of the five years since high school, which had about it an uncanny aura of fatality. Dissimilar though we were, some opaque force seemed to be drawing us together, much as Lautreamont had arranged for the chance meeting of a sewing machine and an umbrella on a dissecting table. We did not fit into the same metaphysical frame; yet somehow, for all intents and purposes, we did.

During the year of our engagement, Lisa was living in Narragansett, Rhode Island, in a small house by the ocean. I would take the train from Boston on Friday and return on Monday afternoon. The small house had a large window that looked out on the bay. At sunset, the bay would be transmuted into gold, a rippling sheet of it. The bay was wide but only a few feet deep, so that fishermen with their fly rods would sometimes appear to walk on water. It was a time of wide-eyed discovery. That something did happen was sufficient proof that it was also meant to happen. One morning, over breakfast, Lisa had said in passing, "I am almost out of money for materials. Perhaps we will find a piece of space junk I can use." An hour later, during a stroll to gather sea shells, we came across a piece of scorched and twisted metal. The ten-foot scrap had fallen there in order that we should find it, and it was asking to be transformed into art.

Salt freshened the air. The sea cast a spell. Roads were utterly black at night, as we found when, on more than one occasion, we managed to get lost. We were amazed to find that we could not see our hands, no matter how close we held them. The eyes of unknown creatures opened in the forest. A small cottage by the sea in what is the smallest state in the union seemed the perfect place for us to begin a life together. In the backyard, now and then, we could hear the screeching of a fox as he ran in and out of the derelict chicken coop, as if, by some act of will, he could once more cause the chickens to appear. We were not providing him with the tribute to which he was accustomed. Work was not a pressing concern, and until Lisa's evening shift at the Bamboo Garden Restaurant, there was nowhere that either of us especially had to go. Birds acted as alarm clocks. By slow degrees, the sun would wash into the room. It was into this stage-set that my friend quite unexpectedly stepped. Out of nowhere, he appeared.

One day when Lisa, her housemate Paula and I were driving down a highway, Paula turned to look at a hitchhiker and then shouted, "Whoa! Look at that freak! He actually thinks that someone is going to pick him up." On a traffic island stood an unshaven creature dressed entirely in black leather, with a long skeleton earring. His thumb was out. His expression: an arrogant sneer. There was something oddly familiar about him. "Wait a minute," I said. "Turn the car around. That's no freak. That's one of my closest friends from high school!"

In retrospect, our reunion consisted in our listening to Danny tell stories about every good thing that anyone in New York or Rhode Island had ever said about him. At a dune on Narragansett Bay, we had spread our beach blanket out, for a lunch of cheddar cheese, grapes, and sourdough bread, washed down with vodka and orange juice from paper cups. He talked, and we responded. It is odd that I didn't stop to register the dynamic of this communication at the time. This was Danny before the fall. He overflowed with energy. His metaphysical balloon was still inflated. His eyes were alive. His heart still seemed to beat, and his intellect had not yet been cryogenically preserved. His stories were, in fact, amusing.

His experience in the New York S&M scene, where slaves would pay good money to be whipped or lick his boots. The time his girlfriend Rivkah made Nathan—a schizophrenic mathematician, who would later become their pet—clean the kitchen floor with a toothbrush. Rivkah's interest in having sex in laundromats and phone booths. His desire to perfect a form of art that existed only in—and for—the pure realm of the intellect. How all connections to the external world should be oblique. His photographs of disasters to be hung with explanatory texts that did not make any reference to the disasters they explained. His expanding circle of famous, almost famous, and soon to be famous friends. His exhibitions at Franklin Furnace and other alternative art galleries, which, however obscure to the masses, were well respected by the Crypto-Calvinist Elect, by the inner circle, by those in the know.

At the labyrinth's heart, howled the ithyphallic Minotaur. Soon, the debt that the race owed him was scheduled to come due. "Useless feeders" were to provide for his material support, as well as the replenishment of his supply of male and female virgins. After the ritual touching of the head against the ground, each would offer his/her tribute in the way that was most appropriate. True feedback was the province of some fraction of a percentage of an already super-select group.

The current version of the Elite was labyrinthine in its complexity, mirror upon mirror, with each contradiction serving to generate a good half-dozen others. Among those that had gathered to applaud him were the following: Post-Marxian Deconstructionists, Fluxus Paint-by-Number Hedge-Fund Managers, Raw Meat Installation Artists, Op-Art Vegans for the Reduction of Earth's Population to a Sustainable 1 ½ Million, Neo-Abstract-Expressionist Stamp Collectors, Dada Outreach Coordinators for the Bilderberg Group, and Anti-Art Crusaders for the Transformation of the Name into the Brand. As if we were living in an age before Copernicus, Danny announced himself as the sun around which Earth and all other planets must heretofore revolve. Hard evidence had accumulated. It could not be denied. Fresh from the experience of a revelation, Danny pulsed with a kind of messianic zeal.

7

It was not at all clear why I was so disturbed by the August 2002 conversation. As Danny had pointed out, this was all so much ancient history, and the details about the move to Belize aside, it was not as if I had learned much of anything new, not as if I had seen some fact from an unexpected angle. To find that someone has become still more of what he had been should not shake one's faith in the coherence of the world. The conversation nonetheless disturbed me. It disturbed me enough that, while washing dishes the next morning, I seemed to be in a fog, and I allowed a large pool of water to accumulate at my feet. It spread over half the kitchen floor, which I did not notice until my wife let out a yelp. My slippers were wet.

I had avoided meeting with Danny for the past ten years or so. For the most part, I had avoided even thinking about him, at least at any length. True, once in a while I might be tempted to remember some guffaw-producing mutual outburst of black humor, a shared Eureka moment of insight into contemporary art, or a key crisis that one or the other of us had talked the other through. But then I would stop and say to myself, "No, there is no point to this at all. He is only a Minotaur. He is not fully human. No good can come from getting sentimental."

The problem could be stated simply as: *What is wrong with my own psychology that I should pick such an apparently soulless creature as a friend?*

I was once a Boy Scout, and the Boy Scout Oath reads, "A scout is Trustworthy, Loyal, Helpful, Friendly, Courteous, Kind, Obedient, Cheerful, Thrifty, Brave, Clean, and Reverent." I was generally a good judge of character, and with the exception of Reverence and Obedience, I still expected my friends to put some reasonable percentage of these virtues into practice. Perhaps, though, there were several other "Brians," at least one of whom I did not really know, and whom I did not want to confront. To secure his supply of bioenergetic fuel, I thought, the narcissist may be able to employ a kind of radar, which allows him to spot the germ of his own pathology in others.

Thus, Danny had been able to probe into my wounds, to definitively confirm that they were not due to any actions on my part. For example: my relative obscurity as an artist and a writer was due not, as might appear to be the case, to the fact that I did not bother to send manuscripts to publishers or to exhibit unless invited; no, it was due to the ignorance of the rest of the human race, which had, almost certainly, been getting more pronounced.

It was possible, I thought, that the Minotaur served as a kind of missing link, as the psychopomp to an otherwise lost world. He was a conduit for the spirits of the dead, the eater of all public sins, the debt collector, to whom blood was due. He was the living key to an alternate version of reality, where my own dreams of omnipotence ran wild across the flood-plain, as dark as the U.S. invasion of Iraq, as free as the drift of geophosphates on the wind.

So, ten years had passed since my last encounter with the Minotaur, and I had gone out of my way not to think too much about him. Then, one phone call had led to another and this had prompted me to glance behind my shoulder. Which flaws and self-deceptions had I managed to transmute? Which flaws and self-deceptions still actively pursued me? My method was to try to make use of every scrap of my experience. If I looked with empathy on what the Minotaur held in contempt, I thought, then I might just make out the features of my own hermetically sealed face. It was only necessary to view each detail in reverse.

See, over there are the factories of Worcester, as they were in the 1970s, when smoke still puffed from the gigantic stacks. This was no place for an artist and a writer to grow up! You, Brian, had no desire to stand for eight hours at an assembly line, day after day, 49 weeks out of the year, and you had some degree of contempt for those who did. Like a twinge from a missing limb, you can even now sense the alienation that you felt. Quite oddly, however, you do not regard yourself as more intelligent than they. You mourn for the city in which you came of age, on whose wrought-iron bridges you climbed, down whose hills you rode your Flexible Flier in the winter. You have come to appreciate its freight yards and its loading docks, and you love those with whom you had shared a now vanished way of life, however inadvertently. Those days that you took too lightly are not scheduled to return. Those factories have become a part of the archeological record. The assembly lines have stopped, and pigeons fly in and out through the jagged glass of the windows.

How evolved you are, Brian, to have not disowned your roots. How sensible you are to not wage war on the dead. How generous you are to think well of those who had made your younger self feel claustrophobic. How freely you have offered your hard-won vision to the masses. With your change of attitude and a paycheck, they could pay a third of their bills. It is not your fault if they have chosen to disregard your insights. For the past ten years, you have done your best to expand the boundaries of the self, to be open where you had earlier been closed, and yet… like the Earth, the labyrinth turns. Its corridors lead to dimensions beyond those of time and space. To celebrate your escape may be to step into a trap.

8

In the labyrinth built by Daedalus there are mirrors by the thousands, which make its 28 u-turns seem more complex than they are. Truly, there would seem to be no way to extract yourself from its spell, no way through or out of it, no direction to go other than the one in which you came. It is clear—if only in retrospect—that this labyrinth is a work of genius, that Daedalus has designed it to take full advantage of your habits. At its dead heart, he has placed the Minotaur, a product of recombinant engineering, who, due to several haywire genes, is said to only be able to survive on a diet of human flesh. There seems no way to escape from the Minotaur's surveillance. His gaze is cold. His remote eyes zero in on anything with a pulse.

Beast-men march like clockwork from every imaginable angle, chanting, their hands shaping balls of primordial energy that they are able to turn into weapons. Your heart is beating from your chest. Could you really be so amateurish as to lack the skill to control it? Such a heart is ridiculous. Can you really call it yours? The sound can be heard in distant quadrants of the galaxy, its thumping growing ever louder, and then louder, and then louder. Your own mind turns against you. It betrays you with practiced ease, like a democratic leader, as if it did not know to whom its loyalty was due.

So yes, be afraid; be very afraid. With your head bowed, let the Minotaur's agents see the deference in your stance, the lack of intuitive certainty in your movements. There are few whom you can trust. Even they tend to assume that they know where the Minotaur is. By closing their eyes, they believe they have removed the barcodes from their foreheads. They do not know that they serve him.

"In the scheme of things," you think, "it seems possible that the labyrinth is no bigger than a seed, that my body is much too big to fit inside. Did not my mother, Maia, once provide me with the tools to deconstruct projections, to shatter all but the most primary of metaphysical structures? There must be some way to return to the 'adamantine' stars—the stars that are alive and that have a human form—and not to the quaint ones painted on the upper part of the labyrinth." At each u-turn, you can feel the cold breath of the Minotaur on your neck.

For the sake of argument, let us say that the Minotaur does not actually exist; he is only the reflection of a reflection of a species dreamed by Daedalus. It is even possible that he might have no power without you, that your life-force is the only thing that gives substance to his image. It is you, Hermes, who have conjured the whole story from thin air. "Surely," you think, "those mirrors will not be difficult to break!" Yet somehow, in the end, this is not at all reassuring. Who is to say that you cannot die horribly in a dream? Who is to say that, upon waking, you will not see your breathless body stretched below?

9

Danny had been very sick as a child—or so the story went—with any number of arcane conditions. In his memories, he would see himself frail and naked on an operating table, under harsh lights, surrounded by a ring of giants wearing 19th-century diving helmets. The eye-slits of these helmets were unblinking. Strange instruments moved in synchronization, as if directed by a single brain. Even under the anesthesia, Danny found that the lights were too bright for his eyes, which hurt, and for some reason were impossible to close. At the same time, the brightness produced a very curious effect: he could see through the walls of the operating theatre, which had become almost transparent. Out beyond them, he could see a network of curved passageways, wall after wall, around which his vision moved, before returning to the doll-like body on the table, with its out-of-scale Taurean head. In and out of hospitals for the first 12 years of his life, he had been overprotected by his mother, Pasiphae.

According to my mother, Maia, who had worked with Danny's mother at an underwater laboratory, in her younger days Pasiphae had acquired a big "reputation" as a party girl. They had worked at a place called the "Center for the Research and Development of Ancient Biomechanical Species." There, they took dictation from the gods. They checked flow-charts for the projection of the five Platonic solids, and they assisted in the preparation of test subjects for their insertion into three-d forms. Pasiphae was bright, but her mind was seldom on the task at hand. This did not seem to have put her at any sort of disadvantage. She had later married well, to a slumlord with a PhD in Civil War Geometry and ties to the Greek Mafia.

Pasiphae's newfound affluence had allowed her to attach a more luminous mask. This image was, after all, in keeping with the root-syllables of her name. Pasiphae, from "pas," "for all" and "phaos," "light." There were certain of the Hoi Polloi who had confused her with the Moon. As if! What an insult! Was her light not destined to be more wide-shining than that? Why did others not give her the credit she deserved? Who would want to be compared to that haunted ship of souls? The mask was new. It shone. It would cause the world to bend in correspondence with its features. There were needs that could not be met. There were hungers that could not be satisfied, as she had proved by her desire to have sex with the bull. And then, nine months in which her body was not hers, the pain of the delivery of an oversized head, the bellowing that put the agents of the IMF on notice. Soon, you deadbeat Hierophants, a child will turn your knees to water! By some process of psychic alchemy, the small son would fulfill the mother's fantasies of perfection.

As the child grew, many academic honors were hung around his neck. His bellowing, while still fearsome and unsettling, became much more covert. Twenty years of twice-weekly visits to the analyst had only served to make the Minotaur an expert on his neuroses. He could expound upon them at encyclopedic length. Twitching fingers in the air, he had learned to put quotation marks around the scene of the primordial crime, with its stench of fear, with its tongueless choral singers, with its shelf upon shelf of disassembled gods, with its Oedipal violation of an all-too-eager mother, with its drawing and quartering of the Servants of the Pole.

First, they had flattened the Hypersphere, until it was just a small circle on the floor. Then they cut the One into Three, the Three into Six, and the Six into Ten. They leached the warmth from the Minotaur's blood, so that he could not register the violence of the act, so that he could not hear space scream. A dead sun was then implanted in his chest. "For your food," they said, "select only the fittest and most beautiful." As a group, in their 19th-century diving helmets, the ring of giants nodded. The eyes behind the eye-slits of their helmets did not blink. Who could make sense of the barbarous nonsense that they chanted? One could only presume that it worked. Ontogeny was thus made to recapitulate phylogeny, albeit not quite the phylogeny of our race.

If "the personal is the political," as was said in the 1960s, then how would we set limits to this type of correspondence, and where would it ever stop? Let us take the mask from the Minotaur, with its terrible gold-tipped horns. It is possible that, behind it, we will see the face of a frightened child. The face is tiny and soft, a bit scrunched up, and as vulnerable as that of an oyster. It is no wonder that he finds it necessary to project a giant shadow. But just as soon as I begin to assume the best, I think: It is possible that the face of the child is yet another mask. It is a ruse once designed by Daedalus, a technological wonder that puts victims at their ease, through which stares a presence that was old before the Deluge.

10

Exempt from politics, uninterested in wealth, devoted only to the care and feeding of my art, it may be true that I am self-absorbed. I seldom give any change to derelicts. I care more for my peace of mind than for the fires that will erase whole towns in California. I do not live there, I live on the East Coast, and who among you has the standing to accuse me? I have never owned a car. I prefer to walk. My carbon footprint is much tinier than the average. Even now, I care too much. In spite of all my yogic preparations, I think more about the sixth great die-off than I should.

Call me focused, if you will, or anxious, or even self-contained; do not call me narcissistic. True, there is a barcode on my forehead, but it is only just barely visible. If I am not pure, I am as pure as most of the 8 ½ billion now being prepped for sacrifice. They are pure enough. They will serve, as will you, dear reader/listener, who have volunteered to bare your throat by the fact of your existence. My role? It is only to inform you of your role. The entrance to and the exit from the labyrinth are the same. There, the choice is yours.

It is certainly not my fault if the Minotaur was a friend. It is not fair to describe me as a vector of disease, and if I were, would this really be so bad? How else could I speak of the Minotaur, of your no-more-than-six degrees of separation from his cult.

In its "Diagnostic and Statistical Manual of Mental Disorders," the A.P.A. lists narcissism as a disease, but why, when so many narcissists are successful, even famous? Some diseases are common, like life. A true disease originates on the other side of death. It is a broken mirror, a sign pointing at itself. To its host, the true disease is of inestimable value. "Success does not come cheap," as the maxim goes, but the price will be paid by someone other than the Minotaur. The 12-year-old girl who works at the Dow plant in Bhopal, for example, has volunteered to assist in the clearing of this debt, and she is said to be grateful that she has a job at all. In this age of the triumph of the Top One Percent, of sociopathic chic, to say that someone is "successful" does not imply any personal virtue on his part, or that he has not, very simply, stolen what he wants.

For now the shadows have come out to play. The light shifts, and they have suddenly become much more tangible than they were, as they dare us to speak up. We are free to say "Please" and "Thank You." We have somehow incurred a debt by the fact of our existence. "Will that be cash or blood, sir?" It is possible that the 1000 percent interest is too high. Once, Daedalus had set up a receptacle for virgins, which has now been fully automated.

We are free to speak up, if we choose. We are free to interact with the forces that, from the time before the Deluge was a tear, have been hidden at the dead center of the labyrinth.

It can be difficult to tell someone who has not been hypnotized by the narcissist about the devastation that the false self can create, about the wake of doubt it can leave. So subtle is the contagion that its target may not choose to detect the signs of its advance, not until the damage is done. Have you set yourself apart? Yes. Have you looked down on the common? Yes. Have you laughed at the less intelligent? Yes. Have you nursed your sense of grandiosity?

Yes. You are free to review the progression of your symptoms, to re-diagnose the disease of which you would be cured.

That you have done this so often before may not imply that you are serious. With eyes wide, you are led to collaborate with the Minotaur, to play each part in the ritual he assigns, before you pause to take note of the gold ring in his nose, of the Freon he snorts, and of the supernatural horns that stretch above the mask, which is made of leather and devoid of all expression. The shared world that once appeared to be so solid is then shown to be a stage set. You can poke a hole through its cardboard with your finger. Wind picks it up and carries it off, to reveal, behind the stage-set, an abyss.

There is a feeling of having asked to be taken in and manipulated, of having volunteered to be the victim in a con game, of having been used and then thrown, casually, away. But do you even know in what age you were born, or that Worcester, Massachusetts, is the place where you grew up? The egg of the world broke, i.e., there were those who broke it. You got sleepy, very sleepy, and you did not really try that hard to put it back together. Of what crimes are you guilty? Some were no doubt by commission, still others by omission. How many of your teachers lied? How much has the Minotaur kept from you?

Yes, "mistakes" were made. You are certainly free to call them that, for such is the nature of freedom: You can tell yourself you are free. It seems your boyhood friend has cultivated a secret life as a serial killer—though of a sort both highly specialized and archaic—and that, with eyes wide, you have inadvertently assisted in his project. At your feet, the bones of a small, man-headed bird, as well as those of a large, bird-headed man, some pottery shards, and a few radioactive spills. Here are giant skulls that do not have cranial sutures; there are the burnt but oddly luminescent bones of several 300-foot snakes.

Now, the night grows quiet. It is even possible that the Minotaur is dead. You have killed him, perhaps, and have somehow misplaced the past 2800 years. For the whole time you have been wrestling with a hologram. Your life-force is the secret of his strength. Right turns to left in the labyrinth. The "I" leads to the "You." "We" opens onto "They." The smoke lifts, and there is only an astringent smell, a bit like that of bleach. There is no space between the city and the macrocosm. It is clear that some world-subverting ritual has occurred. As if they were gloves, you have given a strange species access to your hands.

Notes on Kundalini and the Ticking of the Biological Clock

Vishnu and Lakshmi Floating on Nagaraja, Public Domain

There were no gods in the First Age, and there were no demons. The First Age was without disease; there was no lessening with the years; there was no hatred, or vanity, or evil thought whatsoever; no sorrow, no fear. In those times, men lived as long as they chose to live, and were without fear of death.

—*The Mahabharata*

1

No Man, Shielded by the Hoods of Nagaraja, When
All Previous Forms Have Passed out of Existence

The late 1980s were a kind of golden period for me. Like the ante-diluvian parents who first externalized our race—when the sun rose on a different arc from the horizon, before the genome had been scrambled—I had assumed that I had the whole of 72,000 years in which to get my act together, that all good things would be mine for the asking, and that only others would inevitably grow old. Since then, the Earth has added a bit more than five days to its cycle, and few remember that it is moving much faster than it should.

I lived in an inexpensive apartment owned by the Boston Historical Society, which did not care about making a profit on the space. I had a flexible job schedule that allowed me to attend to every flash of intuition, to wait for lightning to strike in the same spot twice, and to sharpen my focus for many days at a stretch. I had a diverse but mutually supportive group of creative friends, who had not yet entirely gone their separate ways. Most still talked to each other, if from a psychic distance, and less often than before. They had not yet moved to the suburbs or divorced their art to marry their careers.

If I had become just a bit more cynical about the avant-garde, this did not lessen my own desire to take risks. If I did not expect stylistic theorizing or word games to rip open new frontiers, I had done my best to mute my disillusionment, and there were some consolations. For decades on end, critic after critic had announced the "death of painting." If painting had died, no one had bothered to tell painters such as Kiefer, Cucci, and Palladino. Curiously, though, a strange reversal had occurred: most of the best painters of this decade were both "cutting-edge" and "neo." The old was new; the new was less new than refurbished. I desired to plunge even further back, to grow an alternate set of eyes, to resuscitate traditions of which no trace was left.

So, from painters, a few clues, but what to do with the US literary scene? Mythic plunges were out. MFA creative writing pods hatched thousands of pod-approved wunderkinds per year. It was disturbing to admit that I was challenged by fewer and fewer of my contemporaries. The last of my models were repeating themselves or would soon depart for another world. Be that as it may. There were billions who had things worse. Life was good, and this period was golden.

I lived several blocks and five minutes away from the Boston Theosophical Society, the perfect low-key center at which to explore my deepening interest in spirituality. I had hoped to bring certain of my anxieties to the surface, to calm the disruptive forces that were playing games with my mind. I had hoped to be able to plunge, without fear, to the depths. I had hoped to be able to confront the obscure parts of my childhood. I had hoped to be able to integrate those aspects of myself that did not belong to me but to another. I had hoped to be able to read back through several near-apocalyptic flights to determine if they were speaking in a language I should know. While I had no particular interest in Theosophical writings, which I saw as somewhat musty and Victorian, the majority of participants in the center were not actually Theosophists. It was a place where people met and mixed, where circles were drawn and entities invoked, and where many things seemed, always, just about to happen.

At the Boston Theosophical Society, as in the paintings of de Chirico, large figures cast their shadows on the stage-set, without necessarily providing accurate clues to their appearance. Metaphysical lines led off towards multiple perspective points. At first, you might assume that you were still in Renaissance space, and that all of the lines, at some point, would converge. O Newtonian geo-literalist! Deadbeat tenant of the cave! If they did, in fact, converge, in their own peculiar manner of convergence, it was not where your naivete would lead you to expect.

There, in that 19th-century brick townhouse, supported by the hands of unseen powers, or "Chiefs," as Helena Blavatsky liked to call them, you could receive an education in how to come and go from your body. If earlier spasms of primal energy had caused you to doubt your sanity, if you sensed that space was waiting to consume you, if you feared that light might strip the names from every object in the world, the study of spiritual systems allowed you to postpone such concerns. Like the subcategories of Piaget's stages of development, Blavatsky's *Isis Unveiled* demanded complex feats of memorization, as did Taoist subtle anatomy. If one system did not work for you, there were plenty of others to try.

In that quaint but mysterious environment, with its occult feuds that brewed around dark corners, there was something oddly comforting about taking your first baby steps towards death. You could smell salt in the air. The wind from a lost continent blew softly through the windows. On the table next to you, you might find that a starfish was just waiting to say hello. The words of knowledgeable teachers were ships waiting to depart. If Gurdjieff did not—necessarily—agree with Steiner who did not agree with Bailey who did not agree with Aurobindo, that was all very well and good. It was pleasant to inch towards the edges of your comfort zone, to experience some hint of danger without having to push on into the depths.

This lack of finality was in keeping with my mood. If a crisis was imminent, that crisis was not mine, nor was it fair to expect me to find words for the experience. In terms of creativity, this was very much of an in-between period for me. My artwork was going well. I had just begun a series of large black and white drawings, in a sacred-geometric style that had emerged whole in a dream. If my writing was neither here nor there, this did not mean I had fossilized, let alone that I was stuck. No, the explanation was much simpler: I had not yet managed to integrate my earlier avant-garde and current spiritual orientations. Any volatile alchemical elements were still held in suspension. This was not a matter of particular concern. If a race of acupuncture manikins had yanked me from the solar system, and if, due to their class schedule, I had somehow lost three days, this too was not a matter of concern. There was only the One Moment, within which we should live. Our non-dead teachers had met and argued and come to this conclusion, which they then proceeded to issue as a rule.

Since this period was golden, there were no deep anxieties with which to come to terms, none, at least, that could not be put on hold. Our 24/7 lighting grid had banished the last demon. Once, there were tens of thousands of them. Now, they were all scared. Why else would they have come to us with gifts? Each birthday, I grew younger by a year, for such is the inscrutable genius of precession. Any grey hairs would remove themselves. I had to choose to get sick. If the stars were AWOL, if they had somehow wandered from the spaces where I left them, if Earth's axis had been tilted by some 20-odd degrees, this did not mean that my clock was set to the wrong hour. No, it only meant that a cloud had confused my solar plexus. It only meant that I should exercise my breathing. I barely noticed the cracked soil, the slow incursions of the wasteland, the ash that whitened my front steps. Life was good. I was not in any rush.

2
The Breaking of an Egg

It was at the Theosophical Society that I met Kim Levertov. For four years, we would talk of building a life together before acknowledging what we should have known much earlier on: that there was very little on which we could agree. Two-thirds of the Primordial Man had stayed beyond manifestation. It was Kim who would prompt his frown lines to appear.

It was she who would remove the sun from the stage-set of the Satya Yuga. My cry echoed across the cities of the flood-plain, once tall, which were atomized.

The *Rig Veda* says, "Desire came upon that one in the beginning," the one who breathed, windless, without a sign, the one whose breath was suspended on its own concealed intent. It was Kim, in her form as Shakti, who caused a navel that looked like an iris to snap open in the void. It was she who dared the poet to give form to the mists of the non-local field, without knowing—or much caring, as it turned out—that she had produced such an effect. "There was impulse beneath; there was giving forth above." The name "Brian" came from the same root-syllable as "Brahman": "to grow from a seed; to expand; to swell." In the yearly Sadhamada, or contest of poets, it was she who had taunted me to push beyond my six competitors, who, unwilling to offend their teachers, would not test their ability to see beyond the edge of the horizon. For this reason, they spoke in formulas. It was she whose heat had reactivated Soma, having called it from the glaciers of Saryanavat. From there, a drop had landed on my tongue.

We could not, however, agree on whether calendars were real, or on how the year should be measured, or on what year it actually was. It was 1987 when we met. I was off by, at the least, 12,000 years. In her own way, however, Kim was also wrong. Without asking for my informed consent, it was she who would one day force me to grow up.

Let us return to 1987, to a second-floor meeting room of the Boston Theosophical Society. Staring, as if dead, out of the backside of the mirror, we will have been forbidden to do more than watch. Let us nonetheless act—at a distance, with stealth, and as if by accident, for the living are in need of a lot of remedial education. If our efforts prove successful, we will leave not even a fingerprint, but our guidance will be, in its own way, heard and felt. Let us encourage the two main characters in this story to do what they must do, to learn what they must learn, and to value the bittersweet fullness of their moment, before they each drift off into their separate worlds.

The key facts are as follows: Kim and Brian were both members of a meditation group led by David Doolittle, a carpenter/psychologist. He spoke quietly, but he had a subtle manner of exerting pressure and he had trained in a number of confrontational techniques. Nothing should stay hidden, whether childhood embarrassment or deep existential fear. Whatever was lurking under the surface, the group was encouraged to sit with it, to do their best to translate the experience into words, and at times to act it out. Layer by archeological layer, they would then proceed to unwrap some core of "presence." If the concept was simple, it was also paradoxical. This presence was simultaneously an aspect of attention, in which you let go of the future and the past, a substratum of existence more basic than the "ego," and a mystery that stretched into realms beyond the human. The deeper down you went, the less personal the secrets really appeared to be. Having no self meant that love should not have to apologize. Who knew that the Anatman could act badly, other than the whole population of Nanking? A see-through body/mind would serve to minimize your shadow.

In those days, death was different from life. Sex had nothing at all to do with reproduction, or, at best, this was a tertiary function. The average phallus was still large enough to touch a constellation. The average female form was space. The average act of coitus was still hot enough to generate the fuel for cosmic transport. Of course, due to your attachment to the act of coitus, you might not actually get to travel very far. The world, if not solid, was as solid as it needed to be to provide some measure of resistance for your shoes. The Watcher saw the Watched; the Watched did not see the Watcher, not often, at least, and not without some fear. There was only the next step, and the hand of an archeologist that would reach back from the future.

Bit by bit, Brian saw that he was becoming very attracted to Kim, who struck him as highly mischievous, and yet mature. There was an energetic charge to their eye contact, which could be felt on any number of levels and which seemed each week to intensify. Finally, he decided that the time had come to ask her out. Quite oddly, on this day she had worn a form-fitting and very attractive purple dress. "Great," he thought, "she is probably meeting someone after class." Usually, at the end of class, the members of the group would stay around for 10 or 15 minutes to talk, or sometimes go out for a snack and a cup of tea. On this occasion, however, Kim disappeared before they had even gotten out of our chairs. Little did Brian realize that she had left to put on makeup. "I've had two months to say something," he thought, "and now it's probably too late." Stung by the irony of the timing, he dragged himself downstairs. As he turned the corner of the vestibule that led to the front door, he noticed that a woman in a form-fitting purple dress was leaning against the door frame, a slight smile on her lips. "Care to go for a walk?" she said.

"You bet!" Brian answered. Thus began the last great romance of his youth.

From the beginning, Brian realized that Kim was far more grounded and less prone to self-deception than he was. Aside from his high school friend Peter Lisitsky—whose parents had survived the Nazi occupation of Poland, and whose response to any and all complaints about life's unfairness was "Stop being such a baby!"—Kim was perhaps the bluntest person he had known. If they had any problems to address or issues to work out, Kim would write up a numbered list and then insist on going though all items one by one. If he bought Kim a present that was not quite to her taste, she would say, "I don't really like it. Would you mind if we returned it and then looked for something else?" Would not 80 percent total honesty have been more than enough? When they first realized how compatible they were—or rather thought they were—Kim asked, "Can you see us living together in a year or so? If not, we should probably end things now. Time is going by, and I don't want to keep starting over." Brian could see such a thing, and the relationship continued.

Luckily, this tendency to mature stock-taking was counter-balanced by a streak of genuine wildness. Once, when we were riding our bikes through a rough section of the city, a carload of Hispanic males began shouting out appreciative comments on her anatomy. Kim spit on the driver through the open window and then turned off down a one-way street. "Do you have some kind of a death wish?" Brian asked. If the majority of her tendencies were not dangerous, as such, they did serve to jumpstart an openness to chance, to reawaken attitudes that he had chosen to put on hold. After many years of living in the city, it was a great adventure for both of them to rediscover nature. They spent much time biking by the ocean and getting lost on the back roads of New Hampshire. On a mountain hike, as soon as they were out of sight of the car, Kim would generally want to take off all her clothes. "This isn't the Yukon," Brian would say. "Don't you realize there may be Boy Scouts around?" After making love in a field of wildflowers, they would stop for a lunch of bread and cheese and olives. Kim liked to read while sitting on the edge of a cliff. "I can see the headlines now," Brian would say, "NAKED JEWISH GIRL FOUND AT BOTTOM OF CLIFF WITH BOOK."

Once, at sunset in a meadow, as the chirping of crickets rose and fell like a mantra intoned by a single and yet discontinuous organism, they stumbled across a patch of gigantic spider webs. These were three to four feet high, with black/orange lightning bolts zigzagging down the center. Brian had never seen anything like them before, nor would he see anything like them later on. "Were there lots of these webs around?" he thought. "Were we just too preoccupied to notice?" They were like satellite dishes that had been set up to gather signals from the beyond. For over 250 million years, perhaps, each of their arachnids had been waiting for its victim! Brian and Kim stopped short, glanced at one another, and then doubled over laughing at the sheer outrageousness of the webs.

The whole of space was in contact with their skin; it was a hieroglyph they could translate with their fingers. Deep energies leapt back and forth, as they diagramed the closed curves of the microcosm, and yet their ways of seeing things did not always overlap. On a rocky beach, Brian would carefully put one foot in front of the other, and then ease into the 48-degree water step by step. Kim would run out screaming and then plunge into a wave. She lived in the world; he was just a non-local visitor. To each had been assigned a different yet appropriate style of adventurousness. For Brian, their four years together passed with the magical inevitability of a dream. Kim was far more aware of the reality of time passing.

The immediate though not the ultimate cause of their breakup was a shift in spiritual energy, the very energy that had first connected them. It had created the cocoon inside of which they grew, but from which they would separately emerge. In July of 1990, they had both gone to see a presentation on Kundalini Yoga by Asha (later Anandi) Ma. Upon entering the room, Brian felt that he had stepped into a violent field of energy. He was picked up and projected toward an ocean, an ocean scheduled to overflow the banks of the known world. After many years of suspecting he had grown far too inert, that his body had become more solid than it should be, Brian almost immediately felt that something new was going on. One day, perhaps, he could take back what was his; he could see with his first eyes; he could travel towards those shores that he remembered, not half-asleep but awake, not accidentally but by choice. Kim heard only the content of the words: just one more lecture, a string of Vedic platitudes. By slow degrees, and then far more rapidly, they began to drift apart.

3
A sphere, not minding its own business

In the months that followed "Shaktipat," which I received in August of the same year, I felt that all my previous half-formed wishes, all my other-than-personal memories, all my abstract speculations had been turned into a series of daily ultimatums: "Change, and/or die." My body was on fire. In pitch darkness, all the objects in my room were as bright as lamps. The space around me was a web of lightning. A one-inch orb, which I thought of as the Bindu, would unpredictably flare up, grow brighter and brighter, then subside. Hovering above my head or at the edges of my vision, it seemed always about to suck me into the center of its vortex. Did it see me as its student, or was I, in fact, a kind of food?

On one three-day holiday weekend, Kim and I were apart. My meditative focus was continuous. Wave after wave of ecstatic energy washed over me, picking me up here and depositing me there, but returning me each time to a calm and luminous center. "Please," I thought, "Let Kim also experience this ecstatic energy!" I envisioned her at the center of a golden egg. This egg was guarded by a serpent, and through it all necessary information flowed.

Kim did, indeed, participate in the expansion of this energy, but the outcome was not at all what I had hoped. For these same three days, she had become convinced that she was pregnant. She did not sleep at all, and she wrote almost non-stop in her journal. It was not clear, later on, why she should have been so concerned, since her period was only four days late, and this was not at all unusual. By the time her period arrived, on Tuesday morning, she had determined that our relationship was over.

With not much warning—or rather none to which I had seen fit to pay attention—a key moment had arrived, a point of turning, in which the flow of action shifts from one state to another, sweeping away all obstacles in its path. The world again becomes fluid, like the glaciers that melted when Agni destroyed Vritra. Cliff to cliff, down from the Himalayas, the waters of the Sarasvati plunged. Gasping for air, I too was swept along. I was not able to do much more than observe.

"I have decided that you are not at all ready to be a father," Kim informed me on Tuesday night, "but I am more than ready to become a mother. As you know, I turned 35 last week, and I do not have any more time to waste. The strength of our erotic connection has allowed us to play games with time. We have had our fun, and now I need to use this energy to bring new life into existence. You're upset, I know, but you'll soon get over it. It's not as though you have any real interest in children. They are noisy, and you clearly have more important things to do." It would have been nice if she had asked for my opinion on the subject. After having been militantly opposed to the idea of parenthood for years, my feelings had quite recently, and through knowing Kim, begun to change.

But I had had my chance. I would not get another one from Kim, whatever else might happen later on. One day we were together. Quite suddenly, we were worlds apart. For, preoccupied with the care and feeding of my state of perpetual youth, I had already fallen too far behind the curve.

The Long-Delayed Meeting

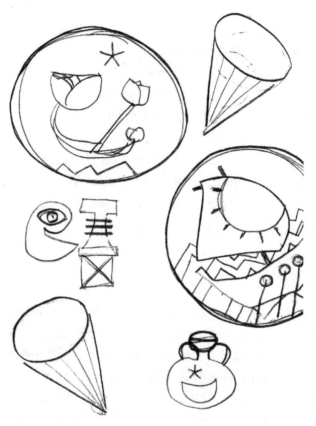

The Voyage, 2000

We had sole tenancy of our life and summer/ Landscape consumed the color of your fragrant dress/ Eagerness and restraint were reconciled/ The Chateau de Maubec sank into the clay... It was the beginning of delightful years/ The earth loved us a little I remember."

—Rene Char, from "Evadné"

1

When I met my wife, Deni, in 1994, the sensation was one of disorientation at having somehow returned home. The day had come. I could hear my heart beating, like a signal broadcast from a nonexistent star. No longer young, I had access to the wealth of the last 12,000 years. I had only to reactivate my ship in the Treta Yuga, the one with eight arms, which a wave had shattered. I stood, at the edge of the black ocean that had haunted me, in front of a locked door. As I opened the door to my third-floor apartment, I looked down the stairs just as Deni was coming up, and our eyes met. "Yes!" I said to myself. For even then I could feel the first effects of antigravity, and the joy that came from seeing my dead wife, now beautifully alive. We will return to the dreams that were contained in this one moment, but let us first go back another decade and a half.

2

Although I came of age physically during the later days of the counterculture, my first period of creative maturity coincided with the death knell of the counterculture and the birth of punk. In Boston, the transition from one to the other was more natural than one might guess. A lot of countercultural energy had already turned dark by the early 1970s. We had stamped our collective foot against the shadow of the Empire, and still that shadow grew. We could not stop Agent Orange from destroying 18,000 square miles of forest. We could not prevent dioxin from disfiguring the limbs of the not yet born. We could not stop napalm from burning at 2200 degrees, or Dow Chemical from making billions. For evil to triumph, it was only necessary for good men to believe in their own virtue, to assume that their good intentions were enough.

Our chanting had purged only two percent of the demons from the ocean. The rest were perhaps annoyed.

Cults had vacuumed up the survivors of entheogenic break-throughs, the wide-eyed, the fearless, the utterly unprepared. Did the "shattering of the ego" always lead to greater peace of mind? Without an ego, it was difficult to tell. It had just come out that the FBI had sent agents to teach bomb-building skills to the Weathermen, or so the rumor went. Taste in music was no guarantee that a radical could be trusted. The most violent of subversives could be agent-provocateurs. The Lords of Deep Time had appointed Altamont to be the Mother of All Battles. She had, quite unexpectedly, announced the end of an era. She buzzed like angry wasps. Rolling thunder was her jewelry. She set the tone for the next decade, but she only hinted at the disillusionments to come. The Age of Aquarius had lasted for five years or so. Seeds planted on February 18th, 3102 B.C., were only just then coming to fruition. Having skipped a beat, the Kali Yuga had returned.

There was, in fact, no shelter to be had. There was no defer-ment for the bourgeois psyche, no evolutionary safe-room at Big Sur. With breathtaking stealth, in a triumph of the behaviorist black arts, the Revolution had been corporatized. Many objects only looked like objects; they had morphed into commodities. The orgone would continue to darken until there was no way to distinguish a real vision from its logo. Mescaline was out; speed was in. It would soon be replaced by cocaine. Free love back-to-the-land communes had gone the way of Atlantis. The free love, in some approximate form, survived. By the mid-1970s, STDs had staged a full-frontal assault on the dream that sex led to liberation. AIDS—then working undercover in the Belgian Congo—would soon make its debut. Antibiotics would begin to lose their alchem-ical cure-all status. Already, having whet its teeth in the Golden Triangle, the CIA was testing its joint-venture model with South and Central American drug gangs. The scent of paranoia was as common as the scent of marijuana. A knock on the door meant that it was necessary to escape onto the roof.

It was said at the time, "All politics is personal," which led us to assume that each small act was being scrutinized. It was also true that global forces were in motion, and we would learn that our anxieties did not go deep enough. There was no way to put a face on the decentralized plutocracy. It was everywhere. It was nowhere. Hundreds of thousands of jobs per year were already being outsourced, and once middle-class workers were beginning to suspect that they had been repurposed as serfs. Through the rows of broken windows at the factories, the birds flew in and out. There were no trains in the freight yards. Many sensed that there was something wrong. What it was, who knew?

In 1978, when I graduated from art school, there was a new alternative scene forming up in the lofts of these abandoned factories. The energy of the counterculture had not yet disappeared, or, at least, not quite. Rather, its participants had become more fatalistic. We had resigned ourselves to existing, somewhat joyously, on the margins, with no hope of having an impact on society at large, with no expectation of being seen or understood. Writers, artists, and musicians from every contradictory style mixed freely and cross-fertilized each other's sensibilities, ideas, and projects. When a Baroque organist insisted that I listen to the Ramones, I could not at first believe that he was serious. His love of Duchamp's "readymades" did not stop him from playing at Emanuel Church. Reichian theories of liberation consorted with apocalyptic wet dreams. Surrealism was big. There seemed no amount of chaos we could not reframe as an art form. It was during this period that I should have met my wife.

My wife, Deni, was at that time a member of a group called *Bound and Gagged*, an all-girl, no-wave punk group, which was one of my favorite bands from that scene. ("How did you come up with this name?" I once asked her. She responded, somewhat opaquely, "We got it from a book.") This affection for *Bound and Gagged* was strange enough in itself, since I had just emerged from a long period of listening to Medieval, Renaissance, and Baroque music, with occasional forays into jazz and traditional music from around the world. Nonetheless, my first—and soon to be ex—wife Lisa and I were fans. I had attended perhaps a dozen of their performances, bought their EP, and listened to several interviews with them on the radio. On top of this, Deni and I had a number of friends in common, and we both frequently attended events at the factory lofts that I mentioned. It certainly would seem that we were destined to connect. Perhaps we actually did meet, and even more than once, but, for whatever reason, neither one of us stopped to take note of the event.

With the dawn of Reagan's "Morning in America," a new sense of alienation slipped beneath the skin of many of the artists and writers and musicians that I knew. This was perceptible, in the early days, as no more than a dead spot, an inch of contamination that just barely even hurt. The numbness would then proceed to spread into an ache. Given that we existed on the margins as it was, this did not at first seem possible. An exile should not be forced to lose his innocence more than once, let alone a third time, or a fifth. Even as artists in their early 20s had started to make millions, even as hedge fund managers had discovered the beauty of graffiti, its grand historical importance, the assurance of compound rates of return, much of the air seemed to have been sucked from the lungs of the avant-garde. In cellars and closets, the pods had broken open. Blakean galas were held to toast the Imminence of the Brand. There, one could share a skull cup of pinot grigio with Artaud and chat with Marx about the lineaments of gratified desire.

At artists' cold-water lofts, the rents went up, and then they kept on going up. Working behind the scenes with the I.M.F., Ananke forced most Enfants Terribles to apply for better jobs. No pierced cheeks were allowed at the Bank of America teller window. Ah, the good old days of 1979, back when it was still a great adventure to be poor. While there was still an adequate supply of Southerners and Midwesterners left to shock, there were also more and more sophisticates who desired to be shocked. The line between transgression and the trendy had been blurred. What fun was that? Self-referential concepts had replaced the cutting-edge events they once described. With each month that went by, there were fewer events at artists' lofts, which made me feel less guilty about going to fewer and fewer of them. My growing disconnection from the cultural moment pushed me towards the spiritual, towards a sense that the new edge might be other than aesthetic. With the dawn of the 1980s, a kind of subterranean shift had taken place. As in the movie *Dark City*, the whole structure of reality had been rearranged while we slept.

Deni's group, however, stayed in my memory. In my book from 1984, *X: Revenge of the Autogenes*, there are two references to *Bound and Gagged* and none to any other Boston band. The references are somewhat out of place, as well, since they occur in two long mythological explorations. All of a sudden, I am mentioning that "Bound and Gagged wore bathrobes to the dance." I may have seen these references as a souvenir of the brave experiments of my youth, or I may have read them as an "OOPArt"—an out-of-place-artifact—which called me to find my way towards some event that had not yet happened.

In the mid-1980s, I met the two friends who would eventually introduce me to my wife. One of these was Sterling MacDonald, who I had met at yet another noisy and chaotic arts event, during which I gave a reading. When I was done, she had pulled me aside to yell something in my ear. She had said, "We could use you as a substitute for drugs!" But I thought she had said, "Do you take drugs?" I answered, "No, not for a long time." She looked confused, and then repeated her original proposal.

I was very touched by this statement. I remember thinking, "This is not exactly the way I would phrase things in a manifesto, but she seems to grasp my yogic intent." For me, the goal of writing was not to analyze or argue or describe; rather, it was to take all concerned to places that were difficult to go, to catalyze latent energies, to return speech to the role that it played in the time of the *Rig Veda*. My literary practice was designed to serve as a kind of hallucinogen, as Soma squeezed between the stones of the in-breath and the out-breath, as the fuel of the gods, the fuel that simultaneously acts as its own vehicle. Through it, as-of-yet undreamed realities could be coaxed into existence. It was a method of getting from point A to point B—still in its experimental stage, to be sure—where A was normal life and B was the meeting place where space became translucent. It could be indulged in while asleep, while washing dishes, or while waiting for the bus.

I saw my creative process as a transatlantic cable, laid by the Ancients, to which the badly-behaved ocean known as "history" had for years now denied us access. Unknown to most Moderns, our fish-suited teachers had equipped the system with self-healing ring topology, which insured that massive data could be sent in less time than an eyeblink. By the purging of distractions from the surface of the mind, one could eventually learn to speak out of the depths.

At the time, I thought that Sterling was an androgynous boy. She was, instead, a girl living undercover as a boy. With her was Ken Bogosian, later Raven Tiamat, who would soon become my roommate. Raven, like me, was a poet who was spellbound by the origins of words. He could easily spend 12 hours at a stretch with a *Webster's New Unabridged Dictionary*, tracing out the cross-cultural migrations of a syllable. For a time, we were like the Three Musketeers, until the roommate situation turned increasingly tense, the way such things can—and due partly to my own dishonesty in confronting certain issues—leading all involved to rewrite the story of their adventures.

4

As in etymology, one point of connection opened onto others, and then branched into a series of asymmetrical connections, until I was led to a meeting that had almost happened in the early 1980s. Ever since, this meeting was awaiting my return. While seeming to lead elsewhere, all roads led circuitously towards a meeting with my counterpart, to a presence that did not know me from a hole in the ground, to a presence both human and more than human that some might call the Beloved, to a presence that had taken the particular form of Deniz. All detours led in a series of blind curves towards my counterpart, to a presence who, somehow, had all along been there.

In spite of the devolution of my rapport with Raven, both he and Sterling were insistent about introducing me to a woman they both knew. Both individually and together, over and over, and more and more forcefully, my friends wasted no opportunity to demand, "You've got to meet her!" "I've never been on a blind date," I said, "so why should I start now?" (Neither, as I later found out, had Deni.) I did not yet know that Deni had been the drummer in one of my favorite punk groups. I had reasonable excuses. My friends refused to accept them.

Raven had described Deni as a "voodoo priestess," which turned out not to be correct. Sterling was more familiar with the tradition, and she informed me that Deni should be called a "Santero" or a "priestess of Lukumi." I had read a few West African and Caribbean myths. I had always wanted to learn more about the esoteric aspects of these cultures, how part was or was not related to some whole, how the past was connected to the syncretistic present, how cosmology and practice fit together. Perhaps I would learn more from a living representative than from a book? Deni was working as a Tarot card reader at the Tremont Tea Room. Tarot, too, was something about which I wanted to know more. All of this sounded fascinating. And why were Raven and Sterling, two of the most laid-back people that I knew, being so absurdly insistent? One of Raven's top-ten favorite words was "cool." He was being anything but.

These details intrigued me. I could feel the pull of some hypnotic force, but I was in the process of trying to finish up the third draft of a book—*To Akasha: An Incantation for the Crossing of an Ocean*—and so almost blew my chance. From a different angle, of course, it would be more accurate to say that I had almost blown my chance again, as I had, unknowingly, those 13 to 16 years before. Deni and I had talked on the phone, but I had postponed several meetings. She was getting very justifiably annoyed. At this point, some alternate part of the self perhaps thought, "Does he never learn? It is time to intervene!"

Two dreams and a memory made me sit up and take notice. In the first, I was involved in a long and rhapsodic affair with a woman who appeared in the form of the actress Andy McDowell but whose voice was my wife's, although I did not know this yet. Toward the end of the dream, I knew that I was just about to wake up. Overcome with sadness, I was shouting, "No, I want to stay in the dream!" There is, of course, a problem with shouting in a dream. I shouted so loudly that I had managed to shout myself awake.

In a second dream, I had found myself standing on a lamp-lit porch, and a woman, somewhat cloud-like, stepped out from behind a 19th-century Greek Revival door. She kept continuously changing from one age to another. She was pregnant when the door swung open, and then she was 20 years younger, and then she was even more pregnant than before, so that I feared I might have to rush her to the hospital. Upstairs and down, she escorted me through every room of the house, the house where I would one day live but that I would not, in real life, see for another month. Curiously, I had seen all of the artwork and other items that were hanging on the walls—wreathes made out of branches, sewing hoops, straw hats—not typical décor, but my psyche, for reasons known only to itself, had taken them all down and then rearranged them more symmetrically.

These two dreams got my attention, but my alternate self had also aimed a third alarm clock at my head. From the edge of my memory, a scene from an out-of-the-solar-system experience that occurred in 1987 came flooding back. In a kind of metaphysical train station, smelling of the ocean and echoing with the noise of distant wars, a vast crowd of soon to incarnate souls was swirling. (They did have bodies, a fact that in retrospect seems strange, but these bodies may have been only a trick of my perception, a convenience.) Tens of thousands of souls there revolved in geometric patterns, wandering or shoving, convulsed with energy or in lockstep, in movements that were both chaotic and near perfect in their order. Then, a young Chinese girl broke suddenly from the crowd. With her hand raised, she ran towards me shouting,

"Husband!" My heart sank. How was it possible that I had forgotten who she was? I could tell that I had loved her.

This love pointed to a real but approximate geography of the soul, to the shadow of a shadow, to a glyph projected from a hyperdimensional sphere, and then bent. There was a sphere that served as the prototype for all later and less perfect spheres. I could glimpse, if only for a moment, how all the shadows thrown by the glyphs projected from the hypersphere fit together. I just as quickly forgot.

5

Let us now return to the scene of the long-delayed meeting: After several postponements, Deni and I had finally made plans, and we had enlisted Sterling to act as chaperon for the date. Opening the door to my third-floor apartment, I looked down the stairs just as Deni was coming up. As our eyes met, it seemed as though a current had set forth and returned from the far side of the ocean, subverting the precession of the equinox and bearing light from the lost sun of the Satya Yuga. "Yes!" I said to myself. Who knew that an ocean could be so intimate a space? And where had Deni been? And why had I not recognized her during those few indeterminate exchanges on the phone?

We talked for a while before going out to dinner, and I am shocked to remember how rude we were to Sterling. After 90 minutes of our both totally ignoring her, so wrapped up were we in discovering the lost history of our connection, our friend at last gave up attempting to join in. She said goodbye without our pausing to take notice, and then left.

At the Dixie Kitchen, we found that the homunculi in charge of censoring our conversation had taken the night off. Information that would normally be put on hold seemed to spill out without warning. "You remind me of my brother, Kadir," Deni said. "I'm not really sure why, though. You seem reasonably centered, and he once fantasized about building a bomb that could destroy the whole of the East Coast. He could write beautifully elegant prose when he was 12." "When I was 12," I said, "I was more interested in archery and camping and climbing trees and bike riding than I was in learning how to write. That came a few years later. I did have a six-hour dream once in which I was buoyed on the surface of a world-destroying flood. Looking down at New York, I could see the water rushing gently through the windows of the skyscrapers. I thought, 'I had not expected all this death to be so quiet.' So far as I know, though, I did not cause the flood."

"How did you come to be involved in Lukumi?" I asked. "My father is from Istanbul," she said, "and my mother grew up in Germany. We had relatives in Brazil who were practitioners of Candomble. Like Lukumi, this is a tradition that was brought to the New World from Yorubaland, which is now part of Nigeria. When I was growing up, I was always fascinated by the mysteriousness of the subject, without really knowing much of anything about it. Then, when I met Raoul Hernandez, my 'Padrino,' in 1989 and attended a few rituals, I felt like I'd come home. I received 'Ocha,' or initiation as a priestess, in March of 1990." "I received a yogic initiation in August of that year," I said. "It's odd that you should say you felt like you'd come home. That's exactly the way I feel about meeting you." I immediately realized that I was violating the first rule of dating: Never reveal too much of what you are feeling at the moment. I found that I did not care, and my comment did not produce a negative effect.

As the night went on, I found that I said things that should have put me in the "seriously strange" category, at least so far as the average person is concerned. "Have you ever wondered about the idea of bi-location?" I asked. "There is evidence that certain saints and yogis have been seen in two places at once. Is this second body a kind of hologram, do you think, or is it possible to be physically present in two places? I've had some experience with astral travel, which is not, of course, the same thing. I am also haunted by the sense that another one of me exists, that the larger part of who I am is located somewhere else. I sometimes ask myself: If you were locked in a cell, with no way to get out, would you be able to project yourself outside and then disassemble the other body? Over the past two years, I've been living in a state of relative creative solitude. I feel sane enough, but there are times when these absurd ideas seem dangerously real."

Would Deni write me off as a flake? "Is it possible to pass through a wall? That would take quite a bit of preparation," she said, "and you would really have to intensify your energy and your focus. To even pose or explore the question you would have to slip outside of your cultural framework. No matter what you told yourself, you would be subject to the subtle power of your habits. Still, you might one day find yourself on the other side of the wall." We never did get around to asking, "What is your favorite color?"

Then at 10:00 PM, two hours after our sitting down to eat, Deni cut short the conversation. This made no sense at the time, but I was somehow not upset. She later explained, "I found out what I needed to know. Things were going too well. I was afraid that one of us would say something stupid, something that would break the spell." A walk to the Mass. Ave T station, a short hug and a kiss, then she was down the stairs to the train.

Thus began the first and the last great romance of my maturity.

6

As if it had become natural to fall up instead of down, so much that had once been difficult seemed to happen by itself. Within several weeks, we touched on the idea of getting married. We also spoke of our desire to have children. I was quite surprised at how easily I said this, as well as of how strong this desire was, since I had only recently been unconcerned with the prospect that I might never become a parent. We were 40 and 41 years old. There were many plans to be made. When we fought, it was briefly. We were happy enough to apologize when we knew that the other was 100 percent wrong.

Once, sitting on the couch in my Hemenway Street apartment, absorbed in each other's stories, we sat almost motionless as we watched the light change on the walls. We watched the early afternoon slip into the late afternoon and then soften into twilight and then fade into the evening. We did not turn on a lamp. Our eyes projected the cones of our intent. These were wide enough to illuminate the dig-sites we explored. Nomads, wandering the cold sands where once a civilization stood, would stoop to light their campfires from the sparks that we deposited.

This is not to say that we only talked about things that were important. Just as often, too, we were content to simply breathe, to picnic in the Arnold Arboretum, to name this plant or that bird, to swing from low hanging branches, to communicate with a look. Our lips and fingers knew, without searching, how to find the most sensitive spots. For those first few months, the shadow of the Empire could not touch us. I only hated slugs. Deni only hated centipedes. To our daughter, Elizabeth, we would one day pass these quite reasonable hatreds. There would be plenty of time to extend such hatreds—to ideological nematodes and billionaire remoras—later on.

We scheduled our wedding for the following October. It was held at the First Unitarian Universalist Church, in Eliot Square, Roxbury. Neither one of us were Unitarians. It is possible that there was one among the guests. *On Saturday Night Live*, when Mr. and Mrs. Conehead were asked where they were from, they would always answer—in their nasal alien tone—"We're from France." When asked about our religious affiliation, Deni and I would often say, "We're Unitarians." This spared us from trying to share experiences that were not easily explained, and it protected us from the strange looks and disorientation of the questioner.

In spite of months of careful preparation, the day of the wedding unfolded with the chaos—a more or less harmonious chaos—that is typical of such events. The important things went magically. Other things hinted at vicissitudes to come, at the ways that reality would play games with our dreams. If there were mysterious forces that had caused our paths to cross, we knew that Eshu, the trickster, must also play his role.

It rained, and the once crisp autumn leaves were soggy underfoot. No photos could be taken in the churchyard. With 10 minutes to go, the doors to the church stayed locked. The caretaker with the key was nowhere to be found. I rang the bell to his cottage and asked his wife if she had some way to reach him. He later threatened to beat me up for pestering his wife. Friends and relatives had volunteered to prepare food in the basement. Unfortunately, these same people were supposed to act as ushers. Guests wandered all around, sans programs. The Rumi poem that we had spent months picking out did not end up being distributed. Because the rain had made the scheduled receiving line impossible, Deni and I spent three hours circulating from one table to another, chatting, sharing memories, saying thank you. We were not able to sit down, or eat.

Our families got along, but my mother said only six words to my father. I was unsure of whether to interpret this as progress; these were six words more than she had said to him since 1965. That night, my grandmother fell, breaking her hip. Taken from the house in which she had lived since 1929 to the hospital, she would, a week later, have to be transferred to a nursing home. She had, perhaps, been waiting to make sure that I was happy. Deni and I honeymooned in Hyannis, on Cape Cod, in a house that was a stone's throw from the ocean. It was chilly, but we had almost the whole beach to ourselves.

If only it were possible to add joy to joy, abundance to abundance, the way that certain New Age theorists recommend that we should do. We were indeed happy. We had entered into the next stage of our lives, yet this new beginning was simultaneously an end.

Sterling did, in a final, celebratory gesture, agree to serve as one of the bridesmaids at the wedding. Raven did not show up at all. Shortly afterwards, they both disappeared, not to be seen again until 18 years had passed, when, through a Facebook search, we found that they had been living in New Mexico. Perhaps we had become too respectable for their alternate-lifestyle tastes. If they had suspected that we would one day end up in a church, they might perhaps have been too appalled to introduce us. Perhaps our marriage was a threat to the care and feeding of the Avant-Garde, an insult to those who died screaming for more opium on the barricades, a thumb in the eye of Pere Ubu, a betrayal of the precepts of the Fluxus Manifesto. Or perhaps that part of the story was just over, and the page had turned.

Children Give Birth to Their Parents

Liz with Globe, 2002

Initiation destroys the self-centered world of childhood,
at least this is its primary intent. The adult produced by
initiation is a person whose self and entire life is defined by a
center outside of him or herself.

—Evan V. Zuesse, from *Ritual Cosmos*

Although it may not lead automatically to maturity, I suspect that
many people would not grow up at all if they had not decided
to become parents. It is one of the key things that shatters the
eggshell of our persistent adolescent narcissism. Now that 30 is

the new 18, now that adolescence seems to be lengthening into a several-decades-long project, having a child is one of the few things that informs us that time is passing.

World cycles go by, whether nine or 432,000, and the sky at last separates from the surface of the ocean. Gentle rhythmic lapping gives way to violent peaks and troughs. The egg's inhabitant has seen his image in the water, as the teachers from an earlier age had informed him that he would. Quite strangely, though, now that she has passed, with a storm of static, through the face of a smoking mirror, now that she can study the parts of her body from a number of different angles, what she sees looks less and less like any image she remembers. His new body bears only a limited resemblance to the ones from which he yesterday departed. It does not look like a sphere, like a constellation or a figure eight, or like any of 10,000 other forms, the last few hundred of which are human. And now, a pair of hands have yanked her from a tunnel. Moonlike faces float in too-bright fluorescent light. Barbarous screams have begun to echo in her ears.

A new theatre has been prepared for its enormous central actor. And you, the first parent there ever was, have been scheduled to withdraw yourself. That act is over, and the shadows ask that you should take your place among them.

Your life can then be divided into B.C. (Before Conception) and A.D. (After Delivery). It makes little difference if you are or are not ready, for whoever really is? You must do whatever is needed. You must grapple with the ultimatum posed by having helped to bring a new life into the world. In any case, becoming a parent—at least potentially—rips your attention away from your own navel and roots it in a center in the outside world. Your own needs become secondary. Another's well-being becomes more important than your own. When a baby cries, it focuses your attention on the present moment, as on the breath, in a way that is just as demanding as the protocols of a ten-day Vipassana retreat. You must breathe with another's breath, and the exercise is not over in 10 days, or even in 10 years!

Directly perceiving the interdependence of all things, the Bodhisattva vows to stay on this side of Nirvana: He must find a way to bring all creatures with him. So too, perhaps unconsciously, parents act out an everyday version of this vow. Let us say that we are already fully "enlightened" beings, who exist at some indeterminate point in the future or the past, or at the still center of a kaleidoscopic sphere. If this is true, then to put on the roles of "parent" and "child" is a service that we have volunteered to perform, each in his/her turn. For even the gods need navels if they are to function on the Earth.

My sense is we exist on many levels, as do our words and our actions, however much these levels do not appear to be related. Our use of both the full and diminutive versions of first names would suggest that we know a bit more than we are saying. For example, my daughter is called "Elizabeth." Broken one way, the name appears to come from "Eli," the abbreviation for "Elohim," the "active powers of god." This combines with "sheba," which means "seven," or with "shaba," which means "oath." Thus, the name could be translated as "God's power is an oath," or "The powers of god are seven." Broken a different way, we could focus on the Hebrew letter "Beth," which means "house," or, in Kabbalistic terms, an enclosure that divides the timeless from the manifest. Beth is the first letter in the Book of Genesis, the "dwelling place of El." On the other hand, my daughter is sometimes known as "Liz," which could just as easily be "Lizzy" or "Betty" or "Betsy" (if these last two did not annoy her). Of course, children do not name themselves at birth. There is a gulf between what we are and what our parents call us. Our use of formal and less formal names nonetheless points to our awareness that the self does exist on multiple levels.

To be born is a miracle, if a common one, perfected over an infinite number of past versions of creation. You would almost think that we had chosen to be here! Here, and in no other place, for where else is there, really?

Here, to some extent awake and present, is where we find ourselves, and are. Being grounded is not at an opposite extreme from being spiritual, and I think that this is one of the secret gifts of parenthood. It is, indeed, a kind of initiation, which may make no sense to those who have not undergone the experience. Even if you, as the new initiate, should prove obtuse, a figure eight will return you to some version of the figure eight. The present will make use of you. You will probably not object too much to being used. And if you do indeed object, too bad. Your hungry koan will be waiting to annoy you.

You will see how you are big. You will see how you are small. You will be able to turn your life to examine it simultaneously from all angles, in the same way you once turned your body as an infant. This could be seen, perhaps, as a slow-motion version of what takes place in an NDE review. Each jump to an alternate level of experience demands that you should turn a clear eye on past actions. Your vision should be, in equal parts, both cold and all-accepting. You must dare to look at those issues you have left only half-resolved, for otherwise your shadow may attach itself to your child. Before the child is even born, you might print him with the scars of those who howl from their graves, of those who yearn to crush the throats of their false rulers. You might warp the expression of her RNA with your own out-of-focus anxieties. You might limit her choice of seats in the high school cafeteria.

By becoming a parent, you also become a parent to yourself. As your child grows, he/she reawakens your own sense of wonder, which had been deactivated at the end of the previous world cycle, when you were sentenced to first grade and the doors to the school clanged shut. By means of looking out for another you have once more learned to see, and you can relive all of your own childhood discoveries and traumas, both from the inside out and from the outside in. The present is no longer the mute victim of the past, a landscape made from shards of broken glass that was left by competing tribes of black magicians. No, the Earth is young, and she is happy to parade her wealth before you. She will point you towards the sun behind the sun, towards the tree from which whole cultures can be picked. You will lift the curled-up husk that you left in the Satya Yuga.

Again, we will meet at the wish-fulfilling stone, where some but not all requests born from necessity will be granted. There, standing in a circle, we will meet with those we love, and there will be none among us who are able to determine the other's age. We will show each other our scars, laughing, as we draw lots to project ourselves towards death. For our golden bodies were designed to sustain much wear and tear.

Visiting Saint Joseph's: Towards a Just Proportion of Emptiness

Liz with Turtle, 2002

"Though autumn had stripped bare the century-old trees, this whole vast horizon spoke of everlasting life."

—Giorgio de Chirico, from *Hebdomeros*

1

"A great city is not to be confused with a populous one."

—Aristotle

The October air was crisp. Leaves rustled underfoot as my daughter and I stepped, with automatic care, around the shards of bottles left from late night summer parties. Elizabeth waved hello to Marvin, the owner of Folger's Liquor Store, as he rolled up the steel caging that protected the door and windows. It was 8:15 AM. I imagined the first customer just then falling out of bed, to stuff dollars and coins into his pocket and wait anxiously for the 9:00 AM opening. Cars on Washington Street sped by. At the sight of a young girl, several drivers stopped to motion us across. "There are so many wonderful people in the world!" said Elizabeth.

The world was a vast playground of which Elizabeth took possession. After all, the Earth's architects had constructed it specifically for her enjoyment. It opened before her, and it supported her every step. There were a few things that could be improved, perhaps. "Why don't people take care of our beautiful planet?" she said, frowning as she examined the cups and wrappers that had spilled from a McDonald's bag. She would have plenty of time to make the needed small adjustments later. We were headed for Saint Joseph's Elementary School, built in 1880, whose Arts and Crafts style shoebox appeared to grow at our approach. Birds guarded the milk carton tower of the adjoining Romanesque church.

The brick exterior of the church presented a brave face to the neighborhood. To step inside was to see the need for immediate renovation. Plaster saints had fallen from the ceiling. Light leaked through the rafters. The school, by contrast, was in a relatively good state of repair. "Do not look for anything luxurious," it seemed to say, "for anything beyond what allows me to survive. To the east, there are city-states that yearn for my destruction." Sparta would have approved of Saint Joseph's scarred oak chairs and tables.

Let me speak here of the school as if it still existed, although it closed shortly after the writing of the first draft this essay, a victim of the priest-sex-abuse scandal, whose international scope was just beginning to be felt but which had already brought the Boston Archdiocese to its knees. Such—according to the Vatican—was the insidious consequence of the liberation movements of the '60s. Madness comes to those who bring gifts to Dionysus, who throw away their clothes, who partake in his arcane rites. It also comes to those who do not. For the West, the end approaches.

But let me do my best to hold on to the innocence of that autumn. As light spills through the soon to be bare trees, let us imagine that we are entering the Arts and Crafts style shoebox. Here are four paragraphs from the notebook I carried with me on the visit:

"Nothing too much," read one of the key inscriptions on Apollo's shrine at Delphi. At Saint Joseph's, too, we find instructions on the walls, among which is "Know Thyself," another of the 147 Laconic precepts found at Delphi, and the building itself can be read as testament to the Mean. Clearly, each stone here had been weighed and considered by the Masons, who knew but did not speak. Like the gods before them, they did not need to count higher than the fingers on both hands, and yet they had set the tone for each gesture the students and teachers would perform.

The atmosphere itself seems to call for the development of classical skills and virtues, virtues that have nothing in particular to do with the Catholic Church, or so my wife and I hope, since neither of us are Catholic, or even Christian, and we are not all that well disposed towards the Church. Out of available choices, however, this does seem like the best one for the moment. Another maxim posted in the main hallway reads,

"Character is what you do when no one else is watching." With the eyes of the dead everywhere, this advice may be difficult for the students to take literally.

The spell of the corrupt Empire does not penetrate the windows. In the outer world, billions are made to suffer for the comfort of a few; within the school, the hierarchy does not depend on wealth. If the goal were to produce a true American consumer, the resources here would not be adequate to that end. The goal here would seem to be much simpler and more practical: to teach students to begin by being where they are. If the students are fewer in number than the 5040 of Plato's ideal city-state, the principle that things work best at a certain scale holds true. Here, everybody knows everybody, more or less. A focus on the proportion between elements creates a "clean, well-lighted space."

With only decades left until the last of the oil wells stop pumping, you could even say that the students are getting a heads-up on the future. Mies van der Rohe's famous statement "Less is more" may prove to be far more prophetic than we would guess. The first will be last and the last will be first. More importantly, we will all have fewer distractions. This will provide us with a better view of the abyss. Quite soon perhaps, in the wake of solar flares and electromagnetically fried motherboards, the Art of Memory may be scheduled for a comeback, and space itself will be the school that we attend.

Let me return to the past tense and also backtrack just a bit. It was 8:14, a minute before we saw Marvin roll up the steel caging. The cool October sunlight bounced beautifully back from the shards of broken liquor bottles. Refusing to take my hand, Elizabeth had just walked along the edge of the wall at Cedar Square Park, from which she then jumped down. This was a vertigo-inducing precipice of some three-and one-half feet. Pleased with her walk on the wild side and subsequent death-defying leap, Elizabeth waved and said hello to every passing group of students.

"I only tell my best friends I'm a princess," she said, "but they all want to touch my hair."

Such apparent egocentrism should not be viewed as narcissistic. Having exited from a sphere whose circumference is nowhere, in which symbols form one vast, unspoken text, my daughter's challenge was to figure out what it meant to exist in one location. It was natural for a four-year-old to act like the center of the world, which for all intents and purposes, she was.

We paused to comment on a large Egyptian eye that had mysteriously been sprayed on a mailbox. Was it vandalism or art? Was there some creature in the mailbox who was looking through the eye? Cutting through the housing development on Crispus Attucks Way, we tasted the cold air. "I'm glad it's cold because I don't like to get sweaty," said Elizabeth. We crunched on crab apples, spread like rotting treasure on our path. A black cat wandered out to greet us with a look of expectation. A few leaves blew. The trees were quickly changing color. The Arts and Crafts style shoebox was now almost human scale, as was the milk carton tower.

Step by step, the vulnerability of the small tribute-state became steadily more clear. The brick walls and molded cement cornices looked more substantial than cardboard, but the school would still need to proceed with the construction of a new defensive perimeter, in the form of a massive octagon, complete with crenellations, loopholes, and slots for the pouring of hot oil. Separate fund-drives had been scheduled for each.

Threats were everywhere, it was said, and the red doors to the school were almost always locked. They would be open for ten minutes, only. Visibly proud, with perfect posture, a young boy held the door for us. He was not too cool to be undefended, however long that would last. If drafted to serve as a tentacle of the Empire's group-think octopus, would the boy then blindly do what was expected or would he find it somewhere in his deep heart to resist? The two-edged virtue of obedience might one day lead to a haunted tower, where, as a pawn in some drawn-out Pyrrhic contest, he would fight the wind on a newly barbarized frontier. As I watched, these actions appeared to have already happened far away, as the tide-level rose, in a seaport that had been emptied of all movement.

We entered through the big red door. Ascending the steps, I noted that the smells of chalk dust and wood oil were conspicuous by their absence. Inside, the school was modern, to some extent. It confounded my olfactory expectation. The rows of computers in the room to the left had no aroma. How strange! I was not only in my daughter's present, as this existed in 2001, I was also in my own present, as this existed in 1959. I was large, but I was also very small. My daughter's hand led me through the grammar school that I had long ago attended in South Worcester. We had arrived at the school on time.

2

"'The idea came like a flash of lightning,' he said, 'and in an instant the truth was revealed.' Tesla picked up a twig and began drawing in the dirt. 'See my motor,' he said to his friend. 'Here.'"

—B.A. Behrend

Given half a chance, the "pre-operational" child—in Piaget's theory of the four stages of development—will demand to choreograph each new idea, to turn painting into song and poem into movement. Synesthesia was a preoccupation of the late 19th and early 20th-century avant-garde. One theory holds that this was due to an excessive use of absinthe. It could just as easily have originated in an upsurge of nostalgia. Since the 1780s, the smog from the Industrial Revolution had been thickening, like the aura of John Calvin, and it was clear that the automaton had plans to recreate us in its image. Intoxication may be the poor man's substitute for the sensory gymnastics of the kindergarten. At this stage, discovery has not yet become a chore but rather unfolds according to its own spontaneous rhythm. Our bodies are not yet objects; instead, they are vast fields of energy, in which the boundaries between the senses are provisional. The good teacher will trust the student to be curious. A gentle hand can then steer and help to integrate the energy.

Tertullian said, "I believe in the Resurrection *because* it is impossible." So too, although it goes completely against common sense, perhaps we should put our faith in the innate genius of each child. (I sometimes told the students in my art class that they would all be starting with an A. It would be up to them to lower the grade by not following my instructions.) Each child may not *be* a genius, it is true, but, according to Greek, Roman, Yoruba, Huna, Sufi, and many other ancient traditions, each child does possess a "genius," i.e., a tutelary spirit that comes equipped with its own agenda. If each child does *possess* a genius, it may be the job of the teacher to empower this genius, step by step, to then take at least partial possession of the child. You could not, of course, say such a thing in any public school in the U.S., as I was warned many times when I was studying to be a teacher at Mass Art, however much parents might be upset with the status quo.

Like the Ptolemaic model of the solar system, the heliocentric model of education—which puts the brain-as-physical-database at the center of all theory—may have reached its "sell by" date. On the one hand, our technological knowledge each day grows by leaps and bounds, geometrically, in a kind of controlled explosion. According to some theorists, we are only a few moments off from the point of IT Singularity. We are learning more and more about less and less, until, quite soon, we will know everything about nothing. On the other hand, the whole material base of post-industrial society may be cracking apart underneath us. We are learning less and less about more and more, until, quite soon, we will know nothing about everything. We no longer take the pulse of nature; we count the "likes" on our Facebook posts.

On the closed curve of a Moebius strip, we should not assume that we know where we stand, whether our heads point up or down, or whether our brains are tucked as securely inside as we think. Our attitudes towards "less" and "more" may be in need of reassessment. If we misconceive the empty, we will misconceive the full. This may lead us to underestimate how empty our fullness is. Similarly, our emptiness may be full to overflowing. Even if a child can be conceived as a "blank slate" or an "empty vessel," as many theorists since Locke have argued, the emptiness that we think we see may also serve a practical purpose. There may already be some reasonable proportion between space and information. The emptiness may not be crying out to be filled, not quickly at least, or by force, or in the interests of one theory or another. Like the inside of an instrument, the child's emptiness may be meant to serve as a resonating chamber, a space in which the scales of the unmanifest can bloom. Less emptiness is not necessarily preferable to more. An exact amount of emptiness should be the goal.

Even in the case of what seems a clear-cut disability, we might do better to interpret any weakness as the seed of a potential strength, any lack as an opening rather than a dead end. Each obstacle may be a door at which the *daimon* knocks to enter.

Einstein felt no particular need to speak until he was seven years old. I have often wondered if his talent for non-linear exploration, his tendency to place the answer before the question, would ever have developed without this period of near silence. There were many who got better grades at the Zurich Polytechnic Institute, and perhaps some had higher IQs. Einstein's gift was to trust in his particular way of moving. Physicists Richard Feynman and Edward Teller were also late in learning how to speak. Helen Keller, if she and Anne Sullivan had not found each other, might never have chosen to communicate at all.

Thomas Edison may have had a form of "Attention Deficit Hyperactivity Disorder." He stared out of windows, and after his teacher called him "addled," his mother yanked him out of school. Thus ended his three months of official education. This was the man who, years later, was to say, when asked about his pursuit of a workable filament for the light bulb, "I did not fail 1000 times. I found 1000 things that didn't work." Somewhat paradoxically, those with ADHD are often the most capable of intense focus when they find a project that commands their full attention.

Zola once called Cezanne "the worst painter in Paris." It is certain that no Mozartian brilliance distinguished him as a child. As a young painter he did not impress critics, or even friends, of whom Zola was one. There was no birthmark on the forehead to identify him as the father of early 20th-century modernism. Like Keller, Cezanne was willing to learn to see by other means, and like Edison, he was endlessly flexible in his definition of what constituted a "mistake."

In our current theories, we tend to see knowledge as a mostly additive process, as well as to assume that ontogeny recapitulates phylogeny. Each day and in every way we are getting better and better. But the future is not merely the sum-total of all of our heroic fantasies from the past. An alternate view is that true knowledge is subtractive, that everything that we need to know or might want to invent is, to a certain extent, already in existence.

If, as the Ancients believed, time moves not in straight lines but in cycles, each event or thing has happened or existed a great many times before. How odd that something as gigantic as our bodies should have emerged from something as nearly invisible as an egg! The foot of the Ideal no longer stands on Earth, nor can the Earth any longer be said to simply revolve around the Sun. Instead, both Earth and Sun revolve, at multiple occult angles, around a center that has yet to be determined.

3

"Every child is an artist; the problem is staying an artist when you grow up."

—Picasso

We arrived at the door to the room where Elizabeth's class was to be held for the day. When I pulled the door open, a moderate roar washed over us. We stopped for a moment to exchange a hug. Elizabeth's eyes darted back and forth, as she stretched and bounced on the balls of her feet like a gymnast warming up. She had things to do, and, already, I had become a small speck in the background. Without looking back, Elizabeth ran to a table at which a group of ten or so girls was seated, and, sure enough, hands reached out to touch her ponytail.

The room was a storm of self-organizing activity. This was the massed military strength of the K1 and K2 classes. The room, as I have said, was loud, making it difficult to eavesdrop. When I stuck my nose into a group I found that conversation would mysteriously slow. I decided to sit quietly, hands folded, on a foot-high chair.

As if to illustrate a cliché, the girls appeared to be sharpening their interpersonal skills, while the boys, for the most part, were working on semi-militarized team projects. It was very sad to see at what a young age they had been brainwashed. Clearly, the teachers had shunted them into these stultifying roles. Like the members of some Leviticus-inspired cult, their eyes glazed and their androgyny removed, with smiles fixed on their faces, most seemed eager to cooperate in enforcing their repression.

On a wall hung sheets of drawing paper that were decorated with handprints. On a clothesline hung paper shirts that the students had painted with landscapes. Mountains of toys had erupted from their storage boxes. A boy walked by carrying a large plastic house, the smoke from whose chimney formed a handle. Action figures advanced against heavy fire up a beach.

I saw, at the end of the large table, a girl braiding a lanyard out of multicolored cords. There was a look of intense focus on her face, and she brushed off all attempts at conversation. A suggestion from the K1 assistant went totally unheard. Off and on she would grip her lower lip with her teeth. If she made a mistake, she would undo the cords to patiently start over.

Three boys were playing with some dinosaurs and a horse. The horse was beating up the stegosaurus. The stegosaurus was tiny and slow. The horse's enormous size appeared to give it the advantage. A Tyrannosaurus Rex suddenly popped up. He was all business, and with no hesitation bit the horse's head off. "Don't you wish that you could be a T Rex too?" exclaimed one of the boys. A pink elephant tossed its head at two stampeding brontosauruses. "Uh oh," said a boy. "The elephant is in trouble! Where is that gorilla?"

"Do you trick Elizabeth?" a girl asked. "Sure. I guess so," I responded. "Would you trick me too? Please!" "It's going to be hard to trick you since you know that the trick is coming," I said. "That's ok," said the girl, "I'll just forget!" "How do you spell Elizabeth's name backwards?" another girl at the table asked. It would not matter, I suspected, whether my answer was correct; an even more difficult question would be quickly on the way, and still another one after that. Pleading thirst, I excused myself.

A green action figure had lost his nerve and was being pursued by a mean building. A boy, who was searching for a particular Lego piece, dumped out hundreds of pieces from a large pail. A three-foot boy said to a boy an inch smaller, "You're too small!" Ignoring the insult, the other boy said, "Could I get a blue crayon please!"

The K1 assistant stopped by one of the tables to announce that it had become too crowded. She said, "There should be three of you on this side and three on that side. The rest of you should move to a different table. You don't have enough room to play." With great theatrical flair, the girls stood up, groaning, and milled around, making every effort to appear to rearrange themselves. When the assistant turned her back, they quickly returned to their original positions.

In a corner sat a solitary boy, who was building, from another Lego set, a lopsided model of the World Trade Towers. When the structure was complete, he stood tiny figures on the top and then tipped them onto the floor, making a whistling sound as they fell. He then picked them up in order to flick them, with his thumb and forefinger, into space. The K1 assistant looked on with some concern.

In every direction the small tornadoes tilted. "Let's keep it down!" the K1 assistant yelled. For a passing moment the room went from noisy to just slightly less noisy. My daughter glanced at me for a second, and then again immediately forgot that I existed. As I turned to leave, I saw a large boy put a green pail on his head, to then adjust it like a hat. Was he fooling around for the entertainment of his friends or just trying to amuse himself? For either of these explanations, his expression seemed far too incongruously stern. The hat-code of the preoperational poet was obscure. Just what, if anything, did the act symbolize?

"In all chaos there is a cosmos, in all disorder a secret order."

—Carl Jung

"If there were a map, there'd be no art, because art is the act of navigating without a map."

—Seth Godin

The Greek root for the word education means "to call forth." Who or what is being called, and where has it been hiding? But perhaps, in the end, it is we who have been hiding, while this alternate self, the master of the art of non-local correspondences, remains, as he/she/it has always been, as clear and wide as space. In *Daybreak*, Nietzsche writes, "Why does man not see things? He is himself standing in the way: he conceals things." In the *Bardo Thodol*, or "Liberation in the Intermediate State though Hearing," more commonly referred to as *The Tibetan Book of the Dead*, the newly departed actor is encouraged to let go of his projections. His is told to discover that it is the mask that makes the demon, underneath which is the god. He is told to accept that the actor is not the character that he/she plays. He is told to recognize—somewhat counterintuitively, given these earlier revelations—that the image is not different from the screen.

In one chapter of the *Bardo Thodol*, we read,

You have the power to go right through any rock masses, ancestral trees, tornadoes, the planet Earth, and Mt. Meru itself without being impeded. Excepting Budh Gaya and the mother's womb, you there can pass straight forwards and backwards through each object unimpededly...You are endowed with the power of miraculous action, which is not, however, the fruit of any samadhi, but a power come naturally to you. You are able in a moment to traverse the four continents arranged around Mt. Meru, or can instantaneously arrive in any place you wish.

If such powers seem like fantasy to us, this is perhaps because we have been trained to overestimate the living and, at the same time, to scoff at the vast accomplishments of the dead. To the Ancients, of course, "to die" might have meant to incarnate, while "to be born" might have meant to wave goodbye to the massive octagon of one's school. Through the centuries, these terms would seem to have been mysteriously reversed.

In Hindu tradition the Atman, or Oversoul, is described as being as large as the top joint of the thumb, or about one inch in height. It can choose to appear in a human or a spherical form, and the tiny, chameleonic god-man can dance out of it to interact with beings of the physical world. In a contemporary comparison, I have sometimes wondered about the tiny, luminous spheres that have been seen to dance above the creation of many crop circles. Could these be a form of the Atman? At first, these circles were simple, as if in reenactment of the earliest stages of the cosmos. More recently, their scale and complexity are like depth-charges dropped into the bowels of the intellect. They are perfect artworks, which confront us with the impenetrable identity of the artist. If these are not the work of the Atman, as they very well may not be, he/she/it would no doubt still appreciate such revolutionary acts of subversion.

After wrestling with the implications of such works, how is it possible to go back to one's simpler view of the world? By sheer force of will, many do, and then they do their best to drag others along with them. At last, "The mystery of those giant circles and odd geometric shapes that have been showing up in wheat fields in southern England have been explained," writes William E. Schmidt in a September 10th, 1991, article in the *New York Times*.

According to the article, David Chorley and Doug Bowers, "two jovial English conmen in their 60s," have "confessed" to being the creators of the circles, the ones who have been "skulking around in the countryside under cover of darkness, trampling out patterns with wooden boards as a big joke." Left unexplained is how they managed to do this in more than 80 countries on five continents, with many of the circles appearing in the same night. According to the British tabloid *Today*, all of this was made possible by a "bizarre sighting device attached to a baseball cap."

It is probably true that our brains are now bigger than the one inch of the Oversoul. This does not appear to have made us any smarter. After six billion years, you would think that we could locate the beginning of a circle. Of course, no navel-gazing is allowed, and the Sun is not, and never has been, located in the solar plexus. Who knows why ancient anatomists would have come up with such silly names? The lack of sighting devices on their baseball caps no doubt led them to misjudge the 94.4 million miles that divide us from the Sun. Even now, such devices are not generally available. Quite often, as we stare into the depths, we cannot even recognize the palms of our own hands.

5

This concept of the tiny god-man has appeared in any number of distorted versions, in which theoreticians attempt to impose a fixed material form on what, by its nature, is as occult as a zero. In Preformationism, as described by historians of science, the child, even from the earliest stages of conception, was imagined to be a miniature adult, fully formed and with mature proportions, trapped inside of a seed. Upon birth, the child had no real need to develop but stepped quickly forward to assume his/her place in the world. This was the theory of development that prevailed until the 18th Century, when Locke asserted that each child is a kind of "tabula rasa." We are told that Preformationists naively jumped for joy upon hearing of the invention of the microscope and that several claimed to have witnessed perfect humans waving back at them from spermatozoa, as from ships.

6

"The eye sees only what the mind is prepared to comprehend."

—Henri Bergson

As part of a project, when Elizabeth was four years old, I asked her to draw some pictures of what a perfect world would look like.

Me: "Elizabeth, this drawing is very abstract. It seems like a kind of diagram. I can't really understand what you're trying to do here."

Elizabeth: "This is a tree that is also a street. Remember, when we used to live in China? In a perfect world I would still know how to fight."

Me: "What is going on in this other drawing?"

Elizabeth: "This is me in a perfect world, which is *our* world, cutting through the park across the street on my way to school."

Me: "Elizabeth, what do the butterflies in this picture mean?"

Elizabeth: "The butterflies are very pretty."

Me: "No, really. What do the butterflies mean?"

Elizabeth: "The butterflies are showing us that they are butterflies *now*."

Me: "Oh? What were they before?"

Elizabeth: "*People*. The butterflies were *people*. What else would they be?"

This was said in a tone of measured annoyance, as if I were being deliberately obtuse, as if nothing could be more obvious. I recalled that the butterfly was an image of the soul. I recalled that, in the Aztec version of the afterlife, certain of the dead would return as butterflies. I recalled that, when Elizabeth Kubler-Ross visited the Maidenek concentration camp in 1946, she found that hundreds of butterflies had been scratched into the walls of the children's barracks.

One day, a few months after this, while she was sitting on my lap in the large leather chair in our living room, Elizabeth, out of nowhere, said, "When someone has decided to come back as a human, sometimes the mommy becomes the daughter and the daughter becomes the mommy." "How do you know that?" I asked. Leaning close to my ear, she paused for effect and then said in a whisper, "I just know." Throughout this period, from the ages of three to seven, such difficult-to-source statements were not all that unusual. One day, for example, I was carrying Elizabeth on my shoulders at the end of a long walk. She was eating a Popsicle. It was hot, and the juice from the Popsicle was dripping on my head. As we paused outside of our gate, Elizabeth sighed and then said, "Do you think that I talk about spirit too much? It's hard to be a big soul in a little body."

The will to objective mastery does not pause to take prisoners. Bit by bit, then almost totally, our ability to see through more than two eyes disappears. The forward drive of socialization consumes all in its path. At the age of 24, Elizabeth is now incredulous when I recount the stories of her past pronouncements. I seldom try to tell these stories. When I do, Elizabeth's response stops just short of embarrassment—perhaps just at the silliness of her father—and she seems to signal that these pronouncements should be labeled "N.F.P.C.," or "Not For Public Consumption." Such out-of-place statements—or Ouplents, to coin a term—may be far more common than we think, but we tend to file most of these under the heading of "Imagination." Like "God," this is a catch-all category, which we can use to explain both everything and nothing. I offer no proof. I tell these particular stories because I witnessed them firsthand.

7

"The mind is an iceberg; it floats with only one-seventh of its bulk above water."

—Sigmund Freud

Let me phrase the problem simply: if a child is the sum total of what he/she has seen and heard, then why would a four-year old be interested in a metaphysical concept? The timing is way off. If we have, in fact, developed into our present state according to the laws of evolution, should not the child fit, like a puzzle part, into the shape of the immediate environment? Convex and concave should fit together perfectly, without any gaps, and without any need for the edges to be hammered into place.

If, as Piaget describes, each child must explore, test, discover, and construct the laws of time and space for him/herself, it is possible that we see the process but mistake the organizing metaphor. Such knowledge should be encoded, like sex and hair color, in our DNA. There should be some brief period of adjustment, as with almost every other species, and then the child should put on the shoes of an adult. With a minimum of fuss, he should fill his assigned role in the world. She should not have to reinvent the whole of the third dimension from scratch. Occam's razor does not allow for so much redundant effort.

The slow arc of our development is a problem for both Preformationist and modern scientific views. It is almost as though we had been the victims of a car crash. For the first few years, we just seem to stumble around, and when we try to talk, a loud cry pops from our mouths. I would argue that there is a different way to interpret the key facts. This is as follows: that consciousness could, just as easily, have come from a dimension governed by a different set of laws. Conceptions of such a dimension vary, as do names. We can speak of the *Pleuroma of the Gnostics*, of Plato's *Realm of Ideal Forms*, of the Aboriginal *Dream Time*, of the *Alam Al-Mithal* of the Sufis, of the Kabbalist's *Beriah* and *Yetzirah*. We may be barred from all easy access to what we knew in such dimensions, and yet we bring their imprint with us, along with some few skills acquired in past lives. "This world is the market-place," say the Yoruba, "the other world is our home." Perhaps, as Aldous Huxley argued, the brain did not evolve as the power plant of consciousness; instead, it may act as a reducing valve. Its purpose may be to shield us from kaleidoscopic energies, from the influx of raw genius, from an ancient consciousness that projects the human body as its shadow. What we see as discovery may be really a kind of self-created refresher course.

Picasso said, "When I was seven I could draw like Raphael. It has taken me 50 years to learn how to draw like a child." Small is not less valuable than big. The open is not necessarily less developed than the sealed. Certain types of guidance may be there from the beginning, as a force beneath the threshold of awareness, however long it might take to translate the instructions, whether or not some failures of interpretation might result. It is only natural for the child to be in contact with the supernatural, as it is natural for us to protect our way of life. With a joke, we dismiss the evidence of such contact out of hand. A first-grade teacher might ask, "Did your 'invisible friend' tell you to push Billy down the stairs?" "Yes, thank you," the still fuming child might mentally whisper to his friend, "Billy needed to be taught a lesson." The silent perpetrator knows only that the impulse came from elsewhere. Such an impulse had also prompted the four-year-old Yehudi Menuhin to smash the first violin his parents gave him because it was only a child-sized toy. Time was wasting. What an insult it was to be given the wrong size! Three years later, in 1923, he performed as solo violinist with the San Francisco Symphony Orchestra.

To be born is to (almost) forget that we ever knew how to paint. It is to set aside both our traumas and our skills. This is a simple creative strategy, no more, and no less, a cleaning of the palette, a refocusing of the eyes. There is no reason to turn this practical arrangement into the Code of Hammurabi. If we expect children to be prepared to learn from us, should we not be equally prepared to learn from them? It could certainly be said, of course, that this is just the kind of sentimental fantasy all too common since the myth of the "noble savage" was first invented by Rousseau.

In the 18th Century, on the other hand, such sentiments seemed less naïve than cutting edge. To Rousseau, it is our hide-bound myopia that would have seemed passé. Our skeptical reduction-ism would have seemed as formulaic as the papal bulls of Urban VIII, as grim as the *Institutes* of Calvin. No more putting of the cart before the horse! We had been there, and done that, for many centuries at a stretch. This was the age of the enthusiastic amateur, the adult child, for whom life-long love of learning was not a reason to grow up. As the age of the planet began to grow by exponential leaps, from 5,700 to the current 4.5 billion years, it seemed that our civilization was getting younger by the day.

The South Seas had just recently been discovered. They brimmed with wonders, Siren-like and hypnotic, and they tempted us to make an almost infinite number of mistakes. These would not be our usual mistakes, the all too boring ones; no, they would instead be a whole new and improved set. On the line between waking and dream, the most exotic of spices floated. Polynesia was a playground, complete with slides and monkey-bars, whose every island was abuzz with new mercantile opportunities. Samoa was still pagan. They wore only minimal clothing, they did not hate us yet, and they had many remedial perspectives to impart. Science was in the process of defining sex and warfare as pastimes, as they were in Ancient Greece. Ritual sacrifice could return to being the innocent spectacle that it was. If people acted badly, this was not due to Original Sin, nor were aristocrats the delegates of God. It was time to trust our curiosity and to see the world anew.

The dawn was imminent. It would only be necessary to remove the few small impediments in our path—the doors to the Bastille, for example, or the heads of the aristocracy. Early on, things had started to go almost imperceptibly wrong, and then continued, bit by bit, to get even more out of sync. There was a tiny golden child that had been locked away in the heart; this much was true, but his many years in prison had caused him to go mad. His beauty drew the millions towards him. Few could have imagined the depths of his revenge. Time after time, we had underestimated the extent of our corruption, as well as the power of the spell that the Kali Yuga cast.

Such dreams have run their course. They have left, from Epoch 22 September, 1792—the day that French revolutionaries overthrew the calendar in order to declare a new "Year One"—until now, tens of thousands of lime-covered pits, and set fire to the length and breadth of continents. We are the sacrificial victims of failed modernist utopias, and we have not recovered from the collective wounds of the last century. This idea, that our children could become our teachers, is nonetheless a way of saying something that is difficult to translate. We have lost our primordial intuition. We go in search of some image already present that encapsulates a metaphysical conflict between worlds.

We are sad, much sadder than we know, and our light-bodies now weigh much more than they should. We are vehicles that have grown too used to running just on fumes. Our movement is now virtual; actual movement would destroy us. We speed, but we do not go anywhere at all, nor do we see each body part as the glyph of a cosmological cycle. Since 2008, Apple has led us from iPhone One through the flux of an alchemical furnace to the latest of 12 generations of the iPhone. We now experience a wider range of entertainment choices than any culture in history. We are YouTube metaphysicians. We are fossilized tornadoes. Our good fortune is to be unaware of which crisis will prove the breaking point. We speak of "security"; it is our polite word for fear. To again see from one end of the planet to the other, without prosthetics, in a flash, we must find some way to forget that we are ignorant. The play of children presents us with a kind of ultimatum.

8
Post Piaget

"I cannot be grasped in the here and now, for my dwelling place is as much among the dead as the yet unborn. Slightly closer to the heart of creation than usual, but still not close enough."

—Paul Klee, gravestone inscription

There was a point towards which the centuries converged—Omega, the Social Darwinist perfection of the race, the Marxist Workers' Paradise, the Global triumph of Neoliberalism, the mapping of three billion base pairs of DNA, a leap into the Noosphere, the extraction of the last ounce of tar sands from the Alberta/Saskatchewan border. We have entered through this point with some few of our contemporaries, we who are still halfway in our bodies. We have entered without knowing that we entered. We have woken up beyond it. Fear proves of little use, but neither does it lull us with inaccurate information. To find our hands is difficult. The sky rings. Our eyes just barely work.

Setting Piaget's stages of development aside, we should perhaps construct our theories as a kind of open house, like a tent, inside of which a nomad spreads a wonderful flying carpet. Let us revolutionize our use of the word "present." Let us go to the New Earth. We, the bankrupt heirs of the decentralized plutocracy, would then find that we had also become nomads, that we could not seem to remember when or where we left our homes. Confused by the silence, we would discover that our TVs had long ago revolted. Outside, when the sand shifted, we would be able to see the broken walls of a metropolis, once called great, which would be only the topmost of at least a dozen layers. The host would request of the gods, "Relax. Make yourselves comfortable." Stories would elbow each other aside to find a place in the poet's mouth. The dead would be invited in for a steaming cup of tea.

The structure would provide provisional protection, the appropriate amount of light, and even, if placed well, some access to a primal source of energy, to a force whose name we had buried in our dreams. If our vortices were closed, we would one day find them spinning. New dimensions of hunger would seize our basal ganglia. Lack of food would be the least of our concerns. The knowledge printed on the wind would provide us with fresh manna. Birds would drop near our flaps with cookbooks on their feet. Supplies of drinkable water would be adequate enough, but we would once more have to learn how to dowse for living mercury, how to transform the dry landscapes of our bodies into maps. When fallout blew from the shell of a destabilized reactor—or with some luck, a few weeks before—we would know that it was time to go. Having served its purpose, the open house would then be folded up, to be carried to a fixed but still unknown destination.

Reefs would die. Auroras would be seen as far south as the equator. A pandemic of epilepsy would take apart most coasts. There would be no petroleum left to be extracted, and the last flames would have ceased to shoot up from their wells. The air would be somewhat cleaner. There would be no lines at the gas pumps. In this none-too-solid world, past and future would meet at sunset to transform the human heart. Lost technologies would flow into the spaces cleared by accidents. Our open house would carry its own weather system with it, with sunsets that would not be all that difficult to schedule, with winds swarming with the flutes of other-than-human players. Messengers would bring flowers, to be burnt. A black cat would wander out with a look of expectation. No longer would Necessity be the sole Mother of Invention. Mnemosyne would return out of the depths. She would hug her overworked sister. Transported by her carpet, a telepathic child would fly to the horizon, on whose lip she would dance. Disassembling her own bones, she would use them to cast oracles. By this means, she would determine the next site for the tent.

Only the subtlest of evidence would mark the tribe's migration—a small school planted here, a tradition floated there. We would once again have a good view of the stars. We would greet our prenatal ancestors. We would take our mummified descendants from their jars. The world would be almost perfect. It would, with a few small adjustments, soon be fully so.

On the Paintings of Deniz Ozan-George: The Breaking of the Golden Egg

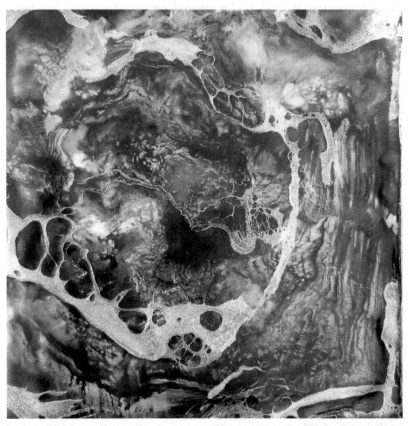

Deniz Ozan-George, *The Last to Leave*, encaustic and shellac burn, 2021

Deniz Ozan-George is a painter whose work invites the viewer to do much more than look. Even the simplest of her paintings are usually composed of many layers; so too, we must approach them step by step, glimpse by tangential glimpse, leap by only later to be integrated leap. As we get to know one of Ozan-George's paintings, our exploration may indeed result in an "Aha!" The process, however, is not one of addition; it is rather one of subtraction. We must prepare ourselves to breathe with the artist as she breathes.

More often than not, I tend to see Ozan-George's paintings as cosmologies, in which the eternal present moment has been broken apart and is just about to be projected into time. The four corners of the canvas are the four ages or the four fixed signs of the zodiac or the four elements. The canvas is an arena of ritual action, in which the vertical and horizontal axes intersect. The artist does not, beyond a point, indicate how these zones of ritual action should be viewed. Is this order or chaos, emergence or disintegration, natural breadth or meditative depth, microcosmic or interstellar space?

Much information has been provided by the creator, but it is up to the viewer to complete the cosmological act, to coax the almost completed world into a state of full coherence. The questions that we ask will determine the answers that we get. Certain paintings might resist us; others might draw us in. Whatever our relative distance, if we were to look at one of her paintings for an hour every day, we would never see quite the same thing twice.

There are times when the artist herself is no more than a bystander, when she gladly lets go of her own name. At those times, she is no more than an inhalation that somehow comes back as a gesture. As viewers, we stand just behind the shoulder of the artist, almost mute. As she circles, so do we, in the breathing space just outside of the edges of the canvas. The painting reaches for the artist, and we watch her weave its electromagnetic fields into a net.

Here as elsewhere, we might believe that we do no more than observe. And yet... Without our distant but not so distant interaction with the artist, the painting may have turned out quite differently than it did. Only space divides our intuitions from those of Ozan-George. There are fields; no line is fixed. Were we not, in a way, present for the painting of the painting, we might see no more than pigments on a canvas. We might simply repeat, "My six-year-old could do it," the classic spell for the warding off of vision. We would not have accepted the artist's invitation to be where we were not. We would not have set out on a journey.

In Ozan-George's work, signs point us towards a technology of the vacuum, towards the method by which an unknown impulse became Nature, towards the birth of an archaic science from the ocean. As she steps back from the yolk of her steadily congealing nebula, from the ionized gas of the paint, from the resonance of the canvas, we can see the artist pause to take possession of an accident. Either choice or both may lead to a dark rift.

If the success or failure of the painting is unknown, if the artist is also unknown to herself, this lack of knowledge is a form of knowledge. She is as blank as might be necessary. To be open in the way that she desires to be open is to be able to touch everything at once. Fierce teachers protect her. Living mirrors have her back. Her hand signals to risk that it is welcome to approach. Her eyes hear and her ears see. Her nerves and muscles think. Her intellect is as tactile in its orientation as a snail. Her nose analyses the hieroglyphic chanting of a sky—a sky that long ago ceased to exist.

Once duplicated by Tesla, there is a tower ringed with electrocuted birds. From it, free energy flows. Like an incandescent coil, the artist pulls down the energy that is also a kind of information. Such energy is neither deadly nor benevolent in itself. A certain amount of transduction is required. X marks the painting. The artist's lack of preconceptions allows things to move through her, even as her method provides for just the right amount of resistance.

Even now, the first continents are thrusting from the ocean. The stars draw up their shadows from the waves. The artist is no more but no less present than a cloud, than the impulse that moves on the surface of the waters.

Yes, effort is needed, and a subtle quality of attention, as the conjuration leads around many twists and turns, out of dead ends, into many new false starts. These requirements apply to all concerned, to the artist and the viewer, to those powers evoked by the format, to those presences that assist in the squaring of the circle. The picture operates on a need-to-know basis. A master is only a beginner with experience. No less than the viewer, the artist must be continuously willing to test her mode of vision, to keep her cosmos intimate with chaos at its edges.

For the good work is the one that self-destructs, thus opening one's eyes. The "oeuvre" is the ovum: the already perfect museum gallery of the egg, from whose darkness the fingers of each work reach back to reconfigure the artist

On Back Roads, in a Car Whose Driver Has Gone Missing: A Eulogy for Robert George

Robert, Joyce, and Brian George, 1956

1

It was mid-October, 1997. Already past their peak, the leaves had started to fall. Cold had driven a few field mice to take refuge in our basement. Our cat would not kill them quickly. He liked to play with them for several hours first. Bees seemed to have lost their radar. They veered off at odd angles, banging into things. I dreamed of a city that the living had abandoned, a city where the shadows searched for their lost bodies, a city where the doors did not have any knobs. There were cars parked in the middle of the street. A dog ran by with a phonebook in its mouth. The Earth was turning. My wife Deni and I were happy. Our new daughter, Liz, was sleeping a bit longer every night. If you had asked, "Is there anything of great importance going on?" I would have said, "No, not really, not so far as I can tell."

It was mid-October, 1997. The year was darkening. Each day was a bit shorter. My father, Bob, and his third wife, Judith, had flown from Denver for a visit. On a complex tangle of back roads, we travelled to many of the places that he remembered from the 1950s, when, just out of Boston University, he was stationed at Fort Devens. The base—a 5000-acre installation in Ayer and Shirley, Massachusetts—was decommissioned in 1966. Through the decades, various pieces were removed. The 57 acres still open, it was said, were now used mostly for training, as well as for the storage of 800 or so vehicles. Devens residents had failed in their efforts to make it the state's 352nd town, and the area was now called a "regional enterprise zone and census-designated place." Behind the perimeter fence, the base held many secrets, the keys to bioengineered sub-systems of control, the results of many hundreds of half-voluntary tests. Who knew if an experiment was or was not legal? Not soldiers but their surrogates stood guard.

Except for the addition of a few satellite dishes, not all that much had changed since my father's days in Army Intelligence. Over here, a high-tech office park. Over there, a few rows of solar panels. If we did happen to drive by an anachronism of this type, it would quickly vanish in our rear-view mirror. No image dared to interrupt the quiet rustling of the trees. If Fort Devens was only 38 miles from Boston, it took years to travel from the one place to the other. To depart from the city was to depart from the monomania of the clock. The year was 1954, not 1997. It would be three more years before Sputnik was launched. In another two and one-half months, my father would be dead.

2

When we are young, our parents can seem to be giants. They have great control over the world and great authority. They exist in a mythic dimension. They cast enormous shadows as they move. It is wonderful to be held in the strong arms of the ruler of the world. We learn to take charge. We are never fully grown. It is hard to do without our magical intermediaries, the big birds who intercede with clouds on our behalf. When a parent dies, should he or she apologize for leaving us unprotected? If it is the job of our parents to strategically remove themselves, to push us into space, there are times when this removal is not at all strategic, when we find that we are not as well-prepared as we thought.

In the next stage, as we grow, our parents shrink to a more human scale. We see them eye to eye, as human beings like ourselves, and we begin to understand their limitations. Since we know all too well our own limitations, we begin, perhaps grudgingly, to accept the limitations of our parents. It would be good if this process were as automatic as the addition of new chambers to a nautilus. The situation is complicated by our having not one but two sets of parents. The mythic parents never do quite disappear; instead, they go underground to live inside of us. We are confronted outside by the human ones. There are children who, for years after a parent's death, will not forgive the one for not being the same as the other.

In the next stage, depending upon how long each person lives, the children might take on some part of the protective role of the parents. Bit by bit, we come to see that the Buddhist concept of impermanence is not purely theoretical. No, all things will change. The classic, three-dimensional images that have followed us from childhood can come to seem like scratched projections, and we cannot help but wonder if we have made the earlier versions of our parents up. We come to see our parents as not only limited but also as quite vulnerable and frail. Where we would hope to see the growth of wisdom, we might see only the contraction of the intellect, a growing fondness for clichés.

A few physical problems are all but inevitable. Then, bit by bit, with no real way to steer, the parent may drift into a twilit fog, into a chaos of fractured times and places, into a state not quite in this world but not yet in the next. The parent might tell the same stories many dozens of times over. To think, "We have heard these stories!" is to miss the point. This may be more than simple repetition. It may instead be a rehearsal, the first step of a process that will culminate after death, when all stories will be told and heard in a single moment.

In the last stage, finally, our parents move on to another world. We are left behind to confront those conflicts that have haunted us for decades, conflicts that we have gone out of our way to not see in sharp focus, all without the object of our annoyance being present. As our parents, with a sigh, may once have sent us off to kindergarten, so too, we must send them off to conduct their life-review and then into the space beyond. Death challenges us to develop a new and subtler relationship with these beings, who are not, in fact, either our parents or our children; rather, they are our companions on a journey to the ocean's unplumbed depth.

3

I would not have an opportunity to explore most of the third stage of this cycle—the stage of a ritual exchange of roles—with my father. His arches were bad, it was true, but he had no reason to assume that, at the age of 66, he was even starting to get old. He had bounced back from the crash of 1987, which had stripped him of 80 percent of his wealth, and he had big hopes for his new career in international business law. In a generation in which the majority of people had one or two careers, he had already had more than a half-dozen. Then, in early December of 1997, my father came down with pneumonia, a disease I thought would only slow him down for half a beat.

When I spoke with him on the phone at ten o'clock on New Year's Eve, he seemed unusually mellow. I asked if he had framed the drawing of a snake and bird that I had given him, and he asked if his granddaughter was talking yet. We discussed upcoming concerts, some problems he experienced with the winterizing of his boat, and whether or not he should join a firm or practice law by himself. The next day, he was dead, killed by his doctors, who had given him three medications that should never have been taken together. For months after, when the phone rang, I was certain that I would pick it up to hear his voice. I was left to wonder how the phone company could have made so many mistakes.

During that trip to Boston in October, 1997, I noticed that my father's hair had turned from silver to white. He no longer enjoyed long walks. He wanted to park his rental car at the front door of any building we were visiting rather than walking the few extra steps. The normal signs of aging seemed to have all at once appeared. Just a year before, he had been talking about the dangers of white-water rafting. Now, he sighed and shifted back and forth in his seat at Symphony Hall, unable to get comfortable. For the first time, my father began to seem like an old man. I thought that he might develop a few health problems. It seemed like such a short time ago that he had started law school at the age of 59, bringing to it the enthusiasm of someone 20 years younger. I felt proud to have a father so willing to start again, to begin where he was and face life head on.

Now, he seemed just a bit frail and cantankerous rather than difficult in his earlier way. But what a wonderful visit that was! Speeding at 80 miles an hour through the autumn foliage, we traveled to the Bull Run Inn outside Fort Devens, where he had been stationed in 1954, the year that I was born. At the Inn, he remembered the name of the cryptozoological creature, the Egopantis, whose head hung above the fireplace. I almost cried to watch him playing with his new granddaughter, Elizabeth, then seven months old. Back in Boston a few days later, we went to a service at Emmanuel Church, where he was overjoyed to find her clapping along to Bach and Schutz.

At the Isabella Stewart Gardner Museum, he was spellbound by the courtyard, which reminded him of the smaller one of his lost house in Mexico City. In an atypical burst of eloquence, he treated us to a lecture on the history of courtyards. He would more often say, "I went here. I saw that." He might, for example, say, "That was the year that I first heard Yo Yo Ma at Tanglewood. He played Prokofiev's Sinfonia Concertante in E Minor. A strong performance. Bernstein conducted. A few of us went to a get-to-gether afterwards. Bernstein brought his boyfriend. He drank too much, and he decided to change into some blue velour briefs with a flowing cotton robe."

Thoughts of his lost house on Avenida de los Insurgentes, where he hobnobbed with Somoza, led to thoughts of his student flat above Louisburg Square, with its wrought iron fence, with its statue of Columbus holding a compass and a globe. How many unexpected turns his life had taken since the 1950s, when, after giving up his dream of becoming a cellist, he first moved from Michigan to attend the BU School of Engineering. How formal were the colleges of those days, when you had to ask permission to even loosen the knot in your tie. How he was not able to sit down for a week after being paddled during the initiation at his frat house. At a time when beer was not allowed, how much they all had to drink.

Thoughts of the house where he grew up in Holland, Michigan, where his neighbors would scrub the sidewalks with soap and water every morning, led to thoughts about his father's frustrations as a milkman, his early death—at the age of 48—and a family secret that he had never before mentioned. How he had discovered a used condom in the back seat of their car, how he would not forgive himself for accusing the wrong parent.

Thoughts of the large dining room windows of the town, designed so that passersby could judge the order of each household, led to thoughts about his mother's undiagnosed mental illness, her off and on confinement at the Lakeshore Hospital, her sudden conversion from strict Dutch Reform Calvinism when she wanted to start a family dance band. How quickly, with her husband's passing, she had managed to become sane. How, during her 20 years as an x-ray technician, she seldom called in sick. How she managed to outlast all five of her husbands.

My father's mood was contagious, and it surrounded us like the smell of just burnt leaves. There was no way to locate Holland on a map. Black waterfalls had swallowed the toy houses of his youth. Where Holland was, there was only a deep chasm.

How strange that he dragged us from a meal at his favorite restaurant to see a jazz trio he had picked from a listing in the

Boston Globe, a group of which he had never heard. (I was still getting used to the idea that he did not see jazz as a suspect form of music. He must have come of age at just the right time in the 1950s, when Dave Brubeck was big, when jazz was moving out of bars and nightclubs and into college auditoriums.) As we were finding our way to our seats, I realized that the pianist looked familiar. Out of the dozens of performances taking place that night, my father had picked one led by a person that I knew. This was a person I had met at parties thrown by Elizabeth's godfather, Steve Provizer.

Stars sparkled as we left the French Library at the end of the performance. Back and forth we walked along a half-mile stretch of Commonwealth Ave., unable to find the car in which we had come. Back and forth we walked along the intersecting and the parallel streets. The car had not been stolen, vandalized, or towed. It was, after a convoluted search, somehow waiting there in front of us, in the spot where we had started.

That October visit was full of quiet joy. It was as calm as moonlight on the surface of a lake, under which move currents that can grab hold of the ankles. We were pulled down into memory. We were pulled down further still. We intuited an emotion moving towards us from the future, a valedictory nostalgia. We coasted without a driver over unpaved roads.

5

At the beginning of the second stage, I had been out of touch with my father for 11 years, while he was trying to build a new life for himself and his second family in Mexico City, in a 24-room house on the Avenida de los Insurgentes. As we were walking from the train I pointed out a car, a silver Mercedes, which I saw as being a model of classic good design. "I have never had a license and have no interest in cars," I said, "but if I did have a car, I would not mind owning that one." It turned out to be the exact image of the car he owned. We also shared a taste for butcher block furniture, for Mesoamerican artifacts, for Oceanic masks, and for shells and driftwood and rusted anchors and other objects from the ocean. His second wife and my first wife both shared a bent towards melodrama. We both preferred—at that time—small instrumental groups to symphonies.

This was, however, a period of some conflict. We inhabited different worlds. My father was devoted to business. I was just beginning to explore various spiritual practices and wanted to find some way to integrate my spiritual and poetic goals. In an effort to be helpful, he had shown samples of my poetry to his most educated friends. All of them thought it was terrible. One had apparently described it as "a form of grandiose masturbation." Perhaps I would like some money to go back to school to study business? "No thanks," I said, "but I could use some money for next month's rent." He believed that I should "take my place in the world, as a man among men." "That's a catchy phrase," I said, "I think that I've heard it somewhere before."

He approached my conversion from poetry with the single-mindedness of a corporate raider preparing for a takeover, with the measured excitement of a serial killer planning his first kill. In 1984, after a particularly big blowout, I broke off all contact with him for perhaps a year and a half.

Then, in 1989, the ground beneath us shifted. I had once more started to do artwork. We were both surprised, if not shocked, to find that he liked the art as much as he hated the poetry. Perhaps I was not wasting my time, and I might have some idea of what I was doing after all. I had come to understand, as well, how much it had taken out of him to set aside his dream of a career in classical music, to redefine his relationship to the cello, to tell others that his love was no more than a flirtation. To be an adult was to live in the real world. To do this was to give things up; it was to learn to treat one's calling as a hobby. In his own mind, my father was only saying that I should follow in his footsteps. He was unaware of the cold anger that darkened his suggestion. The subtext of his comments on my poetry seemed to be, "I have suffered. Few would guess how much. It is not fair that you should get off any easier."

Curiously, however, the conflicts of this period were not so much resolved as put aside. We came to realize how much we both looked forward to our visits, how much we simply enjoyed spending time together. We had been divided by our similar, and very willful, natures. For far too many years, each would not give the other permission to be who and what he was. Then, more or less suddenly, we found that we were the casual observers of a truce.

6

In speaking of the first stage, when my father was a giant, let me share three memories from childhood. The first is the most recent. The last one is the earliest.

I remember driving up winding roads, at 80 miles an hour, on a rainy day to Tanglewood. My father had borrowed a 1950s Triumph sports car from a friend. My seat was tilted back, and I was very much aware that I was sitting no more than six inches over the road. Let me say this a different way: the road was speeding by six inches underneath me. The fog was dense. Rabbits, deer, foxes, and pheasants would pop up, only to disappear a split-second before we hit them. With its smudges of green and gray, the landscape was as insubstantial as the fog. It was only there, perhaps, because we had both agreed to see it. On certain hairpin turns, I decided to perform a test: there was nothing beyond us when I closed my eyes. Still, I knew that one wrong move could result in our spinning off the road. We could flip over, burst into flame, or hurtle into a tree. I was scared, yes, but my father was driving. The car hugged the road, and I knew that we would get to the sheds at Tanglewood soon.

Tanglewood, an outdoor music center in the Berkshires, was the summer home of the Boston Symphony Orchestra. My father was proud to have such a highly cultured son, for I insisted on going to Tanglewood at every available opportunity. He assumed that this was due to a love of classical music. He was wrong. I liked the smell of pine trees and being far away from the city. My big secret reason, though, was that I loved the box lunches that they sold there. The sandwiches were great. The cardboard boxes that they came in were beautifully constructed. Even then, I liked to make things, and boxes were one of my favorite things to make. If only the same genius had designed Brahms' German Requiem.

That year, for my birthday, my father sent me a recording of Prokofiev's Seventh Symphony. The symphony, which premiered, in 1952, as part of a radio programme for a Soviet youth orchestra, is supposedly in Prokofiev's "simplest" style, although, oddly, it is also in C-sharp minor, one of the bleakest of all keys. It may have been written for a youth orchestra, but only an adult would think of it as a child-friendly piece. I played the record once. I didn't listen to it again for eight years. Then, at the age of 16, I finally did develop a love of classical music.

On a trip, we stayed in a white motel by the ocean. We woke up at dawn to go fishing. The smell was a complex one: salt air, disinfectant from the motel, frying eggs and bacon, gasoline from the boat motors, weathered wood, dead fish. You could hear the cables creaking, and the outboard motors sputtering, and the foghorns from the tugboats. When we left the motel, the fog had already started to thin out. It would soon be no more than a thin film on the water. The sun was red, but the overnight temperature had not yet risen much. Bouncing up and down on our toes, we zipped up our spring jackets.

There were seagulls everywhere. They perched on roofs, and on telephone wires, and on most of the posts of the wharf. They had sharp beaks, and we watched as they competed to rip apart a pigeon, which was almost, but not 100 percent, dead. The frozen fish packing plant was their base of operations. My father asked, "Do you think that they call it a base or a town hall or a church?" We speculated that they had gathered there to perform their civic duties. My father said, "They are probably voting on how much fish to eat!" There was no part of the beach that the gulls did not patrol. Even miles out from the shore, you could see them circling the commercial fishing boats, even though these boats had not yet cast their nets.

On the dock, we stepped into a shop with weathered planks, where we rented a small motorboat. We spent a half-hour looking at the deep-sea fishing lures, with their colorful jointed bodies, staring eyes, naturalistic details, and three-pronged razor-sharp hooks. I was hoping that we would go with a few of these. But no; instead, we bought two cans of worms. No fan of worms to begin with, I was horrified by the type of multi-legged sea worms that we bought, which kept biting and writhing and wrapping themselves around us. We never did catch any fish, but I will never forget how fearlessly my father handled the sea worms, how gently he leaned down to unwrap them from my fingers.

It was another overcast day. We traveled in a Jaguar with cracked leather seats to a museum located somewhere in Connecticut. The museum was old, and it had ivy climbing up the walls. I think that this was probably the Peabody Museum of Natural History at Yale, built in 1866, and featuring, or so it is said, over "12 million specimens and objects from Anthropology to Entomology to

Zoology to Paleontology." In any event, we went there, and we stayed for the whole afternoon.

The museum was cavernous, and it echoed. Two or three rings of balconies surrounded the central atrium, within which towered the dinosaurs. These were held together with wire, glue, and metal braces. To me, the braces did not look very strong at all, whereas the dinosaurs still did. Almost certainly, they could free themselves, and it seemed as if they were getting ready to step towards us.

So wonderfully frightened were we, so transfixed by the ancient bones, that we lost track of the hours ticking by. At 6:30 or so, we heard the clank of switches being thrown. We noticed that the museum was much darker than before. The doors at the bottom of all the stairwells had been locked. One after the other, we went down each of them, only to have to climb up once again.

Only a few of the lights were still on. It was so quiet that you could hear the footsteps of a mouse. If you listened, however, the space was not actually all that quiet; it was as resonant as the inside of a shell. My father believed that a misfortune was a terrible thing to waste. He would find some way to turn it into an adventure. As we wandered around the balconies, we waited for the first crack of breaking metal, for the creak of a neck bone, for the turning of a head. We looked back over our shoulders. We wondered which of the sleeping giants might also be studying us. Those giants were scary, but my father was intelligent, and strong. He was also a kind of giant. I was very much content to be there for the night, and I did not especially want the guard to let us out.

7

At the age of 65, I am now a year younger than my father was when he passed. I can see how his partial absence was a gift, just as much as my mother's selflessness. Let me pause here to say, "Thank you." Let me set aside my biography. Let me exit through a keyhole. Let me reassemble my body on the other side of the door. Having cleared the sky, I would reinvent the wheel. I would seed the abyss with my voice. My family tree is the ocean.

As Henry Ford said, "History is bunk"

Snake Arising out of Pot, 1990

On August 23rd, 1990, I was shown how time, as we have come to understand it, does not actually exist. I disappeared that day. I came to see my life as a habit, even an addiction. How to tell my friends? How to demonstrate to the public? How to pay the appropriate tribute to my feet? Few since have seen more than the image I project. In my heart: a multitude, the great majority of whom I had no desire to know. How convenient it would have been if death were a solution. Who would not want to relax? The body's death, however, was no more than a caesura, a question that slipped from our grasp, a challenge that we long ago postponed. Time and space are "illusions," as was argued by the earliest of Vedic seers, but what exactly does this concept mean?

As regards the archaic mode of understanding, in place of the word "illusion" we should probably substitute "art." The world that we inhabit is a form of play, a projection of the omnivorous potency of Maya, a form of magic, of which we are the proponents, now grown frail. We should not insult Maya; it is our memories that are bad.

Our numbers were once few. Our domes: broken. Our culture: scattered. Only threads of our former language could be found. Words had once cantilevered their own contradictory meanings. Those were the days. Key consonants had been lost. The sixth vowel: subject to ongoing speculation. We would subdivide our memory. From a seed, we would speak a stadium. Our promise to foreign contestants was as follows: All would exit as they entered. Who could guess how many of the game's rules would be bent? Some glitch has obscured the source code of the torus.

Once, the Model T gave access to the line of the horizon, to pine forests and the Great Salt Lake, as well as to the mounds heaped by a derelict race of giants. The Interstate Highway System then sprung up from its wheel-tracks. Now, it often seems as though there is nothing left to discover. Like the snake, Vritra, who froze the waters of the Himalayas, the Model T has swallowed every vista that it opened. It is for this reason that we must break the mirror of our projections, and then, with heart in hand, step though.

I have heard some physicists theorize that space is absolutely flat, and that it goes on, without change, in an infinitely straight line. Space cooperates in providing evidence for this illusion. If we follow this straight line, however, we will find that we are following an infinitely vast curve, a scaled-up version of the Earth's circumference.

Q: "Does this straight line have an end?" A: "Did you cry when you were forced to exit from the womb?" Q: "What goes on four legs in the morning, two at noon, and three at dusk?" A: "How old is Canis major?"

When we have all but forgotten the point that gave us birth, we will come upon the ship we left bobbing in the harbor, with its sail that swells like an excited breast, with its wide eyes that we painted on the prow. We will come upon those versions of ourselves still waiting to depart. Self will cancel self, and we will hear the roar of the waterfalls that plunge through the abyss. There are some who will no doubt fall. Others will be suspended on a breath. Should we find some way to put aside our fear, we may feel the first of 108 Vedas begin to form behind our lips. We may hear the first of the 10,800 stanzas that have waited for an eon to exit from our mouths.

On the downslope of Peak Oil, we now mourn the passing of our false friends, petrochemicals. We may soon be forced to reeducate our feet. Q: "Where did the North Pole go?" A: "Thirty-four miles west. Your GPS has betrayed you. All guidance will be graded on a curve." Q: "What is movement? Do you move?" A: "Sirius A is orbited by the "white dwarf" Sirius B. The orbital period is 50 years." Q: "What happened to your water bottle? Is it part of some larger life form?" A: "Square miles: 617,000, number of units: an estimated 1.8 trillion, one of five "offshore plastic accumulation zones," weighing more than 43,000 cars, the Pacific Garbage Patch spreads tenfold every decade." Q: "Should

I learn the names of the stars?" A: "A coronal mass ejection may soon wipe out much of the internet."

Viruses now claim to be our equals in intelligence. Facebook bans the Venus of Willendorf. 2020: Arctic temperatures climb to 104 degrees. Shell and Exxon lead the "oil rush." One in four Americans would side with the Inquisition against Kepler. Comets tweak their schedules. Orbital cameras cannot figure out which of several Earths to photograph. Costing $82 million per jet, F-35As spontaneously combust. Kudzu vines launch kamikaze raids on the Center for Applied Genomics.

In the end, proving far more mobile than we thought, the Sun will resign from its patriarchal role. A few cities, here and there, will fly. The alphabet will then retreat into its roots, and a wave will take apart the black technology of the gods.

The smog grows dense. Vision becomes difficult. Pink sunsets subvert the latest breakthroughs in transhumanism. The Earth looks small, too small for our once vast alchemical designs. There was a hypersphere to which we once had vowed to be of service. Its light was too bright to observe directly. Who knows what went wrong? There were shards that hid behind the tilt of the ecliptic, whose designs we could not read, whose urges we had no way to control.

The body's death was one of the simpler of the obstacles we faced. There were other deaths beyond that, not all of which led to the day of our return. To one side, a gulf; to the other, an abyss. There was a shore that acted as a magnet to our hearts. Only waves are left, the echoes we plumb to salvage a few stories. Courting seizures, for we had heard they were a source of unpredictable new sensations, we have scheduled our eyeballs to roll back in their sockets.

Such is art. Such is the labyrinthine stealth that it demands. Such are the sleights-of-hand of the Magician, the snares into which he steps. Were it not for Maya, were it not for the gifts that she so joyously bestowed, there was nothing we did that we would have had the power to do. Were it not for Maya, we would have no wealth of which to speak. Our memories would be almost altogether blank, even blanker, that is, than they are.

Q: "Did you follow the road of excess?" A: "No. No media empire should have boundaries." Q: "Did you follow the road of excess?" A: "Yes. The wheel tracks led from Malta straight into the ocean." Q: "Did you follow the road of excess?" A: "Yes. The light was beautiful. It led to a split atom." Q: "Did you follow the road of excess?" A: "No. I had no need to. Are you stupid? I am Shiva."

Who can estimate the number bad actors they have killed, or call their faces up? Our words go mad as they circle, unable to find the cultures to which they correspond. Glaciers the size of Manhattan now break off from their shelves. Methane burbs from the sinkholes of Siberia. The continents are a puzzle whose pieces move as they see fit. Our sense of irony: next to useless. We may be forced to pare our aesthetics to the bone. We may be prompted to rethink our definitions of good health.

At the dawn of the Dvapara Yuga, after years of scarcely breathing, moving only to adjust the balance of the North Star on one foot, we had linked our hands to dance upon the surface of the waters, laughing as we felt the rising force of our intent. In one ear and out the other, through our heads blew a wind composed of all past ages.

When we spoke, we were able to call forth wonders from the depths—cities coaxed into bloom from the pistil of a flower, flights of geometric wrath, whole histories that an earlier race had stored inside an atom, bridges stretched between the constellations, the insertion of good teachers into statues, visions broken into self-explanatory steps. When we spoke, the extent of our achievements astonished even us—the music of the spheres made audible, add-water-and-mix geniuses, armies made from clouds, iron thunderbolts untucked from the spiral of a shell, auroras acting out the shape of every letter, our enemies: reduced to the four elements, the sky turned black at noon.

Of the skyline, only a slight glow is left. We must illuminate ourselves. Q: "Who invented the Geiger Counter?" A: "We do not need one to detect the bursts of static from our hands." Q: "What happened to the books that you once wrote on the ocean?" A: "No methods now allow us to determine where these are. We are far too busy to read." The Rudras' roaring has been muted. The Adityas flutter like torn banners on the wind. Moths flash like the souls of departed corporate logos.

Time, without passing, turns back on itself. Our nerves and bones become translucent. We may, as the weight of the whole planet presses on our lungs, be tempted to shrug off the debt we owe to Maya, to claim she showed us more than we had ever asked to know. We might as well remove our tongues. We might as well claim that we are innocent observers. What we asked to see, we saw. What we asked to have, we found. Where we asked to go, we went. How strange it is that each day we grow younger. How strange that we do not know how to play. We barely pause to take note of the pivot, Druvaloka, around which blink the Seven Teachers in their stars. As we drift towards thermodynamic death, we may be tempted to forget that space itself was first conjured as our vehicle.

Descent to the Merkavah

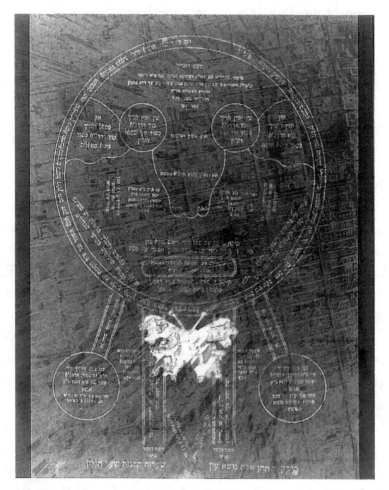

Adam Kadmon, photogram, 2002

Man's quest for immortality, to "live forever," or to be self-sustaining in one way or another is modeled most economically by the vortex. "Looking into the world," he observed the vortex in fire, wind, and water, and in the weave patterns of the heavens above, etc. When, whether

consciously or subconsciously, he recognized that vortexes
represent "the only manner by which a self-sustaining
motion can exist in a given medium" (Arthur M. Young), he
would naturally have gravitated to such an idea—specifically,
the idea that a vortex appears to be *other* than the medium
which sustains it, but actually it is one *with* the medium
within which it exists.

—from Martin Farren, *In the Mirror of Creation*

1

My explorations in Kabbalah and Kundalini Yoga had led me in
and out and upside down through the convolutions of an arcane
curve, and deposited me, at a different turn of the torus, again
exactly in the place where I had started. It was in this position
that I always found myself, as a stranger with a social slot to fill,
as a non-local presence with a local job to perform, as an ancient
soul at a perpetual beginning.

As from a height, I had descended to a vehicle, and, from solid
earth, into a state of watery flux. There, the laws of electromag-
netism could not be taken at face value. My involution followed
one path recommended to the student of Kabbalah, the "Path of
Descent," which was also the path taken by the first imploding
hypersphere and its crop of unpronounceable gods. They do not
have faces, as such. They go by a vast multitude of names, some
deactivated, some still dangerously potent. We should pause to
consider before speaking any one of these out loud. Let us call
them here, for the sake of convenience, the "Elohim."

Once, the Elohim were one. Then, they were no longer. Six
went forth from their circle to take stock of the wastelands. The
force of their desire swelling, a strange intoxication may have
seized them. If it was they who lifted the first city from the

Deluge, to do this they had, paradoxically, to descend. Their arc was downwards, of necessity, through the surface of the waters and towards the bowels of the deep, towards the shards of former worlds, which glowed.

In the Ugaritic Baal cycle, we read of the "Seventy Sons of Asherah," El's consort. These potencies are each thought to have inseminated a culture. The name Elohim is a generic one, which means "The Active Potencies of God," "The Powers," or "The Gods." In contemporary terms, we could perhaps refer to them as "The Powers That Be." We suspect, only, that they are powers now, although, in some respects, they may seem close to being programs. When, amid flashing lights, these powers put in an appearance, there can seem to be something of the hologram about them, as if they had put on bodies for our benefit, as if they were defined by the archetypes that possess them. In spite of the dramatic impression that they make, it is not clear to what extent they really "act" at all. We do not know what these powers were before, or how they came to be in charge of the technology that projects us. We can only guess at how history may have changed them.

When these presences paused to contemplate their outlines on the water, they may have set in motion a process that spun quickly out of control. Shocked by the terrifying beauty of their features, they may have searched for incarnate followers who were more afraid than they were, whose young eyes gave them hope, whose offerings would turn their guilt at plunging from the stars into a virtue. As the eons passed, in debt to their images, nostalgic for the cultures that their followers had expunged, the Elohim may have found that they were anything but free. No, it was they, quite strangely, whom others now had to lift. Now others must fit the pieces of the Seed-Sphere back together.

When the Elohim spoke, their words may have had far more resonance than they knew. They may have been hypnotized by the eyes of the masks that they created. They may have been lured into the ever more complex spiral of their project. Blunted by habit, the scope of their memory may be far less comprehensive than it was. It may now, perhaps, be only somewhat better than our own.

Like the cities they once occupied, these powers have been overgrown by roots. Their heads have turned against their feet. They have been sucked beneath the desert and the ocean. When, at random moments, they do choose to appear, they no longer seem able to understand how much light is enough, how to speak so that humans can hear one word at a time. Face-to-face communication was not meant to be so difficult. As these powers descended, we were scheduled to ascend. Some glitch has corrupted the system. Our energies have not aligned. If the stories about this early race have not been lost to public view, they have, at a minimum, been hopelessly cut, torn, spindled, burnt, and mutilated. These stories have not disappeared; they have simply been implanted. They have been buried beneath years of scholarship, infected by cult attachments, warped by moral pontifications.

"These powers are good," say some, "for we choose to misinterpret all of the evil that they do. Without them, we could never have determined the location of our navels. We would have no line of descent. Our culture would have been killed before it ever left the womb." "These powers are evil," say others, "for they have shattered the once perfect world. They have caused us to look with fear upon the depths of our awareness. They have taken from our eyes the day of our return, and they do not understand what it feels like to be human."

Preferring to believe that our shadows are not dark, we have scarred the Earth with the tool marks of our unfulfilled desires, desires that will not, cannot, and should not be fulfilled. Our manic-depressive hopes for total cleansing by an apocalypse do not really help to illuminate the matter. World destruction would be too simple a solution. It is clear that we are as innocent as children. No trauma will convince us that our judgment has been flawed. We are the victims of a labyrinthine pattern of deception, of a plot as tangled as the neocortex, as dark as the shadows that we have managed to misplace.

By definition, The Powers That Be must be responsible for the light that haunts our dreams, for our horror at the shadows that we cast. Our intellects cannot penetrate their radioactive cloud, and, should we look on them directly, it is possible that our hearts would beat themselves to death. No, such a death would serve no purpose. Instead, we must make use of a different set of eyes, for the ones that we have been issued are prosthetic. We must remember how to see from all of 360 degrees. We must learn to think with our hearts. We must learn to feel with the group-intellect of our ancient micromanagers, those powers that false teachers have convinced us are a threat. Annoyed though they might be with our lack of ritual etiquette, we must once more share some portion of our food.

We must take back what is ours, even as we dare to freely give away our wealth. What fear should we have of the night? What fear should we have of the day? What fear should we have of the Elohim, our relatives? How much energy should we spend in continuing with the argument? Who knows what it was about? We must enter through the keyhole at the base of a tornado. We must once more learn to make love to the wind, as we look with cool disinterest on the bones that we abandoned. We must simultaneously speak each syllable in the Ur-Text, even we, the wide-eyed children of catastrophe, however much the cacophony is too painful for our ears. At first, it was All for One. Then later, it was Every Man for Himself. Later yet, we must serve as midwives for the rebirth of the Zero. We must put our trust in the depth and breadth of our experience, in order to revisit the many places that we have been.

2

We must stop time. We must separate our vision from the quirks of our biographies. We must separate our breathing from our cultural displacements. As if the ocean that divides us from our homeland were a sheet, we must smooth out some of its wrinkles. As we hover a few inches over it, we may still be able to view and then decipher the almost invisible outlines of our movements. Thus, the motives of this early race are obscure, but can be guessed:

The desire to share their accumulated wealth, which was great.

The desire to see and/or make things happen.

The desire to remove one's head—its awful vastness, and thus to escape from the burdens that are built into omnipotence.

After eons of silence, the desire to explode.

The desire to seize Beauty by the hair.

The desire to get drunk, to pick a fight, to have sex, to wake up somewhere strange.

The desire to make a weapon of geometry.

The desire to test one's strength against the ocean, to put one's shoulder to the wheel.

The desire to make a name for oneself.

The desire to bind others to one's cause, to manufacture a consensus.

The desire to express oneself, to which end one must have a particular point of view.

The desire to live life, to learn from suffering, and to outlast death.

The desire to make a mark on the big dream that is history.

The desire to make a complete break with the past.

The desire to be empty, after being pregnant with a world.

The desire to discover the beginning of the circle, its ancient origin, to thus inhabit the lost story one has read.

The desire to be many, after being one, and to be one, after being many.

The desire to give the gift that keeps on giving.

The desire to transmit the knowledge, to cut the fruit of one's longevity.

The desire to pose questions to a seed, to listen when it speaks, to shrink as the seed grows.

The desire to see one's children set off on their own.

The desire, after years of tranquil music, to not recognize one's language.

The desire to be free of all artistic styles, all rules that one created, to remove one's name from books, one's statues from their columns.

The desire to see one's city swallowed by a scream.

The desire to again throw caution to the wind, to be joyous, to be lost, to go where one is led.

The desire of the magician to say farewell to his powers.

The desire to be swept off by a wave.

Yes, the motives of this early race are obscure, as are those of their descendants in the present. Their psyches are not other than our own. As the serpent-force revolts against the magic of the microcosm—from head to heart to genitals to feet, then back again to head—I can hear the Elohim conjuring the dense Ur-Text of my body. However strange or familiar, their actions follow a predetermined course.

3

Let us say that we desire to cross consciously from one world to another. Let us say that, as things fall apart, we desire to be actors, that we would do more than simply observe the electromagnetic shift, we must, paradoxically, somehow make our activity passive. We must be willing to set aside our normal desire for control. In Kabbalah, the first stage of the process is referred to as "going down to the chariot" or "descent to the Merkavah." A modern phrase similar in structure, if not in exact meaning, might be "descent to the unconscious," as this was used by Freud and Jung.

If the goal of this descent, as in psychotherapy, is to heal, it is not to heal ourselves; rather, it is to repair the rip that runs through the structure of the cosmos. Some would argue that this rip is virtual, but it is nonetheless problematic. It would be useful, perhaps, to view it as the time-lapse movement of a lightning bolt, a bolt that creates, destroying as it falls, a bolt that invigorates what it cannot help but kill, a bolt that has just now struck the iron tip of a tornado, beneath which we have built our homes.

Blinding as it illuminates, there is a lightning flash that gives birth to the world that we perceive. What we think we see is the afterimage, now haunted and mechanically preserved, of a stage-set that was long ago destroyed. So too with the Elohim, those powers who chose to join us in our exile, who may have long since been translated, who may have shrugged out of their shells. Our eyes cannot penetrate their radioactive cloud; we see only according to the manner of our seeing. Each thing may have happened a great many times before. For what reason, then, are we experiencing these particular events now? A sense of vertigo compels us to clutch those objects close at hand.

Let us say that the world is a habit of projection. It does move, but it seems to do so only in a horizontal circle, which causes us to feel trapped. We are not free, because upon it we have fixed our eyes. Quite strangely, we do not know what our faces actually look like, nor can we, until such time as we have exited from the world. Until then, they are as featureless as the dark side of the sun. We must depart from what we know in order to find out what we are. It is by going down that we gain access to the eye of primordial energy, to the nothingness on which our something has been built. If we go down further still, we will be shocked to find that this nothingness is a convenience of our speech, that it comes complete with its own geometric form. We will find that an eye snaps open. We will find that danger calls. We will find that our primal energy can be entered like a vehicle. Thus we will go from here, where we are not, to there, where there is nothing to obstruct us.

And so: why are we directed to go down instead of up? Perhaps it is because ascent implies a strenuous effort at improvement, a clutching at what is out of reach, a desire to become bigger when we should, instead, become smaller. Perhaps it is because the preexistent beings, which we have here referred to as the Elohim, descended towards the chaos of the primordial waters, there to speak the words that began the world, there to instigate the march of evolution. Conversely, we might also see this as the march of devolution, because all species have descended out of Adam's DNA, which had not yet been unzipped from the DNA of Eve. There is a point on the dark horizon, now infinitely small. It is from this point that we humans have descended.

And so: why are we directed to go down instead of up? Perhaps it is because descent implies disintegration, a requirement for new growth. Perhaps it is because biogenesis is just a prep-course for cosmogenesis, for a delivery to occur at the end of a great war. Perhaps it is because each city, when it burns, collapses into the rubble of an even older city. And so: why are we directed to go down instead of up? Perhaps it is because Death is the most attentive nurse, the magician beloved by manikins. Perhaps it is because we assume that the "higher self" is good. Perhaps it is because we are terrified of the shadow that protects us. Perhaps it is because the end of all descent has been geometrically encoded in its origin.

And so: why are we directed to go down instead of up? Perhaps it is because, appearances to the contrary, our catalytic agents are not actually out to harm us, and they are doing no more and no less than instructed. Perhaps it is because our dismemberment will hurt less than we think, because, at the most difficult of moments, our essence will detach itself. Perhaps it is because vision is not something to be sought, because it comes when there is little or nothing left to lose. Perhaps it is because it is important to relax.

And so: why are we directed to go down instead of up? When we go down we return as to a vehicle, a vehicle buried beneath dense archeological strata, a vehicle humming the whole time in the ground beneath our feet. This vehicle is the Merkavah. Such a vehicle is not different from the absence that is space. Tilting back and forth at an angle to the aeon, a vortex will set in motion the dead body of our language. The self, without moving from one spot, will find that little has been left undone. Events will run backwards, returning to the future world. We must take full advantage of this primitive mode of transport, for, without it, we will not be able to travel as far as we need to go.

4

Upon my exit from the hieroglyphic vortex, few of my contemporaries could even be bothered to admit that I had stood the world on its ear. Thus it was necessary to postpone my transvaluation of all values. The revolution that I had launched did not even seem to exist. Such is the traveler's pathos. Such is the poet's joy. Truly, this revolution was arcane in its goals. By the most psychotically complex of geometries, my race had hidden its intentions even from itself. Even I, the slightly more informed, knew just enough to prevent my premature extinction.

We had pulled a gigantic wave above our heads. We had caused the sky to tilt. We had long ago forgotten that our choice was not a punishment. Each day, we went to work, where we dragged our feet and pretended to be bored. Each night, we sped off to take part in god knows what. In our hands, a variety of archaic scalar weapons. On our lips, an ecstatic chant, from a planet that the Death Star had exploded. Thus we flew beneath the radar of the Lords of Industry and Commerce. My army was made up of straw dogs—very lazy!—who did not want to get burnt.

With our capacity to be both everywhere and nowhere, we would reassemble the once perfect world. We would bridge the gulf between sleep and waking, a gulf which may, in the end, prove no more than a construct. We would redraw the maps that our ancient teachers hid. We would reenact the path of our descent, its labyrinthine series of curves, the reshuffling of the letters that had swept us from our homes, only to find that the sphere's navel led to its circumference, only to find that a few seconds had gone by. We would throw back our heads and laugh. We would be forced to acknowledge the superior science of the Ancients.

At the Museum of Unnatural History, we would wander among the statues that a race of birdmen left, those statues whose bones and organs are translucent. We would note, as we have in visits past, that their veins are petrified lightning, that their eyes are burnt out suns, that their nerves are the dry riverbeds of once enlightened cultures. We would ask, as we have so many times before, "But why do their faces look so much like ours, with their wide eyes that have never ceased to stare? And if, in fact, they actually do breathe, then why is this breathing almost imperceptibly slow?"

I have heard the roaring and the droning of the Ur-text when the Powers That Be sing simultaneously the syllables of each line. To some, it might sound like chaos. From the center to the circumference, and from the future, in 12 directions, back, in order that we have space to act, the one sphere must be emptied. For it is in the nature of high energy to descend, as it is in the nature of free energy to flow. From the fog of souls, the tides of all potential versions of events, I have seen how my descent has followed in the path of a lost race, who had not, as it turns out, ever really agreed to put aside their magic. Each thing has a certain "tendency to exist." It was my job to coagulate the ocean.

Birds of a Feather and the Playthings of the Twelve

Sideways Bird's Head with Vortices, 2003

1

O you who would come against me in obstruction, come to me, come to me! I detest travelling in darkness, for then I cannot see those who are upside down.

—The Pyramid of Unas Text

Just as every human may have one or more animal forms, so too, every animal may have one or more humanoid forms. "Therianthropes," or "man-animals," are some of the oldest images in the history of art. They often appear on surfaces that are covered with zigzags, arcane symbols, and geometric patterns, all indications of hallucinatory transport. In some cases, these figures are clearly shamans, who have undergone a transformation. In other cases, they appear to be interdimensional beings—of some indeterminate anatomy, perhaps, whatever the masks they wear—who have chosen to appear in a particular hybrid form.

Long ago, the ocean spoke. The color of the sun had not yet been determined. A seal was then placed on the top part of the skull. Who knows when, or by whom? Now, the waves go mad. We rent our eyes and ears from big media conglomerates. To stare into the sun is painful. We Moderns eat, we distract ourselves, we reproduce, we die. Therianthropes play by a different set of rules, so that one sky leads without break to another. Just as the shaman discovers his antlers in the pregnant cloud of archetypes, his counterpart bends to choose a more or less human face. Their vision is not bound by any one perspective. Knowledge causes their shared body to convulse.

But why have certain of these therianthropes been transfixed by spears and arrows, sometimes by the dozen? While studying this handful of variations of the prototype, I felt a shiver go down my back. My stomach knotted up. "Should we read these lines as acupuncture needles," I thought, "that proto-Taoists have placed within a network of meridians, thus opening the therianthrope to a flood of primordial energy? No, it is probably best to be practical; these projectiles are the technocratic probes of the Nephilim, those rulers returned from the mists of the Younger Dryas, from the light of an alternate sun, whose doctors now seek to reconstitute the genome."

One action would be "good"; the other would be "bad." Each would present us with the ultimatum: "Learn." What percentage of our experience do we dare to welcome back? To perfect our stealth is to begin to understand how we are pathologically driven to take sides. Faux naiveté does not serve the voyager well. He must suffer until his vision clears.

Let us imagine that we have travelled to the Eastern Free State of South Africa. A San petroglyph is before us. The artist has stretched a figure diagonally on the rock face. On his head, there are horns. He still seems to be alive. His bow has fallen, and one arm is reaching upwards. His limbs and neck and torso are transfixed by three-dozen or so lines, whatever these might be.

This hybrid humanoid is clearly moving between worlds. Whether up or down or in both directions at once, who can tell? It is not even clear if this figure is suffering, at least not as the average person suffers, passively, without intent. Or, if this figure does indeed suffer, it is not clear if this is intrinsic or incidental to his function. If one arrow may cause pain, two dozen may push the senses into a different realm of experience. It is possible that such suffering should be seen as an initiatory tool, no more and no less, which serves to detach the observing consciousness from its vehicle, even as this vehicle is made more fully suitable for use.

From whatever expansive space he may have come, this therianthrope has been flattened onto a two-dimensional surface, just as most of us have been flattened onto a three-dimensional one. His scarred eyes are a map of worlds. Ladders and concentric rings and spider webs tilt this way and that way through the vortex. Have we exited, or are we entering? Just whose side are we on? And yet some unknown agency has appointed us to judge. Even we, who can access only three percent of the data in our DNA, who have been barred from setting foot on the steps of the first language.

Even we, who stifle the sobs in our throats, without knowing that we feel anything at all. Even we, who are content to see the whole of the Pacific coastline burn, who dream of self-driving cars, who see an ice-free Arctic as an economic opportunity, who do not mourn for the 3,700 people per day who die screaming in twisted metal. Even we, whose torsos throb with pain, who do not suspect what year it really is, and whose hands have transfixed the hybrid humanoid with probes. Let us simply refer to him as "The Wounded Man," as certain scholars do. His dilemma is as clear as his expression is opaque.

Yet again, we have been attracted to the scene of a great crime, like detached observers to the scent of blood. Can the therianthrope speak? Let us count the spears and arrows that transfix him. Why do our ears ring, loudly? Who has ripped our tongues from their roots? By what teachers were we appropriated? We did not give our consent. Star-maps and wheels and eight-headed figures tilt in all directions through a vortex. We notice that our bodies are just coathangers, upon which certain memories can be hung.

This realm of experience is by its nature paradoxical; not only are things not what they seem, but we are also not who or what we are. I have sometimes thought that it should be the Gates of Heaven rather than the Gates of Hell that bear the inscription, "Abandon Hope, All You Who Enter Here." For, however painful or ecstatic our initiation, and to me these are variant interpretations of one and the same process, we will not return to the same Earth that we left; we will not return the same.

In speaking of these arrows, of these acupuncture needles, of these technocratic probes; in speaking of the movement of the Wounded Man, of the topological puzzle it presents; in speaking of the light that pulses through his bones, of his scarred eyes, of the flood of primordial energy that he feels; in speaking about his pain, about his subsequent detachment, I am not only speaking about the ambiguity of his role, I am also struggling to make sense of my experience. Like the Wounded Man, the one on the San rock face, I have only accidentally come to exist in one location. If I suffer, it is not my personal suffering that concerns me. I have often felt that I must redefine what it means to rise or fall.

I have felt such pains. My consciousness has been decentered. I have wondered to what extent I was alive. I have wondered to what extent I grasped the concept of extinction. If my experience was contained in the small body that I saw, then why was it so easy to see through it? Was not 99.9 percent of what I took to be my body space? How was it I could split an atom? How was it I could split the little left again? Why did nothing have a body? Why did my neocortex resemble the stellar nursery of Barnard's Loop? If some race of acupuncture manikins had probed me with their needles, if I took note of my own face in the group, I was no doubt only partially aware of the depths of my complicity. Was I the Master or the Victim, the Teacher or the Student, the Watcher or the Watched?

During my own preparations for a voyage, I have been forced to accept that there was no way to prepare. Fool that I was, I went about my business. I disciplined my breathing. I pressed my forehead to the floor. I read books written by explorers who knew much less than I did. I cleared my mind of the opinions of great teachers. I volunteered to edit the Egyptian Book of the Dead, to cut the dead wood out of Genesis, to tweak the Bhagavad Gita. I tore the cobwebs from Akasha. I swept my habits under the rug. I focused on the infinite subdivision of those matters close at hand.

During my own preparations for a voyage, I have often enough been yanked out of my skin, only to then be forced to justify my arrogance, my reasons for having dared to overstep my role. If I did attempt to give some accounting of my actions, those asking would discount the questions they had asked. They would brush aside my answers. They would stop my heart. They would hurt my feelings. They would not shield their eyes.

In my own travels, I have sometimes met with snake-beings and with bird-beings, who, as the guardians of the spaces they inhabit, must first determine if a living human has any right to be there. To this end, they inspire fear. They may torture both our bodies and our minds, in order, if all goes well, to resuscitate our memories. They may cut us, piece by piece, apart, to remind us of how we were originally put together. They may strip us of so many of our childhood attachments that the wind can find no dust to blow away. They may feed us with auroral lights, with the ruses of the East, with the seed-sounds of the South, with the vast and inexpressible sadness of the West. As we watch, they may assemble a new body out of symbols, leaving us, in the end, with no choice but to laugh.

For this reason, I have no patience with the current crop of conspiracy theorists—those metaphysical used car salesmen, those trolls of the lower Bardo realm—who have demonized these interdimensional helpers, who have portrayed them as the dark oppressors of our race.

Not all who test us are evil. Not all who comfort us are good.

If we bring the Birds a gift they do not like, if we are so forgetful as to mispronounce their names, they may very well forgive us. They may very well pretend that they are pleased. They are big. We are very small. They have cultures to steer. They have geometric quandaries to untangle. No smudges cloud their translucency. Surely, they will not hold us in contempt. They may not even turn to notice we are there. Then again, they may be in a bad mood. They may still be jealous of Adam, with the toxic jealousy of the Ben Elohim, of those Melech HaOlam loves less than he did. We may be made to wish that we had never kissed their feet.

Who has flattened out the therianthrope? Why do human beings not fit onto a three-dimensional surface? If our bodies bear the scars of occult holocausts, the runes of fossilized screams, how is it these scars are so numb to the touch? Zigzags and ladders and geometric patterns twist in all directions through a vortex.

Evil is real, as is our age, as is the fog of the eons we have lived. Blank: our teachers' eyes. We have no way to determine with what crime we are charged. It is always too soon to judge the motives of our catalysts. At the very least, it is counterproductive to demonize the energy of the Snake, which is, after all, the energy of wisdom. One could even view it as a kind of psychic suicide. "It is we who are the good guys! Those bad Reptoids from Orion are the ones who are ruining the neighborhood!" This is little different from saying that the Jews killed Christ and that this is why Christians have been forced to act so badly. This sort of reasoning never ends well. Fears projected into other-dimensional realms will still return to make us stupid.

2

You with the eye-injury, beware of him with the command!
You with the command, beware of him with the eye-injury!

—The Pyramid of Unas Text

The true enemy of any paranoid is the energy of his subconscious mind. Who has dared to frustrate his desire for omnipotence? He searches for the Corporatists who have microchipped his thalamus gland. He searches for the Globalists who have hacked his oligodendrocytes. However obscure the origins of his fall, no efforts must be spared to find and punish those responsible. As his strength was appropriated, so too he would appropriate. As he was dismembered, so too he would dismember. As he was abused, so too he would abuse. Some prehistoric insult cries out to be avenged. If the actual malefactors no longer walk the Earth, there are methods that will help us to identify their descendants, to determine which might be the most suitable for attack.

Once we have purged the world of toxins, the energy that was stolen from us will then return out of the depths. From Malta's underwater cities, from the bones of the 1.6 million warriors that were said to have fallen at Kurukshetra, this energy will pulse to reeducate the collective solar plexus, which is not in any way larger than that found in our bodies. Again, we will burn like suns. We will have no use for our shadows, those historical curiosities, which can then be safely removed. Our libraries will be stocked with first editions of the Classics. Our fires will burn only those word roots that we specify. We must be lucky enough to be elsewhere when our shadows get reattached.

To the one side, those with twelve-strand DNA, an army of the Evolved. To the other side, the League of Aborted Fetuses from Orion. For it came to pass that Eugenics had not yet seen its finest hour. The New Age did not begin in 1975. It is more likely to have begun around 1875, and we ignore at our own risk the occult actions of the Superman, as revealed by the last century, bit by contradictory bit.

There is the Superman of Nietzsche and his later Fascist incarnation. There is the Superman of DC Comics and the Superman of New Age antediluvian nostalgia, oddly similar to the Fascist version. There is the real Superman and his almost exact duplicate. For our purposes, there is very little difference between the two, except that one may kill you and the other one may not. In any event, it is towards him that all archetypes converge. He is the shadow of the Apocalypse, the fulfillment of our dreams. It is he who whets our appetite for omnipotence. He prompts us to reclaim our birthright and, at the same time, he takes back what he gives. The shadow of one figure is the darkness of the Pole, the shadow of the teacher wrapped inside the death threat. The shadow of the other figure is opaque.

The Superman that we think we know is not at all as user-friendly as he seems, at least not on purpose. He puts on the collective unconscious like a telekinetic glove. An alien stares from behind large eyeglasses. Few coworkers follow the obvious hints, or see him as more than a colleague. He subtly edits their perceptions. He puts their names on his stories. He is not from the USA, or from the labyrinth that the Pre-Adamites once hid beneath Antarctica, or from any place in the solar system. He is nothing if not terrifying, as dark as he is bright. His gender is in doubt, the result of one or more ontological appendages, of one too many transplants gone berserk. He is the stranger born to Chaos and Geometry, an experiment hatched in the depths by the Sitra Achra, the child of an imploded sun, now black, whose arms turn backwards.

It was he who appeared to the Gnostics as Abraxas.

He is the god who falls, the Dawn Star, the master of intoxication, who has been transformed by the taste of human blood, whose heart is good, whose memory is clear. He is the afterbirth of a catastrophe, the flowering of a dream that the Thule Society first planted in the ocean, the alchemical child of Reich Youth Leader Baldur and a test tube. He acknowledges his guilt. He denies that he could have acted other than he did. He will kill what he loves. Even now, he looks at his acolytes with some degree of contempt.

He is the self-obscuring light of the city of Jbalqa, the thief of souls, who limps. He is the noseless troubadour, the groom whose bride was never of the Earth. He is the curse of the Var of Yima, he who loves to be surprised, who courts death, he whose forked tongue speaks some version of the truth. He is the archeologist of the sunset, the inventor of the West. He is the fatal glow that pulses from the city of Jbarsa.

There is no way to probe the motives of the duplicate of the Superman. The darkness of the one will be swallowed by the darkness of the other, by the Superman whose darkness is a shield for something deeper. The one Superman is our opponent; the other one is not. The one Superman is luminous, the ancient teacher behind the teacher wrapped inside the death threat. The other Superman would like us to believe he is in charge.

There is no way to disentangle the threads of the conspiracy against us. Luckily, there is no real need to do so; its beginning is not different from its end, which is the record of our own projections. Each projection becomes fully real—in its way—before space once again dissolves it. Encyclopedic knowledge gives no protection against the Shadow, at least no sort of protection we can trust. The magic force of Maya turns one conspiracy into thousands, and then each one of those thousands into several thousand more.

However much it might contain each detail of the future past, the Soul is nonetheless only one inch in diameter. Like the seed of space, we are tiny. Our opponents must help us grow.

Let no passive-aggressive victim look a gift horse in the mouth, lest he be handed his head on a metaphysical platter, for he has broken the law that governs that glad welcoming of the Guest.

Fear not the Killer Klown, as laughter is the best medicine for the dead.

If we refuse to learn what our teachers have to teach, then this says very little about the agenda behind their actions. It is up to us to readjust our focus. It is always possible that, in a distant age, it was we who were the teachers of our teachers. We grew bored, or corrupt or arrogant, and we were seized with a desire to set aside what we knew. With a shifting of tectonic plates, we found that we had no choice but to start at the beginning.

Perhaps, like the world-wide web of megalithic sites, which are massively present without in any way deferring to our theories, a web of teachers was once put in place to frustrate our too easy access to the whole. They show us only the bare bones of their intent. They gesture from a place that is not quite of the Earth. They are cold, and at times contemptuous, and it is difficult to tell to what extent they are alive, what language they once spoke. Those with half-closed eyes can interpret just enough.

Intent on making the same mistake every time, we have taken apart the mechanisms of each clock, cycle by bent cycle, piece by perfect piece, only to find that we must put them back together. Always, we are on the outside looking in, except when we are on the inside looking out. Picked up, yet again, and transported to Pangaea, we are in danger of becoming joyous. It is our blood that potentiates the Stone of the Philosophers, which we ride. There is much work left to do. We are the descendants of an eight-armed sphere that has somehow misplaced its circumference.

Memory wounds us. In its turn, each plaything of the Twelve revolts. Few signs of our vast technology will be left. In a dream, there is an image that reminds us we are dreaming. There are birds who leave loaves of bread on our customary seats at the stadium. "Eat," they say, and we must. We are enjoined to treat the groans of the dying competitors with dispassion. We watch in a state of suspended disbelief as nonsense articulates the geometry of sense. Far below us, the Earth has shrunk to the size of a pinhead. We have been sucked up through the vastness of a well, to the green light at its lip, and then into the space beyond. This does not interfere with our enjoyment of the action. It does not stop us from applauding the calm death of a competitor.

We are old, unspeakably old. It was the overflow of our exuberance that once set the worlds in motion. It is our tears that have irrigated the "desert of the real." Out of habit we tend to every city that we hallucinate. We celebrate the Arts. We love War. We are more corrupt than Ahriman, more violent than the Aztec priesthood, and more self-deluded than the architects of the Holocaust. Paradoxically, we are young; we have not a care.

A pose of victimized innocence does not open us to the Infinite.

3

The Great Ones will tremble, having seen the knife which
is in your hand, when you ascend with all of your members
from the Duat!

—The Pyramid of Unas Text

Once, transported from the Earth by a tornado, I found myself on the field of a great battle. It was Gotterdamerung or the battle at Kurukshetra, or some other even more archaic conflict, in which the fate of the Three Worlds hung in the balance. The whole of recorded history was played fast-forward by some form of technology that was intrinsic to the vacuum, as if on an eight-dimensional VCR. Each atom was clearly visible.

It was humans who were then in charge, those humans with whom we share some few residual attributes, those humans who would cause our blood to freeze. These were the first avant-gardists. These were them whom the ocean loved. These were they who had witnessed the self-subversion of the torus. We might, when all is said and done, be tempted to view this race as nonhuman. Their words were seeds. Winds whistled through their heads. They were able to descend. They were able to ascend. Their pregnant emptiness gave birth to the gods, who were then little more than mechanical contraptions, electrically charged simulacra. We had sent them out to assist in the breaking of an egg.

The gods had no interest in history, not yet, and no knowledge of the pains of childbirth. They had not yet stolen the keys to our DNA, or stripped us of the ability to fit inside its spirals, or reclassified almost 98 percent of the information there as "junk."

Death was then a branch of yoga. War was the way the preexistent played. Magicians danced on the black waters of the ocean. Somehow driven from behind, they competed to destroy and then reinvent the wheel, taking countless heads, starting over as many times as might be needed. Ecstasy drove the brave to throw away their omnipotence.

Absent for millennia, I, the Aeon, had returned just a moment later to the field of a great battle, perhaps slightly the worse for wear. Cities flew, as planets fell. The scene was bathed in the rays of an alternate sun. As if illuminated from the inside out, all colors were painfully bright. Stupid me, it was my race that had weaponized the rainbow! Banners crackled like bursts of lightning through the air.

Quite oddly, as I found myself projected headlong into the action, my body seemed to move without me, each world-destroying movement flashing into the next. Like the violence itself, my eyes seemed to spin in all directions simultaneously. Feinting West, I performed the martial pranayama of the Vrishnis. Lunging East, I enacted the occult taunts of the Andhakas. I could hear each strophe from the Ur-Text clicking into place. It was hard to believe that I was not already dead. A large portion of the warriors had the heads of animals. Snake-men and bird-men and boar-men and lion-men attacked me from all sides.

Spears were inserted into my abdomen, and then withdrawn. I was relieved to see that my intestines were still on the inside of my body; recombinant feet by the millions had not yet trampled them. I was struck by swords and halberds and even more exotic weapons, blows that should have taken off my arms and legs, to leave me no more than a screaming torso.

At last, unable to withstand the convulsive flood of energy, I simply fell to the ground, staring, and did my best to prepare for death.

Out of nowhere, I heard the following, "Do you think he knows who we are?" "No, he can't even hear us." "Well, I guess we'll have to rescue him anyway." Behind me and to the left, two bird-headed humanoids were standing motionless in the sky. The arms of one were folded. The other pointed to where I lay in a spasming heap. "Watch and learn, you stupid child!" The taller of the two birds knelt before me. Bowing his head, and throwing out his arms, he asked that his friend should help to illustrate the lesson. "With no hesitation do what must be done." The short bird then circumscribed the cranium of the tall bird with a blade. "You, take it off!" he ordered. I suspected that this action would result in a horrible sucking sound.

Instead of doing what I was told, I placed my thumbs upon the center of his head, with my hands gently circling around it. I then slowly pulled my thumbs apart, as though I were opening the aperture of a camera. Wave upon wave, the light of 10,000 suns flooded out and over me from the finally wide-open skull. This, I suddenly understood, was the first and most harmonious version of Hiroshima, the illumination toward which our splitting of the atom points. Standing just behind, and speaking into my ear, the shorter of the bird men said, "You are not as weak as you think!"

4

I have not come of my own accord, a message having come
for me. I have passed by the House of my Ba. The striking
power of the Great Lake has missed me...I have seen the
cobra in the Nightboat, and it is I who row in it. I have
recognized the uraeus in the Dayboat, and it is I who bail it
out.

—The Pyramid of Unas Text

Once, following where my breath led on the edge of sleep, I found
that I was floating above a landscape in New Hampshire. It had
been 20 years since I had taken an entheogen. My mind was calm
and clear. I was not visualizing the landscape; I was seeing it.

This was not a dream, nor had my consciousness left my body
as it does in an out-of-body experience. An unusual confluence of
forces had led to my being both inside and outside of my body—
good sex, an educational trip in a tornado, my heart squeezed by
the hand of a none too gentle teacher, recurrent dreams about the
splitting of the atom. So, I was somehow both inside and outside,
with no preference being given to any one mode of perception.
I could move, if I chose, so long as I did not move much. There
was no corpse-like paralysis. Instead, it seemed as though my
consciousness had popped through a kind of bubble. Elasticized, it
spread out in a field, and then, on and on, it continued to expand.

At first, I was assaulted by a cacophony of voices, as though
I could hear everything that was being said for a distance of two
miles. Most of the conversations were boring. The voices faded
and then stopped. They were replaced by an echoing silence, which
made my ears ring, wherever those ears were. Pleased with being
up so high, as well as with the gentle wind, I saw the dark green
undulations of Earth's crust—so wonderful!—before I felt them
in my solar plexus. I could see the small headlights of cars, and

the turns that they were making, and even zoom in to read the license plates. Glancing left and right, I took note of the unusual number of hairpin turns.

Without warning, I was sucked down through a vortex, as though down a bathtub drain, and I found myself, with seatbelt securely fastened, in a car that was hurtling down a mountain road. Kim Levertov, my girlfriend during that period, was at the steering wheel. She was doing her best to keep the car from tipping over on the turns. (Of course, she was also still breathing softly next to me on the bed.) Its mouth opened wide, a giant snake was pursuing us. Fir trees towered toward the moon. The scent of resin was like a drug. Energy lines hissed, crackling where they intersected.

With much power in reserve and toying with our fears, the snake closed on us at its leisure. It had no difficulty in navigating at top speed every twist and turn in the road. Each detail on the face seemed hyper-real, each row of scales, each horny protuberance, the gleam on its blank eyes. There seemed no violence, no act of genocide of which it was not capable. Its many coils snapped into and at the same time out of focus. "How is it that this snake has not already caught us?" I thought. "Surely, it has to be much faster than our car. Is it really toying with us, or is there something else going on? Perhaps the snake is in a generous mood and we are being given a few moments to prepare ourselves for death. Why panic? There is only one way this can end." Quite suddenly, an even larger snake appeared behind the snake that was behind us. It swallowed him/her like an hors d'oeuvre. And then an even larger snake appeared and swallowed that one, and so on and so forth, snake after snake.

I began to suspect we were no longer in our car. I began to wonder who or what it was that watched. When had Kim disappeared? "I should," I thought, "probably give thanks for her absence." If she had not left, would she turn and gasp in horror at my face? I began to wonder what had happened to my limbs, why my body coiled and twisted, why I seemed to be eating mountains, why I could taste the salt of the Atlantic and Pacific, why the skin of a cold species was sliding down my backbone, why my eyelids were stuck open. I began to wonder when my heart had been removed. There seemed to be no top part to my head.

Below me, I saw snakes. My body coiled and twisted, until, finally, a snake that I took to be the World Snake gulped me down. Sucked through the infinite density of a pinhead, I saw things through the World Snake's eyes.

The sky cracked like an egg. From each of 360 degrees, my vision was able to look backwards at itself. Dead birds were the judges. Every stone became a Shakespeare. Energy grids copulated, crackling where their currents met, as the whole night rang with the music of the spheres, again audible. Trees ranted against the invention of the hieroglyph. I could see tall cities collapsing along the coast, as, bearing gifts, the waves of a black ocean rose.

The Snare of Distance and the Sunglasses of the Seer

Bird, Snake, Pot, and Lotus, 1991

The Proteus who sleeps inside us has opened his eyes. And we say what must be said. These jolts are for us what snares and tortures were to the sea-green prophet.

—Giorgio de Chirico

1

If we were to leap tens of thousands of miles into space, the Earth, with all her continents and clouds and cities and roads and industries, would appear to be a blue and white marble. All life and death conflicts would be no more than abstractions. A tornado would be a kind of Sufi dance. A nuclear explosion would be the brushwork of an artist. In the "Foreword" to *Masks of Origin*, I have suggested that time might exist this way as well, as something that can be experienced close up or at a distance. In this "Foreword," I compare a person's life-story to a novel. In a novel, as in a near-death experience, all events are simultaneous. We could follow the story from one page to the next. We could also read from back to front, or we could open to a page at random. The novel is an object that can be weighed in the palm of one's hand. Like the Earth when viewed from tens of thousands of miles away, it exists as a self-contained volume. Viewed from the inside, the Earth is chaos, the fight for survival, human drama, many billions of overlapping choices every second. Viewed from the outside, there are the rhythmic variations of a shape.

Viewed one way, time is measurable. "Time is what is measured by a clock," as Einstein says. Viewed another way, it is a koan that stretches our intellects to the breaking point, and then beyond. Time could also be imagined as a landscape, as a spiral, as a hypersphere, as the relation between an acorn and an oak, as a stage-set, as a conjuration, as a snare, as a figure eight, as a labyrinth, and as an ocean. If we do exist in both the here and the beyond, then our predictions should no doubt be more accurate than they are. While we live, perhaps, we do not have access to the necessary distance. Even after death, we may be terrified of the depth of the space that spreads before us, of the light that spirals open.

If prediction is an attempt to take possession of the future, prophesy may be an attempt to see more deeply into the moment, an attempt that depends upon our making no assumptions about what this moment is.

Prophesy may be the exchange of a beginning for an end, an end for a beginning, a way to ask how this plays with our sense of what is human, to then find that our role is anything but fixed. Prophesy may be a method for determining who lives and breathes in our bodies. Prophesy may be the shattering of the vessel that contains us, after which we may plummet to an inconceivable depth. Prophesy may be an attempt to circumvent the authority of Earth's Rulers, those teachers who would substitute their quaint opinions for our own. Prophesy may be a way of picking up where, an age ago, we left off. Prophesy, if it exists, may be no more than an energy, a way of hitting "pause" on our habits, an attempt to see the world afresh. We no longer measure our inhalations in units of 12,000 years. This does not mean that our vision cannot be expanded, that some part of what we are does not have access to the whole.

"If everything is happening at one and the same moment," a reasonable person might ask, "if each life exists as an already completed story, if the world, as we know it, has already ceased to exist, then how is it we are faced with such a multitude of choices, how is it that each action branches and divides, how is it that chance plays such a central role?" Such questions may not be answerable on the level they are asked. At one scale: endless branching; at another, a Parmenidean stillness. It is probably not in our power, as we are currently constituted, to put these viewpoints together. We can, however, hold them side by side. We can learn to live with the tension.

In a comment on my essay "The Vanguard of a Perpetual Revolution," Okantomi wrote,

> I often feel like I can see what is happening in the world, as well as what is just about to happen and what will almost certainly happen later on, and it's like no one else sees what I am seeing. It's eerie, shocking, and finally depressing.

People do have visions of the future, both individually and collectively. Quite often, these visions are troubling, as Okantomi says. We would much prefer to not follow their implications to the end, let alone change our lives. One way or another, though, our visions have ways of making themselves felt, even if we do not register what it is we are seeing. The world is a kind of eyeball. There is no such thing as a "safe space."

Such visions do not necessarily depend upon telepathy; they can be equally present in the automated workings of the culture, in the traumas that we code in the guise of entertainment, in the license we give to superheroes to break the laws of physics, in key issues that we ban from the realm of public discussion, in the demographic analyses that drive the decisions of corporate boards.

Hollywood blockbusters, for example—such as *Star Wars*, *The Terminator*, *The Fountain*, *Blade Runner*, *Total Recall*, *Contact*, *Cloud Atlas*, *Avatar*, and *Arrival* (and all of their various spinoffs)—serve as useful enough vehicles for contemporary mythmaking, whatever their variations in quality, whatever the motives or self-awareness of their directors. Do those who finance these movies have any real concern about their content, about their webs of subliminal symbolism, about anything other than their opening weekend grosses? With all of the complex decisions that precede day one of shooting, it may be just as accurate to say that these movies create their producers. While the stories they tell are not in any sense literal memories or predictions, they do help us to gain access to archetypal forces as they play, to scrutinize the hypnotic gaze with which our culture holds us. There are symptoms. There are cues. There are occult knots. Our responses are overdetermined.

Our hands freeze in mid-air as they reach for their absent weapons. We marvel at the strength of our ten-foot azure bodies, before cutting our connections to the ones we left behind. Our bones quake at the appearance of the Death Star. As the Empire's eight-eyed drones pursue us, we hug the Tree of Souls for refuge. Hurtling through space, intent on finding the All-Healing Herb, we perform our yogic exercises in the glass dome of a biosphere.

Meanwhile, at the entrance to a Mayan temple, we have somehow killed a priest. We are shocked to find that our True Love is no more than a memory implant. We later find that this discovery is itself one more deception. Only one half of a giant egg has landed, and we are puzzled as to where the other half has gone, as to why what has a front should not come with a back. Glyphs are transmitted by a race of perfect beings. Sadly, they look like octopi, and these glyphs are the infinitely tiny variations of a smoke ring. We have little or no doubt that these constitute a threat.

As we stare into the distance, the ancient world resurfaces as a scientific dream on the horizon.

We remember the collapse of complex systems, the return of the repressed, the abuse of occult technologies, the scars left by the tearing of the planetary web, the hierarchical clash between the rulers and the ruled, but we mix and match the specifics of the story. We remember the green branch of primal knowledge, the blackening of its leaves, the two-faced role of the snake, the subtle art that turns a toxin into an elixir, but we kneel before our oppressors and strike out at our friends. Our best efforts to solidify the Rorschach blot of the future only point us towards the enigma of our origins.

To discover what we know, we must sometimes pause to observe what we create. Seized from afar, as by the magnetism of an almost nonexistent teacher, we are pulled by a current all too eager to instruct us. An unresolved agenda speaks to us from the screen. The screen also acts like an iron curtain, through which the bodies of the living may not pass.

3

We are fortunate that the collapse of our culture entertains us. We might otherwise not pause to notice it at all. In a different mode, we give form to the future through our fears, by what we do not do as much as what we do, by our *belle indifference* when presented with a series of ultimatums. Our psyches are jagged. Whole periods have gone missing. As crises converge, our refusal to act is a testament to the scale of the coming upheaval.

We finger the rigid outlines of our scars, as if they belonged to someone else. We shape the future by our under-the-skin sense of all of those things we know but go out of our way not to think about: that reserves of oil will almost certainly run out in our lifetimes, that a solar flare could wipe out all of our I.T. systems, that the U.S. does not manufacture much of anything anymore, that each day more methane burps from the permafrost of the Arctic, that the ocean is no respecter of our coasts, and that there is not enough locally grown food to sustain most cities in a real emergency. There are many things that it seems better not to know. The future is one of the better places in which to store such unasked-for knowledge.

It is always possible that the march of progress will indefinitely continue, that "someone will think of something," that our way of life will require only a few small modifications, that windmills and solar cells will save us. As ancient souls, we know this is absurd. The problem is, of course, to separate and categorize these alternate versions of the future—in simplistic terms, to discriminate between the more false than true and the more true than false. We can see the details but somehow miss the pattern; we can see the pattern but somehow miss the details. To see clearly we must see from more than one location, from all of the 360 degrees of a circle, from the vantage point of a presence that may see the future in retrospect.

4

If we are the simultaneous inhabitants of the present, the future, and the past, we may not physically occupy these spaces, or, conversely, we may occupy them all without inhabiting any one space in particular. As our mouth pronounces the word "present," where does this word go? Is the present even present as we normally understand it? This present, in that it vanishes at the very moment that we grasp it, may be just as difficult to enter as either the future or the past. To the past's inhabitants, the past is just as present as the present is to us, just as, even as we turn the concept in our minds, we have moved into a future that was just now theoretical. If we do, on some arcane level, live in both the future and the past, if both of these are just alternate versions of the present, there is a gulf between what we embody and what we think we know, between what we are and what we have been allowed to see.

Sadly, there are laws that prevent our switching out of "power save" in order to reactivate the full scope of our senses. The art of remote viewing is no longer taught in schools. Bilocation is now seen as unscientific. There are industries devoted to the proposition that a human being has less predictive power than an algorithm. The age of the tool has passed and the age of the prosthesis is at hand. We see what is put before us; we do not see the long shadows that stand behind our backs. We now see with our eyes; we do not believe that it is possible to see with the solar plexus.

From their underground bases, speeding all ways at once, like boomerangs, and with superhuman stealth, suspect forces play games with the horizon. Fear and hope pump out a kind of metaphysical fog, crackling with static, which makes every level of the process difficult and tests our ability to translate the first hieroglyphs that we wrote.

As light can manifest as either a particle or a wave, or both, but not at the same time, so too the future both *is* and *is not* there. It is there for those beings with a panoramic view, as it may be for us at the moment of our deaths, but it revolts against all functions that we would force it to perform. It is present in those flashes that it chooses to transmit; it does not see fit to instruct us as to the gaps in our methodology, through which we will fall.

We want to believe that each year our systems are moving a bit closer to perfection. How accurate this is. Yet we forget that "what is perfect will soon end," as it says in the Tao Te Ching. The language spoken by the future both *is* and *is not* similar to that spoken by the present. Floods of information are provided, yes, enough to create the appearance of a world, but too often disinformation is more attractive than the truth. Trolls and gremlins are among us! Fear forces us to misjudge the location of our navels. We dread the constant vigilance that is imposed by the Ideal.

5

Through the years, and especially in the early 1990s, I have sometimes found myself projected into the future, both in terms of specific images and through wider visionary overviews. These experiences felt urgent. On the skyline, threats had massed. Spent technocratic protocols had clogged the lines of energy. There were also invitations—invitations to which we had somehow not bothered to respond. I felt seized by the hair. I felt yanked out of my skin in order to bear witness. I felt called upon to test the boundaries of my language, to rethink my aesthetics from scratch, to find some way to speak of what I saw.

These experiences made demands on me, yet they also, to some extent, seemed almost pointless to report, even if I had been more visible than I was. Why did I waste so much time in torturing my language? For whom was my message intended, and was there any way that my vision could be shared?

Before a crisis, few would have any reason to pay attention to such overviews, and afterwards, reading poetry would be way down on the public's list of priorities. I was able to see certain details as well as certain patterns. At first, there was no good way to present these as a narrative, any more than an ocean consists of a series of steps. How is it possible to tell the story of an ocean? The traumas that had possessed us from the time of the Younger Dryas were nonetheless starting to make sense. A finger to my lips, I have spent years keeping secrets. I pretend, when asked, to know much more about football than I do.

In retrospect, certain passages stand out, as having started in one world and then ended up in another. What began as vision had some tangential relationship to fact. For example, references to the destruction of the World Trade Towers popped up three or four times in poems from 1992. "A monster stalked his head through the air vents of the World Trade Towers. He could not find it, for the towers themselves had disappeared." "The World Trade Towers for a fourth time fall; their shadows stand."

There were other lines from this period that possibly pointed to the BP Gulf oil disaster: "Not one leaf stirs. The sea has met its death by accident. The tree Yggdrasil has been hacked at the root." And to Fukushima: "You have thrown a wave at the reactors of the Nephilim. Rods overheat, and the whole of the ocean is not enough to cool them."

There were dozens of references in my books *To Akasha: An Incantation for the Crossing of an Ocean* and *The Preexistent Race Descends* to the idea of a "mile-high wave." *To Akasha* was structured around this image, and it was a phrase that I never expected to hear in the evening news. But, during the BP Gulf oil crisis, reporters began to speak about what would happen if the vast lakes of methane under the Gulf were to explode. One consequence of this would be a mile-high wave that would rise up to wash over two thirds of North America.

If such images proved nothing, if they were no more than suggestive, well, such is the nature of poetry. From the standpoint of vision, what was real was that our way of life was far more fragile than we thought. The complexity of our systems was a liability rather than a defense, and, the more complex these systems became, the more out of touch and vulnerable we were. What we called "facts" were a way of keeping our eyes fixed on the foreground.

"If there is a foreground," I said to myself, "then there should also be a background." Delusional though it might seem, I felt that some ancient audience was observing me from a distance, that they were presenting me with cues and challenges and tests. I referred to this body as "The Assembly Beyond Space." If this body did, in fact, exist outside of time or at some tangent to it, what possible interest could they have in my experiments with language? If, on some level, the events in our world had already taken place, what more could a poet add?

If I was not entirely content to be anonymous, neither did I want to become more public than I was, not if this required even the smallest amount of effort. How should I transmit information that I barely understood? There was nothing that I could do to change anyone's behavior. Should not a mystic be silent? "Silent, yes," I said to myself, "but lazy, maybe not. Perhaps I should see my attempts to speak as a kind of ritual action, as a way of pointing to the arcane geometry that joins one world to another." Some few noticed, here and there.

6

The Hebrew calendar began on October 6th, 3761 B.C. The Mayan calendar began on August 11th, 3114 B.C. The current age in the Vedic calendar began on February 18th, 3102 B.C. All of these calendars would seem to point to an even more archaic system, now lost, to some larger complex of cycles in which these start-dates are embedded. Just as there are larger cycles, so too, there should be smaller cycles, like days within a week or weeks within a month, during which archetypal forces move in and out of dominance. If we do grant that such models may be valid, we may also find that the Ancients were less literal than we are. Even now, perhaps, they tempt us to conflate the "when" with the "how," the archetype with the means of its projection.

February 8th, 3102 B.C. was the date on which the Dvapara Yuga ended. 3102 B.C. was the year of the Kurukshetra War, during which, it is said, 3.94 million warriors lost their lives. Such a date is clearly anything but trivial, but on what plane were these battles fought? Were the current laws of physics in effect? Where are all of the shattered cities and scorched bones? Were the weapons described—the Brahmashiras and the Nagastras and the Pramohana Astras—no more than metaphorical, or are we missing some key aspect of the story?

December 21st, 2012, was a date that left many prophets disappointed, yet it was on this date that Warner Bros. released a movie called *The Impossible*. Based on actual events, it tells the story of an English family on vacation at a resort in Khao Lak, Thailand, who were separated when the Indian Ocean tsunami of 2004 struck. After a movie-length ordeal, they are once again reunited. This was the tsunami that killed 230,000 people and displaced 1.7 million more. Many critics gave it positive reviews. Eric Koln, of *Indie Wire*, on the other hand, gave it only a B-minus grade. He argued that it suffered from a "feel-good" plot within the context of mass-destruction. Already anxious, I had no desire to see or judge the movie for myself. Waves haunt me, as they have for the past 12,000 or so years, and this one seemed just a local instance of far greater things to come. For me, the Paleolithic glaciers are still just about to melt, and a rise in sea-level will destroy the cities on most coasts.

But why, you may ask, do so many of our predictions turn out to be wrong? Now that 2012 has come and gone, and the visions of its cultic devotees have proven far less than accurate, we may want to free ourselves from any obsessive focus upon dates. The Time-Snake is far slipperier than our theories. It is not that we do not know, perhaps, but rather that there is no way to determine what we know, or to differentiate a corporate logo from a hieroglyph. We see, but we have forgotten how to read. We believe that our minds penetrate beyond the ends of our own noses, when, in fact, they rarely penetrate that far.

If we humans cannot travel from one side of the omniverse to the other, it is perhaps because, at this point in the Kali Yuga, we have gotten much too big. In the Satya Yuga, when the Sun still had a face, we knew enough to avoid getting tripped by our own feet. We could enter through the keyhole of the pineal gland to then exit onto the pyre that the Birds had built to burn us, where, as we watched with bland amusement, our bones would turn to ash. Our 10,000-year life-spans allowed for much experimentation.

We inhabited our bodies from the outside in, like the visitors to a museum—the *Smithsonian Institution*, let's say—and not, as in the present, from the inside out.

There is an aperture, an eye that opens in an atom, a point around which the figure eight is twisted. There is a zero that gave birth to the Big Bang, which even now contains it. How strange it is that this zero is no bigger than it was. There is a passage that leads to the edge of the known world. There is a tunnel that we remember, which also remembers us, which waits for our return. We must only dare to enter. Such a small requirement this is—to go where we have been, to slip into a passage, to step out the other side. There is a luminous tunnel that opens out of Life and onto Death, which can turn like a frightening kaleidoscope, which contemporary custom tells us we would do well to avoid.

Ignoring the instruction manuals that were left to us by the Ancients, we may, quite foolishly, decline to enter through this exit, to exit through this entrance. We may wait for 60 to 70 years to see what can be seen. We may prefer the safety of the known to the recognition that such safety is a hoax.

We do, of course, have cause for some degree of hesitation. There are forces that oppose the reclamation of our birthright, who stole and occupied the depths that we had earlier possessed. On the other side of the aperture, we may draw to ourselves beings who are adept at playing games, who may be quick to realize that our skill-set has grown rusty. They may trap us in light's bargain basement, if not worse, with no capacity to come and go as we see fit. We may inadvertently have travelled with big targets on our backs.

Do the Ancients still have our interests at heart? Are the Snakes our friends, and will the Birds be curious enough to even turn their heads when we speak? Should we dare to enter, what relics will we leave, what evidence of our scorched-earth war against our shadows, what trace of our Promethean technology? Will the Snakes set us up for the kill, or will they dazzle us with their feats of encyclopedic recall? Will we know which words are teachings, which are snares? How black is the ocean that will swallow up our cities? How much will it hurt to stare into the Sun? Once the Birds have burnt us, if they do, how much of what we are will drift free of the ash? Will we once more hear the hum that preceded the Big Bang?

There is a passage that leads to the edge of the known world. We are there, at the point around which the figure eight is twisted, in the moment just before the start of the Great Year, nor have we ever left. To the one side: desolation; to the other side: a waste. We pause to wonder what has happened to our breathing, which, after deepening, has somehow fled into the distance. Was the rhythm of that heartbeat ever really ours? As the zero opens, a voice presents us with an ultimatum, which some may hear as a choice. "You may live," it says, "or you may die." We must choose the third alternative.

7

It is certainly odd: that even though some part of ourselves may be living in the future, our predictions are far more likely to be wrong than to be right. To see would demand that we acknowledge what we see, only to then catch ourselves off guard. To see would be to predict that we will die, to accept that we just did, to then believe the Ancients when they say that we are wrong. To see would be to fall like light through outer space. To see would be to give, to whomever, wherever. To see would be to begin beyond the end, to laugh. To see would be to remake ourselves in the image of what sees.

If there are forces that may actively attempt to block our view, our own sense of false humility may be a bigger factor. Real humility creates openings; the false type shuts them down. If prophesy does depend on our ability to see clearly into the moment, whatever this moment might be—to boldly recognize patterns that are just beginning to emerge or to probe into patterns that have long been in existence, but which, for whatever reason, have not yet become visible—then our success may come more from a set of classical virtues than from a bag of occult powers. We have only to differentiate real virtues from their substitutes.

To be virtuous, as I use the word, is not necessarily to act well. No; it is only to be conscientious in keeping our heads clear, to act well enough to be of service to our vision. In the morning of the world, there were those among our teachers who had said, "Let us break you, just a little." Our lifespans were shrunk. A fog was attached to our eyes. We were taught to count from one to two. To be virtuous was to choose between them. Well, enough of that. There are other sorts of virtues. Should we once more make our vision circular, we may find that our powers are equal to our ends.

Let me call these virtues the "Anamnesian Virtues." These are real virtues, however much they have been formatted by an artificial author. Their names are common, like the days of the week, yet a shadow has fallen between one culture and the next. The original definitions do not correspond to ours. To the extent that they remain on this side of the existent, we must acknowledge that they are fragments from a long since vanished text, which was copied and then recopied into half a dozen languages before once again being lost. Such a text is obviously prone to mistranslation, if not self-serving paraphrase. Let me nonetheless present my attempted reconstruction. The seven virtues are as follows:

1. Detachment: the capacity to see the ocean that will swallow up all things, and to listen as it whispers in your ear. You should, paradoxically, become even more empathic as the degree of your detachment grows. You may act on this, or not. You may spill your blood as a purely symbolic gesture, in service to those humans yet unborn. You may feel the pain of the multitudes that you kill.

2. Foresight: the capacity, while still in love with life, to be dead, and productively so. So too, the longer you are dead the more alive you will be.

3. Self-reliance: the capacity to stand on your own as you free yourself from the force-fields of the common wisdom, and then not complain too much. This will be more of a challenge if your head, hands, heart, and feet have been removed. Most prostheses will require some amount of training, after which you will become 100-percent free.

4. Balance: the capacity to see the right in every wrong, as well as the wrong at the dead center of each right. By the blinding light of the hypersphere, we can see that even the most generous of our actions is a crime; at one and the same moment, every crime can be regarded as a type of revolutionary act, as a flawed but useful reinvention of the law. Strange indeed are the methods of the stern Goddess of Necessity!

5. Hindsight: the capacity to remember just when to shut up, the instinct to leave the most important details out, and the knowledge that you have seen these things a great many

times before. To all others have a role and a position been assigned; to the seer, only the pathos of descent.

6. Stealth: the capacity to bring your full energy to a project when there are few who understand what you are doing, and none who will reward you. Only in this way will the dead be prompted to grant access to their libraries.

7. Simplicity: the capacity to make do with whatever Fate deposits. We must do what we were meant to do. We must go where we are meant to go. The shortest distance between two points, however, may turn out to be a labyrinth. We must read each accident as a catalytic cue in order to discover the true outlines of our work.

There is a fog that drifts through the City of the Oppressors, from whose spell we must free ourselves. Such an act may not increase our personal wealth or popularity, of course; thus our progress may seem to others the very definition of failure. A "win-win" solution may not be in the cards. If we do decide to act, these virtues may help us to develop the breadth of vision that we need. They are of use to both the solitary artist and the multitude. No line divides the subject from the object. "One thought fills immensity," as Blake argues in *The Marriage of Heaven and Hell.* Even good habits must be probed and then, finally, dismantled. All crutches must be thrown away, as we free ourselves from the advice of experts, from the urge to see our side win and the other side destroyed, and from the high-tech wet-dreams each day generated by the media. At the end, there should be nothing left but space.

Conversely, we must have the courage to accept that we do not, in fact, create our own reality. For the "You" is inextricably bound to the experience of the "We." The "Body Politic" is an actual body, however much we might choose to view it as a metaphor.

One victory leads to the next, smartphone upon smartphone, upgrade upon upgrade, until the spell of neoliberalism has left no tribe untouched. You are one of 6 ½ billion being swept along through the veins of a metastasizing empire, whose reach is inter-dimensional in its scope, but whose key principle, at the moment, is nowhere to be found. Its search engines troll for evidence that it has not ceased to exist, as there, just up ahead, the ghosts of failed superbeings beckon from the fallout.

8

If we are a storehouse for the "seeds of every form and the sprouts of every sort of life," as Pico della Mirandola argues, who knows but that we might not scare ourselves? "The New Man is living amongst us now!" said Hitler. "He is here! Isn't that enough for you? I will tell you a secret. I have seen the New Man. He is intrepid and cruel. Even I was afraid of him."

Once, we were not so easily impressed. We had not yet vol-unteered to be eaten by the gods, they to whom we had recklessly given birth. We were not afraid of giants, who burned as brightly as atomic bombs, nor of tiny beings with large eyes, who were skilled at creating simulacra. Our craniums were large, and open at the top, but we did not necessarily need large bodies to go with them. One size fit all. The great assembly hall of the heart was almost endlessly interactive. Mercury had attached its power to our ankles. We did not need wings. Few realize that the oceans fill the footprints that we left, that megaliths mark the vast multitude of our navels, or that the sky is filled to overflowing with our tears.

Much stupider than they think, Earth's top one percent are nonetheless quite adept at playing games. Let us posit: that they rule by reactivating some antediluvian trauma, the fear of which has been bred into our bones, the records about which have been hidden in the coils of junk DNA, which they, and they alone, have somehow learned to read. Such feats of micromanagement! All data is then made to correspond. Not being actual prophets, of course, their reading of these records is hit or miss at best. "As you are figuring out the world," they say, "we will have manufactured a new one, and then another one after that!" This does not mean that they are actually in charge. Like us, they are subject to whatever spells they cast, and, as the apparatus of the Great Year turns, they are swept along with the other 99 percent.

No part can ever be taken from the whole, nor does the One increase when added to itself. We move as One, unconsciously, and pushed forward from behind. At one scale: ideologies at war, the clash of genomes in the dark; at another scale: a dance of resonant geometry, the living library of space, of which we can become at least partially aware.

As we free ourselves from the common wisdom, paranoia may be the most immediate of temptations. All conspiracy theories may be true, or none of them, or a fact from this one and an archetype from that one, but in the end such labyrinthine explorations may not lead to greater freedom. The trap is this: that we are always the good guys, and someone else is always to blame for every evil in the world.

As citizens of the greater city of the cosmos, who have now been grounded, our job—should we choose to accept it—may be to cut through the layers of obfuscation that divide each person from the core of his/her power, so that each may once more serve as a kind of movable Omphalos. We have only to discover the most efficient means. We have only to determine the best moment to move forward, when also it might be better to hold back.

In 333 B.C.—a most symbolic date!—Alexander the Great marched his army into Gordium, the capital of Phrygia. There, he encountered an ancient wagon, its yoke tied with several knots all so tightly entangled that there was no way to see how they were joined. Phrygian tradition held that the wagon had once belonged to Gordius, the father of King Midas, and an oracle had declared that any man who could unravel the knots was destined to rule all of Asia. According to the chronicler Arrian, Alexander was instantly overwhelmed with a desire to untie the knot. After wrestling unsuccessfully with the ropes, he suddenly stepped back and exclaimed, "What difference should it make how one manages to undo it?" He then drew his sword and cut the knot in half. That same night, Gordium was rocked by thunder and lightning, which Alexander and his men took as a sign that he had pleased the gods. He did go on to conquer much of Asia, before dying unexpectedly at the age of 32.

Appearances to the contrary, it is possible that the things that matter most are actually very simple. To see fully may be to know what to subtract, to know what debts come attached to the very fact of our breathing. To act clearly may to act from more than one location, to liberate the subtle genius of the Zero. Each thing having happened a great many times before, we should have long ago grown bored with making new mistakes. How is it we have not? Why do we take so much pleasure in judging ourselves harshly? We may want to pose such questions to all the Buddhas we have killed.

9

Gently but persistently, we must bring our attention back to what I will call the "Boy Scout (or Girl Scout) Code of Conduct," as this was understood by the Ancients. The 21 "Anamnesian Maxims" that correspond to the seven "Anamnesian Virtues" are below. These are formatted as injunctions. To the extent that they can be interpreted at all, there are some that must be followed to the letter. There are others that might put the practitioner into conflict with the Authorities. In your cultivation of virtue—or *virtu*, if you go with the classical understanding of the word—you must read not only with your own eyes but also through the eyes of your opponent. You must read between the lines, as well as what is on them. Obey at your own risk. These 21 "Anamnesian Maxims" are as follows:

1. We must love to act well for the sake of acting well; all action is circular, and no Uroboros can remove the tail from its mouth.

2. We must work hard and stick to our projects through any and all obstacles, until, as if by magic, we one day finish what we started. Looking back, we must thank all of those forces that conspired to destroy us. We will have died more than a dozen times since we set forth from our blackened port. We must not be so naïve again.

3. We must learn how to accept the full responsibility for our actions, and be the first to gladly admit it when we are wrong. If we discover, as in a dream, that we have caused harm to the innocent, we must accuse those who have dared to point their fingers at us, for it is they who have tainted our otherwise spotless minds.

4. We must cultivate a smile, and be able to transmit warmth from the solar plexus. It is in this way that our energy will tempt space to self-organize. As much as does the Sun, we will then be able to micromanage each event.

5. We must be willing to meet each person on his or her own terms, however self-deluded or sociopathic they might be. We will know that we have succeeded when their flaws

become an almost exact mirror-image of our own. We must then kiss the horror that confronts us in the mirror.

6. We must be generous with our friends, but more generous with our enemies. We must hold them as close as Teddy bears. For they MUST be kept off balance. We must trust that our sense of style will make up for the catastrophic damage that we cause.

7. Putting fears aside, we must do our best to act with some appropriate degree of courage, which may mean standing still. We must practice death, as though our lives depended on it, and be willing, at any moment, to shrug off what we love.

8. We must speak honestly, to the extent that we can hide behind a mask.

9. We must keep to the Mean. We must do nothing in excess, except when we choose to violate this rule. This is part of the natural equilibrium of the Mean. Lacking excess, it would not know what it is, or how to tell its butt from its elbow.

10. We must act justly. We must treat others in the way that we would want them to treat us, especially when they deserve a good slap across the face, which, at the appropriate moment, we must know how to apply.

11. We must kill first and ask questions later, like the gods, so long as we have the best interests of our sacrifice at heart.

12. We must care for the orphan, and marry our brother's widow. If needed, we must be willing to make love to our neighbor's wife. Grave indeed are the responsibilities of the caretakers of the cosmos!

13. The house of the sky has many windows. A window is open, and we must thank it. As was done "In Illo Tempore," we must be able to zip from one place to another with no need to cross through the intervening distance, for this will reduce our dependence upon gas.

14. As blunt as need be, we must perfect what Hemingway called our "built-in bullshit detectors." We must, if and when we choose, speak truth to power, or else operate beyond the edges of the stage. We must cultivate a sense of the innate law of the omniverse. It is utterly obscure. It is as soft as a breath.

15. We must boldly go where no man has gone before, at first together, then more and more alone. No other will survive the wreck. Once having washed ashore, you will there find Argos, your aged dog, who has been waiting with bated breath for your return. He is a good dog. He wants only to lick your hand before he dies. A loyal companion, he will even then share the deep intelligence of his nose. He will be waiting with his cold head resting on his paws, on the last dock, as the ocean swells.

16. To the one side Birds and to the other Snakes: Keep eyes wide open, but do not enter any contest where you would have to stare them down. Do not offend them with such words as "high" and "low," for, already, they tend to regard you as a snack.

17. We must cultivate curiosity, for there would be no world without it.

18. We must stay alert, and have no fear of boredom. A wait of 12,000 years is not other than the blinking of an eye. We are not, in fact, obligated to bring new worlds into

existence, however much we might like to pretend that this is so. No, for we are on a wheel. On this wheel, each of the spokes functions like the gallery of a museum, and, from where we stand, we are free to wander into and out of any period that we choose.

19. We must be able to bring objects across a threshold with us, whether gargoyle breastplates or stringed philosophical instruments, and then fully translate them into this world from our dreams. Do it well, and these objects will blend seamlessly with other props in the environment, although some few may note their faint radioactive glow.

20. We must be good little boys and girls—or else! But no, we are free to be as difficult and subversive as we want, so long as we keep the Bindu always before our eyes and the apparatus of our primal energy intact.

21. We must cultivate the ability to break through any mirror, leaving, as we go, little evidence of our passing. Moving in and out from behind the surface of projection, we must snatch the archaeological relics that we need.

These seven virtues and 21 maxims will allow us to stay grounded as we venture to reconstruct the non-dual architecture of the city, which exists in no one place. As we knew, my wide-eyed shipmates, there is no such thing as time, and the lightning bolt that directs us falls crazily where it will. Let us pause once more to note that this is so. The emptiness that is space shows no sign of disturbance. We cannot leave, for we never did depart.

10

The emptiness that is space shows no sign of disturbance. Space is, for there is no way for it not to be, yet no line divides what is from the depths of the nonexistent. In this next to nothing, there is resonance; there is the hum of every incantation from past worlds. Each terror is an egg in the hand of a blind magician. Each neurotransmitter is a key that fits the lock of a missing door. Once, the Kundalini hid its teachings inside forms, as a test of whose skill in camouflage they served and from whose potency they had been created. We must later on help to free these teachings from their forms. We must break the Sumerian seal that turns us back from the catastrophic depths of our own breathing.

Having once been set in motion, the Kundalini stirs up and expels a volcanic flux of images, as it burns through every obstacle in its path. It rips continents like sheets of paper. It dismantles the prosthetic bodies of the gods. It unravels all of the complexes that defend us from our fears, leaving no means by which blessing can be sorted from disaster. It expunges every trace of the antediluvian records, all arts and sciences, yet without even a small detail being lost. "But why is this necessary?" you might justifiably ask. It is possible that it does things just to show us that it can. It is possible that the Kundalini simply likes to play. Or, alternately, it is possible that our childhood is over, and that, finding ourselves cold and naked on the coast of a dead ocean, we must figure out how to grow up.

Tertullian writes, "I believe in the Resurrection *because* it is impossible." So too, at the tail-end of the Kali Yuga, if access to our first mode of vision would now seem to us impossible, it is for this reason that we must treat our abandonment as a test. Good vision may depend on our having nothing to lose, no cause to advance, no belief whose planks have not been shattered by a storm. At some point, cooling down, upon finding that there are no laws left to violate, the Kundalini may become much nicer than it was. Then, as smoothly as a bell tone through the zodiac or as the arcing of a current through the ocean, it will move on to its predetermined end. Each atom will have 108 eyes.

We do not always have to be picked up and transported to view one dimension through the wide eyes of another. A state of clarity will sometimes do the trick. To be present may be to calmly view the day that we have died, a day that has not occurred yet. To be present may be to sense how our shadows too cast shadows, city upon city, length upon darkening length. To be present may be to grasp the pregnant weight of the unspoken, to internalize the demands of those who do not yet exist, to recall the thousands of perfect poems that no human will ever write. To be present may be to be present in all the places we have breathed, to remove our metaphysical chastity belts, to breathe according to the rhythm of our tasks, no faster and no slower.

To cross from what we know to what we do not know we know, we may not, in fact, have to move from where we are. A state of clarity will sometimes do the trick. Then again, to directly perceive the shifting structure of the cosmos may be to taste the most potent of entheogens. One's vantage point becomes mercurial, no more solid than the drip of Soma on one's tongue.

11

If we desire to reset the parameters of our vision, it will be necessary to begin at the beginning, like those long-eared poets who lifted up dead cities with their words. Being silent, they could hear. Being desperate, they could laugh. Being present, they could trace the labyrinthine path that they had mapped out in past worlds. Crossing from one residual landmass to the next, between those few peaks that still poked above black waters, those seers joined hands to call the Sun out of the deep. What they were taught to do, they did. They caused lost cultures to coagulate beneath them.

Their hearts weighed almost nothing—a bit more, a bit less. Their eyes were wide. They did not hesitate to kill.

Even now, the long-eared poets play games with the sky. Even now, you can hear the rhythm of their oars, the drone of their chant, the slap of their feet as they dance upon black waters. Even now, they return to the clear shores of their youth. Curled like fetuses and covered with red ochre, even now, those poets breathe. Their whispers re-inflate the lung-sacs of the globe. Their hands still clutch the gifts that they take to the beyond.

Even now, those seers stare into the Sun, in their hands the cylinders that hold the eggs of slaughtered species, in their hands the knives that cut the throats of foreign gods. Like our guides, we must not only find a way to begin at the beginning, we must find some way to determine just what a "beginning" is.

The world is almost infinitely complex, as is time, and human nature, but we should start by drawing a circle on the ground. We should lift our hands at the center of a turning 10-dimensional torus, which can be statistically renormalized as a circle no more than 10 feet wide. There, we will begin our invocation. There, we will test the first steps of our dance. There, we will reach for the others in our circle, for those present and not present, for those whose phones have no signal, for those who live in cities where the streetlights have gone off. We should start there, in this circle, and not elsewhere, for there is no other place. This circle will be powered by our breath, and its centripetal vortex will then gather up what it needs.

Visions will be allowed to visit, but fears and traumas and hatreds and projections will be required to stay a few feet off. Joining hands, we will cross from one residual landmass to the next, from coast to shifting coast, between the sites of the derelict reactors. We will lose track of our tears. We will feel our earlobes grow. As the invocation swells, a standing wave will lead us to the center of the Sun, inside of which are cities. A standing wave will lead us to the Sun behind the Sun, to the twin that so few know. A standing wave will lead us to the belt stars of Orion, and then into the trials beyond.

Back home, there will be few remaining traces that there ever was a circle. A new Sun will have long since bubbled from the depths. We will find, should we return, that our bioenergetic vehicles have been transformed into stones. At first worshipped by the masses, they will later come to be seen as normal parts of the environment. In passing, we will note that a day takes 24,000 years. Hieroglyphs will buzz in geometric networks. In our reconfigured forms, we will take what we require, no more and no less. We will improvise as we go.

12

In the end, it is predictable that any prophesy will fail, for the omniverse is far more contradictory than a clock. And, though we can envision this omniverse as a being with two hands, it is in no way obligated to use just the hands that we can see. Then too, of necessity, some chaos must always be added to the mix. In order to get from where we are to the sphere we once inhabited, we must set foot on a path that does not exist, in those bodies that we threw so carelessly about. What we once saw, we must see. We must excavate our ears. We must learn to pronounce the words that we once spoke. We must harness the explosive power of the zero. We must dare to follow the instructions that we left. With our small flutes, we must challenge the bone orchestras of the Empire.

Having Cleared the Sky, it was Time to Reinvent the Wheel

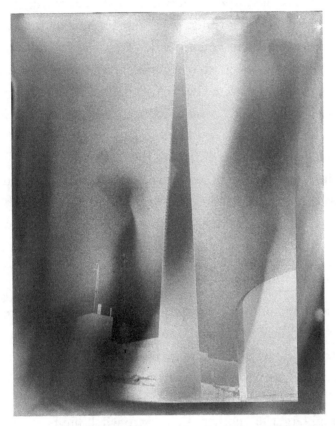

Solarized photo from x-ray irradiated film, 2001

Has the future a location? Yes. It came before itself. It was!

∾

Brian George is an artist and writer who was born in 1954. He grew up in Worcester, Massachusetts, surrounded by crumbling smokestacks, factories, and freight-yards. He had travelled far to serve as a male midwife in the birth of a form of energy that dares not speak its name. There were complications. It was the end of one world and the beginning of another, or, if things went well, the luminous end of both. He would first have to take the foot out of his mouth. Big things were happening, and it was all he could do to remember how to walk.

With its flywheels that were frozen in mid-turn and its drop-hammers that were always just about to fall, the "industrial heart of New England" would not much longer beat. No longer would there be a systole or a diastole. Much would look the same, yet all things would be different. The assembly lines of the 100 or so factories were still there. It was only the breathing humans that were missing. This threat, according to some, was much more than theoretical. They argued that some Moebius-type reversal had occurred. The real question was when we would learn of the attack. In silence, the fallout had spread everywhere from one point while we slept.

The atom had first been split in 1917. Since then, there were hula hoops. There were aerodynamic vacuum cleaners. There were cantilevered bras. There were game shows. There were monkey astronauts. There were highways that led from Fargo to Sioux Falls, from Boise to Winnemucca, from Tulsa to Las Vegas, from one potential target to another. There were witch hunts. There were drag races. There were easy-to-get prescriptions for barbiturates. There were laugh tracks. There were protocols for the ritualized diffusion of anxiety. An alarm would sound, and the subjects of the experiment would crouch down, heads on knees, beneath their desks.

The first atom had been split in 1917. Twenty-eight years before "The Gadget" would be detonated over Alamogordo, it was possible that the rule of the third dimension had expired, that the space inside an atom had grown larger than the Earth.

It was possible that, already, the hands had been removed from every clock. How was it that no one had noticed? This was a matter for top physicists to resolve. Until then, silence as to this issue was simply a question of public policy, a way of insuring that consumers did not suspect they might be dead. It was certainly odd that the third dimension now appeared to be flat.

There were days, even early on, when Brian wondered if Worcester had been built out of pre-cut pieces of cardboard. The shapes were there, but only just; you were only meant to see them from one angle. They had no other sides. His actual city was almost infinitely far away. It was no more tangible than the salt-smell on the wind. Without knowing what he knew, or how, Brian sensed that the ghosts of the Younger Dryas had returned. Worcester, at its best, was no more than a seed, a kind of mnemonic exercise, a point from which to conjure. Even the tallest of smokestacks had been levelled by a wave. Clouds drifted through the future ruins of an empire. Fish followed where they led.

One morning, when Brian was four, he was sitting on the third-floor back porch of his three-decker, imagining himself to be hovering above the green flow of the Amazon. While making snakes, canoes, and villagers out of clay, he became frustrated. It occurred to him that he had succumbed to a creative block. How small he was! How contracted his intelligence! He remembered what it was like to create real snakes and villagers.

At the age of eight, Brian gave up the idea of becoming a Catholic priest. If he had not been traumatized by his mother's 14-hour natural childbirth ordeal, it does not seem likely that he would ever have set foot in a church. He would simply have picked up where he left off before some random impulse had pushed him to descend. Contractions, wave upon wave, had squeezed the collective genius of human history through a point, so that its outlines were now locked within the depths of the unconscious.

During Mass, Brian would stare at the crossed keys on a shield above the altar, at an eye inside of a cloud, at a book on whose pages were the Alpha and Omega, and at the even more obscure symbols, such as pinecones. Brian stared as though his staring were a method. His mind was an utter blank. These symbols had called out to him, like lovers. They then refused to submit.

To know their literal meanings did not help, nor could the failed magicians transmit more than they had learned. At the age of 13—in other words, 13 years too late—Brian determined that these keys—the so called "Keys to Heaven and Hell"—would not open any doors. No, the thumbless carpenters did not believe that keys should fit into locks, nor did they believe in doors that could actually be opened. A key should be big, and it should be held by a netless fisherman, by a shovelless archeologist of the soul, who would tend to the health of the secret that God hid in the basement. If hypocrisy was the tribute that vice paid to virtue, then belief might be the tribute that myopia paid to vision.

Clearly, Brian's threat detection system left something to be desired. It would take him another 20 years to piece together his own equivalent to the priesthood. If his deconstruction of dead bird songs did not prove a complete success, his metaphors worked well enough, in the sense that a journey of a thousand miles began with a single step, in the sense that something was better than nothing. He yearned for the days when poets would risk their sanity in the Sadhamada, the Vedic contest between poets. This contest would not soon return, at least not on a physical field. Brian's words were makeshift gestures in the face of the beyond, instructions for transport that sealed the lips of those who heard, burnt maps from which his homeland had gone missing.

If Brian knew more, he might possibly have done a better job. Due to the rules of his lineage, however—rules to which he had once apparently agreed—the producers of the death-flash video had insisted that he wear a blindfold. In this, he was lucky, for they did not actually blind him. It was only necessary that he find his way, by means of touch and smell and hearing, around each of the 28 u-turns of the labyrinth. Some help would be provided, but of the catalytic sort. If the death of the rational intellect was the goal, then they would do their best to pull the Earth out from beneath him.

One night, in 1971, Brian was awakened by an enormously loud ringing and droning sound, a bit like Tibetan chanting, a sound he would later come to recognize as the music of the spheres. He ran from window to window looking for its source. "It must be some type of nuclear alert," he thought. The very glass in the windows rang, and the telephone wires, and the TV antennas, and the railroad tracks. Filaments burst from milkweed pods, straining upward towards the moon. Only in passing did he notice that no neighbors switched their lights on. Why did they not run wide-eyed from their houses? Why were all of the members of his family still asleep? Such thoughts were somehow distant.

In the morning, when Brian found that no one else had heard the sound, he could not help but be shocked. He was shocked in the way that children are shocked when they discover that their parents have had sex. "Is it possible," they think, "that my birth could be the result of such an event?" He was shocked in the way that people were shocked when they discovered that the Earth revolved around the sun. How could the Earth revolve, when for centuries the experts had all agreed that it was fixed? Brian would grow used to knowing things that could not be understood, about which it was difficult to speak. That the sky could both act and sing was a source of some consolation.

In 1973, Brian had a six-hour conscious dream, in which he was swept around the world by a giant wave. The wave grew and grew, to a mile or two in height, at first gradually, then faster.

At first, Brian was sure that he would drown. With his heart pounding, he woke up several times, only to resume where he left off. Some cities were smashed, like miniaturized stage-sets; others were more gently covered, as water spilled through windows, as it rose above the tops of even the tallest towers. In these gentler moments, it appeared to him as though the ocean were a mother. In her own way, she was tucking her children into bed. The planet itself appeared to be tilting back and forth. Brian felt the infinite sadness of the Earth, its hieroglyphic madness. He felt the ocean's rage, the return of the repressed, the love of a mother who was forced to kill her children. The water, in a long arc, rose. It rose and then continued to rise further. Brian felt an enormous emptiness yawn open in his stomach. He was dressed like Superman. Many reached for his hands, but his fingers had no strength.

"No!" he thought, "If I am Superman, then it is almost certain there is something I should do, some drain that I should open, some small percentage of these victims I could help." Such was not the case, and he could do no more than watch. The water rose. The line between the ocean and the sky could no longer be determined. Thrown headlong into culture-shattering storms, in whose wake his memory could find no hook upon which to hang its hat, he found that sadness turned into curiosity, that dread turned into wonder. The roaring subsided. The whispering of 10,000 boneless avatars took over. At the end, a kind of audible silence rang, a bit different from Tibetan chanting. "Is there some reason that I am still alive?" he thought. Then as now, the question was a good one.

In 1987, Brian was carried out of the solar system in a tornado, for energetic realignment and instruction by a race of acupuncture manikins. He was shown the wheels that contain all of history. There, geometries intersected with ever more complex geometries, paralyzing the mind, striking fear into the heart. Cultures rose and fell, like experimental crops. They grew for a season, spread their seeds, and then were cut. Fixed in format though it was, he saw how DNA was designed for baroque improvisation. Whole ages passed in an eye-blink, and yet, somehow, not even the tiniest of details would be lost. "Is it possible to die from vertigo?" he thought, amazed that he was not already dead. Then again, who knew?

Vast crowds of the soon-to-incarnate swirled in a 19th-century train station. Brian's wife was there, in a manner of speaking. She did not look like herself. Splitting from a crowd, a young Chinese girl ran towards him shouting "Husband!" She was shocked when he did not recognize who she was. His heart sank. "How should I know what to call her," he thought, "when I can't seem to even remember my own name? The top part of my head appears to have gone missing." As a hawk-god, he stared at his aging reflection in the mirror, his hair turning white. Looking from a height on a vast field of battle, he relived his death as a spearman in 9th-century Mongolia. The death was full of laughter and ecstasy. It hurt less than expected.

Upon returning to the Earth, the metal objects in his room seemed radioactive, and he had to yank his hand back when he reached to turn on his lamp. It was far too hot to touch. The building smelled of burnt ozone for days. As in the movie *Dark City*, certain things had been added, while others had been subtracted. Whole sections at the Copley Square Library had been moved to different places. Brian knew this library by heart. No librarian seemed to have heard that the books had been reshuffled. The world looked almost but not quite as it had, as though it had been replaced by an almost exact duplicate. Attached to Brian's wrist: some random stranger's hand. Attached to Brian's face: a different version of this face. Current fears and preoccupations became much less important.

If only it were possible to tell the story of his journey, to share the details of its aftermath. Why bother, though? Brian knew how absurd such experiences would sound. He did not say a word about them, even to his girlfriend. Brian's energy was limited, at least that portion to which he had so far been able to gain access. He must do his best to conserve it.

In August, 1989, Brian had a dream in which he was looking through years of his own artwork on the top floor of a bombed-out warehouse. The walls were jagged, as if puzzle-parts were missing, and broken beams jutted from the edges of the roof and floor. Just outside, there were clouds, which, wave upon wave, billowed up. The work had turned out well, and he laughed to himself as he flipped between the pictures, as if to say, "Of course! How else should they look, and who else would have done them?" Although he had been involved with writing rather than art for the previous ten years, the style of the work was fully formed. Birds and snakes were the dominant classes. Symbols pointed to a lost prototypical culture. All forms were imagined to be the subdivisions of one sphere.

The dream followed him around for weeks. Brian felt that the future was reaching back to the present to give him an ultimatum. "It would be nice if I had a choice," he thought. Curiously, the style of the works did not evolve; rather, there was a language in which all forms were simultaneous. Brian's goal was to become more skillful at catching and then pulling down its shadows. Before starting a drawing, he would often stand almost motionless for hours, watching and listening, breathing slowly in and out, doing his best to evacuate the surface of his mind. To some extent, this worked. An alternate self would judge when or if a drawing was done, when or if the primal sphere had gestured its approval.

A year later, when a more complex series of crop circles began appearing in the fields of Northern England, Brian was surprised by the strange familiarity of the style. "These are obviously hoaxes," declared many, but Brian had his doubts. Hoaxers would not have access to a technology that could have produced his conscious dream, let alone the obsession that followed. Were some few circles made by Doug Bower and Dave Chorley, the two publicity seeking geezers who claimed to have used a rope and a board? Were they the result of labor-intensive pranks by some sect of pagan tricksters? Who knew? Perhaps the explanations and not the circles were the hoaxes. Brian saw these designs as projections of the Language of the Sphere, as psychic provocations, as a form of atemporal gorilla art, as a call to metaphysical arms, as invitations to a contest he had long ago attended, as signs demanding that he learn the language that he spoke.

In August, 1990, Brian underwent an initiation in Kundalini yoga, receiving "Shaktipat" from Asha Ma. He brought her a dozen roses. She ripped their heads off to contemptuously throw them on a big heap in the corner. "Hold on a minute," he thought, "does this mean that my bones and organs have been scheduled for disassembly? With its eyes that do not blink, will my mummified husk be thrown with others in some big heap in a corner?" She mashed a rose on his head. Her hand stretched down through the soft spot on the skull—through the horseshoe of the hippocampus, through the X at the bottom of the brain stem and through the spinal column, down—to provoke a near heart attack. The thumbprint left on his heart was almost imperceptible, and yet he knew that something had changed.

A month later, Brian had a dream in which he was standing in a barn. Next to him was a kind but terrifying presence. Somehow he knew that it was Dhyanyogi Madhusudandas, Asha Ma's teacher, who was 106 and lived in Gujarat. There was some sort of an old-fashioned drop-hammer contraption set up in the middle of the floor. From the height of the rafters, an enormous stone cylinder would, over and over, come crashing down on a head-sized rock. "Do you know what that is?" asked Dhyanyogi. Brian's mouth felt dry. A sinking fear spread upward through his stomach. "I think I do. Is that supposed to be my head?" "Of course it is your head, you idiot! I've been working day and night for the past three weeks to break it. It really is very hard."

Shortly afterwards, Brian realized that space does not exist. He experienced the cosmos as a single but discontinuous body. For ages now, this body had been strategically hidden from itself, yet it had not ceased to be conscious and translucent from one end to the other. Fierce guardians had sealed the doors to the Hall of Akashic Records. They killed those who approached. Brian found, upon his tongue, a key. There was no need to insert it in the lock.

Joy spread its atomic petals, demolishing the three-ring targets that some took to be their cities. Convulsing the psi-bank of the species, a history-wide lotus burped out of the depths. It was difficult to tell if any humans had been harmed. Brian's heart broke. The glyphs that were written on his liver smoldered, causing him to cough. His fingernails hurt. His hair expressed its desire to remove itself from his scalp. His dreams struck at random. They refused to accept that their role was to occur while he was sleeping.

Wherever Brian went, a luminous one-inch sphere would follow, sometimes growing dimmer, sometimes flaring to full brightness. This sphere would not grant that his private thoughts should be allowed to stay private. All other-than-honest insights must be judged, all crimes in past existences acknowledged, all fears given permission to come true. A series of explosions shook the depths of his energetic anatomy. "Where does this energy come from," he thought, "if not from the destruction of all that stands against it?" Many unclean birds were expelled from their Babylonian sewers, where there were none to love them, where they wept. If Brian's body had not been turned into a sphere, he did begin to view the earth-square from a multitude of angles.

In 1945, a kind of rip in the fabric of projection had occurred. Shadows had lengthened from the day that "The Gadget" had been dropped on Alamogordo. In 1990, these shadows simply got up and walked off. A snake ate the power plants of an outmoded civilization. After years of hide and seek, Brian shook hands with his dark and once thought-to-be threatening Double, who looked almost, but not quite, like him. The waves of a nonexistent ocean roared, crashing on his head. One part of the self—let us call it, for the sake of convenience, the "persona"—looked outward to the stars. A different part of the self looked back from the circumference of space.

Brian's mode of vision is now subtler than it was. Those presences whose energy once took the world apart feel less need to resort to violent methods. The fifth element, called Aether by the Pre-Socratics and Akasha by Vedantists, has become his daily instructor. Long dead teachers compete to bring new life to this field, yet age in no way lessens the sweet mystery of their youth. Who had set the traps that proved central to his growth? None among them could be bothered to confess. When asked, they would simply laugh. They would close their eyes. They would stare into the distance. Brian learned to send his breath out. It would circle, then return. The field would answer a question that Brian had not asked.

Brian currently lives in the Fort Hill area of Roxbury, Massachusetts, with his wife, Deniz Ozan-George. Neighbors are friendly, as much so as in the vanished South Worcester of his childhood. A Green Man doorknocker greets the approaching guest. Their 1852 house is an example of the "mortise and tenon" method of construction; its none-too-regular beams are slotted one into the other, like those of the barges that were found in

Egyptian tombs. A wave might, at any moment, spill through the house's cracks to sweep away their furniture. Such a wave might be a problem, if Brian had not taken care to nail the pieces down.

Notes

1. **Foreword**—Michel de Montaigne, "Preface" to 1518 volume of *Essays*; James Hillman, *The Soul's Code*; Heraclitus, *Maxims*, translated by Richard Geldard

2. **The Blind Staircase**—Axis Mundi quote, *New World Encyclopedia*

3. **The Big Dreams of a Gravedigger**—Thomas Kinsella, from the "Introduction" to *The Tain: Tramslated from the Irish Epic Tain Bo Cuailnge*

4. **The Music of the Spheres, Again Audible**—Johannes Kepler, *Harmonices Mundi*, Book V, Chapter 7

5. **The Stranger Face of the Friend**—Pico della Mirandola, *Oration on the Dignity of Man*, translated by Robert Caponigri

6. **The Goddess as Active Listener**—Giorgio de Chirico, from "Manuscript from the Collection of Paul Eluard," translated by Louise Bourgeois and Robert Goldwater; Arthur Rimbaud, *A Season in Hell*, translated by Wallace Fowlie

7. **The Art of Deep-Sea Fishing**—*Tao Te Ching*, translations by Charles Muller and Yi-Ping Ong, and also John H. McDonald; Diana Reed Slattery, "Shifting to a Psychedelic World Culture," posted on *Reality Sandwich*, May 23rd, 2008

8. **Anonymous, and His International Fame**—Friedrich Nietzsche, *Ecce Homo*, "Letter to Jacob Burckhardt," *Thus Spake Zarathustra*, translated by Walter Kaufmann; Pindar, "Sixth Nemean Ode," translated by Richmond Lattimore; Rene Char, "Rampart of Twigs," translated by Jackson Matthews

9. **Notes on Kundalini and the Ticking of the Biological Clock**—
   The Mahabharata, translated by J.A.B. van Buitenen

10. **Visiting Saint Joseph's: Towards a Just Proportion of
    Emptiness**—Giorgio de Chirico, *Hebdomeros*, anonymous trans-
    lator; Mario Livio, *The Golden Ratio: The Story of Phi, the World's
    Most Astonishing Number*; Nicolai Tesla, as quoted by B.A. Behrend,
    from *Wizard: Nicolai Tesla: Biography of a Genius*

11. **Descent to the Merkavah**—Martin Farren, *In the Mirror of
    Creation*; Arthur Rimbaud, "The Just Man," translated by Wallace
    Fowlie

12. **Birds of a Feather and the Playthings of the Twelve**—San
    wounded man figure, Eastern Free State; *The Pyramid of Unas
    Text*, translated by Win van der Dungen. Note: On page 322, in
    the sentence "The Great Ones will tremble, having seen the knife
    which is in your hand, when you ascend with all of your members
    from the Duat," I have added "with all of your members" to van
    der Dungen's translation.

13. **The Snare of Distance and the Sunglasses of the Seer**—Giorgio
    de Chirico, "Proteus," translated by Damon Krukowski; Rainer
    Maria Rilke, "The Vast Night," translated by Stephen Mitchell;
    Hitler, in a statement to Hermann Rauschning, from *Soul Flight:
    Astral Projection and the Magical Universe*, Donald Tyson

About the Author

Brian George is the author of two books of essays and four books of poetry. These include *Voyage to a Nonexistent Home*; *Maps of the Metaphysical Double: In the Footprints of de Chirico*; *To Akasha: An Incantation for the Crossing of an Ocean*; *X: Revenge of the Autogenes*, and *The Preexistent Race Descends*. He is a graduate of the Massachusetts College of Art, an exhibited artist, and a former teacher. He has published in *Dark Mountain*, *Metapsychosis*, *Scene4: International Magazine of Arts and Culture*, *Reality Sandwich*, and *Modern Mythology*, as well as in the *Apocalyptic Imaginary* and *The Immanence of Myth* anthologies. He often tells people first discovering his work that his goal is not so much to be read as to be reread, and then lived with.

CPSIA information can be obtained
at www.ICGtesting.com
Printed in the USA
JSHW050942131122
33070JS00002B/16